The Attack
of the Killer
Rhododendrons

My Obsessive Quest

to Seek Out Alien Species

GLEN CHILTON

HARPERCOLLINS PUBLISHERS LTD

HarperCollins Publishers Ltd
2 Bloor Street East, 20th Floor
Toronto, Ontario, Canada
M4W 1A8

www.harpercollins.ca

Library and Archives Canada Cataloguing in Publication

Chilton, Glen, 1958–
The attack of the killer rhododendrons : my obsessive quest to seek out
alien species / Glen Chilton.

ISBN 978-1-55468-364-2

1. Chilton, Glen, 1958—Travel. 2. Introduced organisms.
3. Biological invasions. I. Title.

QH353.C45 2012   578.6'2   C2011-905760-3

Printed and bound in the United States
RRD 9 8 7 6 5 4 3 2 1

To Dr. Lisa Chilton, whom I treasure more than my next breath

Contents

The Attack of the Killer Rhododendrons

Introduction

I WANTED A DOG. I got a turtle. Imagine my disappointment. Try to imagine the disappointment of millions of children who got turtles instead of dogs. Dogs are really good at returning affection. Turtles are really good at dying, which mine did in fairly short order. I swear that it wasn't my fault. It was reluctant to eat much of anything, and I tried just about everything. So I got another turtle. It came from Kmart and cost 25 cents, which says something about the value that was put on the lives of animals back then.

In the 1960s, 3 million turtles were imported to Canada from the United States each year. Given that the human population of Canada was less than 18 million at the time, you have to be impressed. Most of those turtles were red-eared sliders, native to the Mississippi Valley of the eastern United States.

Well, that second turtle died too, so I got another. And so it went. Eventually I got a little better at turtle husbandry and my turtle didn't die. Over the period of a few months it even managed to grow a bit. So imagine my rekindled disappointment when I was told that my turtle was a health threat and had to go. Like millions of other children, I released my turtle from captivity to live a happy life in the wild.

It seems that someone in a position of power had made the link between turtle ownership and diarrhea, cramps, and fever in children. Salmonella bacteria live in the digestive tract of turtles (and a wide range of other reptiles), and they shed some of these bacteria with every bowel movement. Turtles suffer very little from being infected by salmonella bacteria. The same cannot be said for people, and so a ban on the distribution of turtles was put in place by the U.S. Food and Drug Administration in 1975. Not all turtles were banned, just those under ten centimetres in length. The FDA figured that young children wouldn't stuff larger turtles in their mouths. The Centers for Disease Control and Prevention in Atlanta estimate that the ban prevents 100,000 cases of salmonella poisoning in children each year.

Imagine the disappointment of the 150 turtle breeders in the United States, who were producing upwards of 13 million pet turtles a year. When the ban came into effect, some of these business people gave up, but the rest saw the obvious solution. If you can't sell turtles domestically, then ship them to places that haven't enacted prohibitory legislation. By the mid-1990s, 6 million turtles a year, bred in the United States, were being exported overseas. Parents in the receiving countries eventually got the salmonella message and liberated their children's turtles into local waterways. Freed from the haphazard care of young children, many of the released turtles prospered. And so, from their humble beginnings along the quiet backwaters of the Mississippi Valley, red-eared sliders came to inhabit the world. Populations are established in Belgium, Saudi Arabia, New Zealand, Japan, France, Israel, Bermuda, Guyana, and, very likely, wherever you happen to be reading this book. The red-eared slider is considered to be one of the 100 worst invasive species in the world, outcompeting and hybridizing with native turtle species and eating other freshwater fauna.

It seems likely that as long as humans have been humans we have been shuffling the deck, picking up plants and animals from one spot and plonking them down in another. The general consensus among biologists is that, nine times out of ten, the newly introduced creatures will simply die off. Something about the new habitat will fail to meet their needs or will exceed their tolerance, and the potential invaders will fail to establish a self-sustaining population. Even if the newly arrived creatures beat the odds to survive and flourish, nine times out of ten they will blend into the background without causing any hardship to native fauna or flora or to humans. No muss, no fuss.

However, one time in one hundred, the creature that has been transplanted over some geographical barrier to dispersal proves itself to be very, very unwelcome. The guest is now a pest. What was once exotic is now unwelcome. The introduced species is now an invasive species. And so we find Australia covered with rabbits, the North American Great Lakes filled with zebra mussels, Africa's Lake Victoria choked with water hyacinth, and pigeons hanging out in every town square in the world. Indeed, the only place in the world without introduced species is Bouvet Island, an incredibly remote and tiny chunk of rock poking out of the South Atlantic. The word "pest" is probably an enormous understatement. Along with habitat destruction and overexploitation, introduced species are considered to be one of the greatest threats to global diversity.

I had just completed an around-the-world expedition to find every stuffed specimen of the extinct Labrador Duck. Sales of the resulting book, *The Curse of the Labrador Duck,* had gone some way to replenishing my savagely depleted bank account. It seemed the perfect time to throw myself back into penury by circling the globe again in search of introduced creatures. I wanted to jump from one continent to another, examining the alien pests that were creating biological Armageddon. If possible, I wanted to speak to someone who had actually made an introduction, and to the folks charged with exterminating the foreigners. Could I distinguish between noxious aliens and innocent victims of our tendency to move plants and animals from here to there? Examining the effects of an exotic disease might be fun. Perhaps I could even find an introduced critter whose presence was having a positive effect on the local landscape. Was it possible to put the whole issue of introduced species on a scale?

It was time for a quest.

CHAPTER ONE

The Last Place You'd Look for a Wallaby

REASON NUMBER ONE FOR INTRODUCING A FOREIGN SPECIES: BECAUSE IT'S MY ISLAND, AND NO ONE CAN TELL ME WHAT TO DO.

IN THE NORTHERN SCOTTISH CITY of Inverness, the museum and art gallery has an enviable assortment of landscape paintings and artifacts of local human history. It also has a representative sample of stuffed Scottish animals. For school-aged visitors, Felicity is probably the most popular attraction. Felicity was a mountain lion, discovered wandering the highlands in October 1980. Native to the wilds of western North America, Felicity was a fair few kilometres from home. She was trapped and transported to a wildlife park near Kingussie, where a keeper described her as overweight and unnaturally tame. There was little doubt that Felicity had spent her first ten or so years of life in the care of someone who released her after finally realizing that a house in the Scottish glens is not a naturally tenable place for a mountain lion. She lived her last five years in the wildlife park before shuffling off, apparently of old age. Museum taxidermist Philip Howard had given Felicity the look of an overgrown tabby just waiting to be scratched behind the ear before devouring the family poodle.

There is no shortage of tales of large cat sightings in the less

5

populated portions of Britain, some dating back to the sixteenth century. Further, there is no shortage of other introduced mammals wandering that green and pleasant land, including feral goats introduced some 4,000 years ago, ferrets introduced during Roman times, the so-called yellow rabbit brought from France in the eleventh century, North American grey squirrels introduced in the late-nineteenth century and now not-so-slowly pushing out the native red squirrel, and American mink from the 1950s that are chomping their way through Scotland's population of water voles.

The tale may be apocryphal, but it seems that a tanker driver had a small role to play in what must surely be one of the strangest introduced species stories in the United Kingdom. According to an article in the *Glasgow Herald* from October 16, 1982, local police were investigating the story of a tanker driver, hauling a load along Highway A82 on the west side of Loch Lomond near the village of Luss, who claimed to have collided with a kangaroo. Normally, this sort of claim calls for a Breathalyzer test. But five years earlier, several kangaroos had escaped from the Loch Lomond Bear Park at Cameron. Could one of them have been hiding out until clobbered by the truck? Alternatively, the creature in question may not have been a kangaroo at all, but rather a red-necked wallaby. A wallaby might have swum across a narrow channel in Loch Lomond from the island of Inchconnachan. How did red-necked wallabies come to be on Inchconnachan? The part of me that loves a good yarn wishes that they had something to do with warfare between the highland clans in the murky past. Luckily, reality is almost as much fun.

The lives of people with titles like "Lord" and "Count" are an open book. We know, for instance, that our protagonist, Fiona, Countess of Arran, formerly Miss Fiona Bryde Colquhoun of Luss, married Sir Arthur Strange Kattendyke David Archibald Gore on June 11, 1937. December 28, 1958, was a pretty good day for Sir Arthur, when he became 8th Viscount Sudley of Castle Gore, County Mayo; 10th Baronet Saunders of Newtown Gore, County Mayo; 8th Baron Saunders of Deeps, County Wexford; 8th Earl of

Arran of Arran Islands, County Galway; and 4th Baron Sudley of Castle Gore, County Mayo. Sir Arthur passed away in 1983, but the family has assured me that the Countess lives on. Fiona has had great adventures in her long life. For instance, in August 1980, she became the first person to surpass 100 miles per hour on water when her powerboat achieved 102 miles per hour on Lake Windermere in England; for this she became only the third woman to be decorated with the Segrave Trophy, awarded to those who demonstrate the great potential of travel by land, sea, or air.

In 1972, the Countess reportedly released a pair of collared peccaries, native to Central and South America, on Inchconnachan. I suppose that she had every right to do so since her family, the Colquhouns of Luss, owned the island. One peccary vanished and the other was removed in 1984. As part of a plan to establish a small wildlife park, the Countess released red-necked wallabies on the same island sometime in the early 1970s, and these have persisted to the present. The current population is thought to number somewhere around forty.

The Countess of Arran probably didn't have to get her red-necked wallabies shipped from Tasmania by FedEx. As early as 1933, Whipsnade Zoological Park in Bedfordshire had wallabies in its collection, along with gnus, dromedaries, dingoes, hippopotami, and polar bears. Now called the ZSL Whipsnade Zoo, the institution still counts a herd of 599 free-roaming wallabies among its attractions, and it seems that this is where the Countess got her stock for Inchconnachan. Fiona and her husband, "Boofy," reportedly also kept albino wallabies on the grounds of Pimlico House, their home in Hertfordshire, along with alpacas, foxes, and badgers.

I first heard the story about wallabies on Loch Lomond in a Glasgow pub, which made me initially doubt its veracity. Asking around, it seemed that about 50 percent of Glaswegians had heard the story. But knowing about wallabies on an island is one thing; actually seeing them is another. Although Inchconnachan is part of Loch Lomond & The Trossachs National Park and is designated a Site of Special Scientific Interest, it is still owned by the Colquhoun family. My reading of the Countryside and Rights of Way Act (2000) seemed to suggest that I had the right to walk all over the island without asking permission. The Land Reform (Scotland) Act (2003) seemed to suggest the same. Even better, the Scottish Outdoor Access Code (2005) made it pretty clear that as long as I stayed away from residences, didn't commit an obvious criminal act, didn't harass the wildlife, and didn't let a dog run free, I could pretty much tramp over any bit of Scotland that I pleased. No need to ask; just do it.

But that sort of behaviour just isn't in my personality. I am more likely to ask for permission than for forgiveness, and so I did, and was rewarded with official sanction from Iain Sheves, factor of Luss Estates Company. Sheves asked that I write to a ranger in the national park to let officials know I would be on the island, and said I should stay clear of a small, environmentally sensitive spot on Inchconnachan, but otherwise I was welcome to have a poke around.

This still left me without a means of getting to Inchconnachan. Luckily, through mutual friends, I had struck up an acquaintance with Klarinka Farkas. Klarinka was an architect from Hungary who had visited Scotland eight years earlier and had loved it so much that she stayed. Klarinka was far more comfortable out-of-doors than in, and being particularly fond of marine sports felt Scotland would provide her with greater opportunity than land-locked Hungary. To a large extent, she was able to ply her profession from the home she had purchased in the tiny west coast community of Mosachbean. Beyond her own gear, Klarinka had a spare kayak, a spare tent, a spare sleeping bag, and all of the other outdoor equipment that I didn't have. Further, she was willing to spend a few days away from her computer to have a paddle to look for wallabies.

THERE ARE FOUR SONGS of enduring fame to have originated in Scotland. The first is the rock classic "I'm Gonna Be (500 Miles)" by the Proclaimers. The second is the bagpipe classic "Danny Boy." The third is that other bagpipe classic that everyone knows, but no one can ever remember the name of or the words to. "Aaaa reee braaaad daaa daaa daaaaaa, Aaaa reee broooo daaa daaa broooooo"; you know the one. The fourth is "The Bonny Banks o' Loch Lomond." No one seems to be able to agree on the lyrics, but one version goes:

> Oh, I'll tak the high road,
> An you'll tak the low road,
> An I'll be in Scotland afore ye,
> But me an' my true love will never meet again
> On the bonny, bonny banks o' Loch Lomond.

There are endless notions about who composed the piece, when, and under what circumstances. My favourite story involves Donald Macdonald, a Scottish soldier awaiting trial after his capture at the Battle of Culloden in 1746. Sitting in Carlisle jail, Macdonald was pretty sure he would be executed the following day for his role in the Jacobite Rebellion. Convinced that his soul would reach Scotland from the gallows before some of his fellow prisoners who would be set free to walk home, he wrote the poem for his beloved Moira. Whether or not Macdonald wrote the words to "Loch Lomond," he appears to have escaped the gallows and lived for another twenty-four years.

Death is not the only way to get to the bonny, bonny shores of Loch Lomond. If you are keen on staying off the gallows, you can take the train from Glasgow's Partick station, and for just £3.10, it will drop you off forty minutes later at the town of Balloch, just a couple of hundred metres from the loch. This is what I did.

I didn't want to be late for my rendezvous with Klarinka, so I caught a train that got me into Balloch an hour early. I plonked myself down on a stone wall to wait. Showing typical Hungarian efficiency, when Klarinka pulled up she had already purchased all of the groceries that we would need for our three-day trip. I would have appreciated the opportunity for a bit of input on our meals, but her efforts meant that we were away that much sooner.

Klarinka drove us up the west side of Loch Lomond to one of the park's interpretive centres. We unpacked all the gear from her car and moved the kayaks from the roof rack to the water's edge. Now, I am generally a whiz when it comes to packing a lot of stuff into a little space. I have even been known to get two bodies into a single sleeping bag. But when it came to getting drinking water, food, and camping gear into the holds of Klarinka's spare kayak, I just couldn't make it work. After Klarinka had packed her kayak, she took over packing mine. Then we went through a checklist—or rather, Klarinka went through a checklist. Did I have sunglasses? No, because I was wearing eyeglasses. Did I have a rain jacket? Yes, because I was not an idiot. Was I wearing sandals? Yes, because I knew that shoes never dry on a kayaking trip. Did I have a hat? Yes, it was perched right there on top of my head. It all left me with the rather uncomfortable feeling that I was being directed by a Girl Guide leader.

I love to canoe, and I love to kayak. I haven't done a lot of either, but I claim to be reasonably confident in either craft. This made me feel all the more incompetent when my kayak was as tippy as a Glaswegian on a Saturday night. Klarinka got back out of her kayak and steadied mine while I got in and adjusted the spray skirt.

Then we were underway, en route to an adventure with wallabies on Inchconnachan. Less than 30 seconds into the three-day trip, I discovered that my kayak had no rudder, which Klarinka described as a "North American thing." No matter what I did, with every pull on the paddle the kayak pulled to port, and I didn't have a rudder to counteract it. It wasn't just that I was paddling harder on the right side; as soon as I stopped paddling, the craft coasted in a lazy arc to the left. I was told that I must be sitting wrong. I tried shifting my weight, but I had to choose between a position that made the pulling bad and one that made it even worse.

My progress was slow. Klarinka, a semi-pro with a paddle, kept looking back over her shoulder to see why I wasn't keeping up. Then I twigged that Klarinka had the impression that I was a lot more experienced in a kayak than I am. She waited twenty minutes before asking how long it had been since I had kayaked. I told her that it had been seven years, but really it was closer to ten, in the same way that I am closer to forty years old than to thirty.

Three days was going to be a long time if I got too hung up about my inadequacies, so I settled into a pleasant, if glacial, rhythm. Being a Sunday morning in June, the waters of Loch Lomond around Luss were littered with powerboats towing water skiers, but we slowly pulled away from the noise and confusion and entered quieter waters.

As we approached Inchconnachan, I was surprised by how big it was. On my ordnance survey map, it was shorter than a paper clip, but it took us a considerable period to paddle around it as we looked for the best place to set up camp. In various spots around the island, several big cruisers lay at anchor, their occupants drinking fancy beverages with ice cubes. We gave them a wide berth.

At the far southern tip of the island, we found an idyllic little stretch of beach for the kayaks and a wide green verge for our tents. Midges made themselves known the moment we stepped on shore. These tiny biting flies are known by the scientific name *Culicoides impunctatus,* which translates from Latin as "countless punctures." Giving the little devils the diminutive name "midgies" was probably the local way of making them seem less irritating, but the word, strange enough in a Scottish accent, was even odder in a Hungarian accent, "madge ease." Klarinka, an old hand at the Scottish outdoors, had brought midge veils for both of us, and although they looked silly, they were a lot better than a thousand insect bites on my face.

I can erect my own tent in about thirty seconds, but no one can throw up an unfamiliar tent rapidly on their first go. It didn't help that a young boy had arrived in a small horsepower tin boat to chat with me while I struggled. Klarinka had her tent up long before I had figured out mine. "Just let me know if you need help." After coffee, Klarinka set out to do some more paddling; she was in training for a two-week kayaking trip to Finland. I went in search of wallabies.

SOME OF THE ISLANDS in Loch Lomond have no end of fascinating recorded history and claim many famous visitors. Inchconnachan

isn't one of them. It has been called Inchconnachan, or some variation of it (probably a corruption of the name of its owners, the
Colquhouns), since at least the mid-eighteenth century. Residents
of Luss may have made whisky on the island in centuries past, but
that was about it. For an island just one kilometre from north to
south, it has an impressive range of different habitats. Significant
mixed coniferous and deciduous woodlands feature in places,
although the soil is thin, as evidenced by large fallen trees with
shallow root balls. In the swampier lowlands, ferns grow to chest
height, and bracket fungi, white and orange, grow from dead tree
trunks.

After about an hour of tramping, I began to wonder if I was
a victim of a hoax. How do you hide forty wallabies? But then,
on trails about halfway to the summit on the island's north side, I
discovered poop that by its shape and size (rather squarish; it made
me wonder how it got out) couldn't be from anything else. As I
was ascending the peak, forty metres away I spied something that
I wasn't expecting. It was a small, old, hunched Chinese man peeping at me through the undergrowth. Well, perhaps not so much an
old man as a wallaby.

Big enough to be a male, he was greyish-brown on the back and
pale grey below and had a neck that would be described as "red"
only by someone with colour-blindness. He was woollier than I
might have guessed. He shook his head vigorously, probably to dis-
lodge a few midges, and then hopped away. Some trick of the soil
meant that he made a *thump-thump* noise as he moved.

Most people think of wallabies as small kangaroos, although
wallabies themselves claim that kangaroos are oversized wallabies.
The family includes such oddities as rock-wallabies, nailtail wallabies, and hare-wallabies, but if you are looking for a good old
down-and-dirty garden-variety wallaby you could do worse than
to look at the red-necked wallaby. With wimpy arms and powerful jumping hind legs, they stand the better part of eighty centimetres, with an equally long tail. Males clock in at around twenty
kilograms, and females at a slender fourteen kilograms. They are

found along the eastern coast of Australia as far south as Tasmania, where they are also called Bennett's wallaby. Those in Tasmania are considered a different subspecies than those on the mainland. The Tasmanian ones have thicker and longer fur, and they are the likely source of wallabies on Inchconnachan. Red-necked wallabies rest in shrubbery or long grass during the day, emerging at night to eat grasses and herbs and sometimes browse on shrubs. For most of the year they are solitary, but sometimes gather in pubs in winter.

As with everything else in Australia, red-necked wallaby sex is odd. Males have a two-part penis, attached behind the testes, not in front. Not to be outdone, females have two uteruses and two vaginas. When a female becomes sexually receptive, she is followed by a group of enthusiastic, hopeful males, but when she is at her most fertile, a single dominant male chases all the other suitors away. Unlike the situation in placental mammals, the embryo doesn't dig its way into the wall of the uterus. About a month after conception, a tiny joey climbs from its uterus and into its mother's pouch, where it stays for about seven months before getting the courage to climb out for a hop around. The joey will continue to pester its mother for as long as six more months. If a female lives to a ripe old age, she will give birth to about nine young. In the warmer parts of Australia, red-necked wallabies breed throughout the year, but in Tasmania, cooler weather makes reproduction a summertime thing.

Red-necked wallabies are protected from persecution in Australia, unless they become pests, in which case they can be killed with a licence. Red-necked wallabies are hunted in Tasmania, where their meat is a delicacy. A non-commercial licence costs $25.60, and the season runs from February 23 of one year to February 22 of the next. Wallabies in Tasmania are a nervous lot.

When Klarinka returned from her paddle, we had a meal of pasta, cheese, and vegetables cooked over a propane flame. We couldn't get a fire started because all the wood we had gathered was too wet. In the fading light, I took a walk with Klarinka to try to find wallabies. After a tramp through some marshy bits and up a slight rise, Klarinka called out, "There's one." At first I couldn't see it, but said that I could. I figured that she might be seeing a wallaby-shaped bush in the diminishing light. Then the bush hopped onto the trail. As we peered at it, and it peered at us in return, it occurred to me that a Scottish wallaby was a sight that most people will never get to see. Introductions of red-necked wallabies have been attempted in Czechoslovakia, Germany, Hungary, and the Ukraine, all without success in establishing breeding populations. A small number of red-necked wallabies were introduced to the south island of New Zealand from Tasmania in 1870 and 1874, and they went on to become a forestry nuisance. Between 1950 and 1960, 5,000 to 6,000 wallabies a year were destroyed there.

Back at camp, we had one more try at a campfire, but either the wood was too wet or neither of us was as woodsy as we claimed to be. Instead we used the camp stove to make hot chocolate and retired to our tents. I tucked myself into the borrowed nylon sleeping bag using its nylon bag liner. It is much easier to launder a liner than a whole sleeping bag after you have loaned out your bag. But this created a problem. The liner was slippery, the bag was slippery, and the inflated sleeping pad was slippery. The situation is probably like trying to be smoochy with someone in silk pajamas, while wearing silk pajamas, lying on silk sheets. I changed into my running tights and a T-shirt, deflated the mattress, and tossed the bag liner to one corner of the tent. It took me a very long time to fall asleep, but insomnia is not nearly so bad a thing while camping. I woke very early to the songs of Chaffinches.

UNLIKE MOSQUITOES, which are mainly nocturnal, midges are perfectly happy to rise early and have a little nibble. Therefore, Klarinka and I had our breakfast of muesli, powdered milk, and hot water while walking briskly up and down the beach. We returned to the campsite periodically to have sips of sweet, black coffee. Western Scotland would be an unbearable place in summer if it weren't that midges are comparatively wimpy. They don't seem to like bright sunshine, and they don't seem able to cope with even a modest breeze, rain, loud noises, or an unfavourable stock market report. Unfortunately, what they lack in tenaciousness they make up for in number, and I discovered just how painful tickling could be when a midge flew up my nose.

Then it was time for a paddle. The water was mirror-calm, and all of the Sunday boaters had gone back to their weekday lives. By paddling three times to the left for every two strokes to the right, I managed to keep my kayak in nearly a straight line. Klarinka was clearly disappointed in me.

First we coasted by a "floating island" in the channel south of Inchconnachan. When the loch's water levels are low, I gather there is an exposed gravel bank on this spot, but when the waters rise, the vegetation is left to float eerily. Even though it isn't much of an island, written references to it date back more than 400 years, and legends claim that the island literally floated about the loch. On we paddled, past the sandy beaches of Inchmoan, which, like Inchconnachan, has been owned for centuries by the Colquhoun clan. The island is almost a kilometre and a half long, but low-lying and boggy, and it is said that the inhabitants of Luss had visited it for centuries to harvest and dry peat in summer for use as fuel in winter.

Loch Lomond must have 10,000 stories waiting to be investigated more thoroughly. The story behind Inchgalbraith Castle must be one of the better ones. As an islet, Inchgalbraith is likely a crannog, a forty-metre-long artificial island built as a defensive retreat in the Iron Age or earlier. Above a pile of boulders, brought from the mainland on rafts, and wooden poles driven deep into the loch's bed, a wooden roundhouse would have been constructed. A secret, submerged, and twisting causeway would have led to the nearest island, defeating potential invaders who didn't know the route. In medieval times, the Galbraith family found the crannog sufficiently robust to construct a castle that covered all of the tiny islet. Although the castle has been in ruins for at least 300 years, the walls still rise up from the loch, hidden by trees and shrubs, and serve as home to a family of Canada Geese.

As we curled back past Inchmoan, it became clear that whoever had been using the kayak before me had much longer legs. The foot rests were nowhere useful to me. As a result, my back and upper legs were growing tired quickly. We beached on Inchcruin to allow me to adjust my foot rests. It is hard to believe that the name Inchcruin is taken from the Gaelic word for "round island," since its outline looks more like a missing jigsaw puzzle piece. Some attribute the name to a Gaelic expression for "he is not sane" on the basis of an eighteenth-century insane asylum on it.

On we travelled to Bucinch, whose name may be, but probably isn't, based on feral goats that may have, but probably didn't, roam the island in centuries past. Rising more sharply from the loch than its neighbours, Bucinch is a beautifully domed and wooded island. A short dash brought us to the tiny islet of Ceardach, or Tinkers Island, named for the remains of an Iron Age smelting furnace. The islet is sometimes called Gerbil Island because of the release of two gerbils in the 1960s. It must have been just the two gerbils, because there isn't room on the islet for any more. Klarinka got out for a quick tramp around; I stayed in my kayak, since I could see every inch of Ceardach from where I sat. I saw no gerbils.

After a lunch of coffee, tomatoes, cheese, and rice cakes at camp, Klarinka set off for more paddling as training for her upcoming expedition, while I went off in search of more wallabies. I took along my camera and a small bag of carrots, having read that these are the all-time favoured food of red-necked wallabies. At several likely looking spots, I left behind ten slices of carrot. Then, if some of the slices were missing on a subsequent trip, I could tell if any had been taken. Unless they had all been taken, or I couldn't find the spot again.

I headed uphill toward the highest point on the island. I spotted a wallaby, but it was clear that he had long since spotted me. As soon as I raised my camera, he was away. He was much smaller than the one I had seen the day before, but his feet still made a tremendous thumping noise as he jumped. I followed him uphill, but he darted every time I got close. Wallabies have no difficulty moving uphill.

Toward the top, I spied one resting between a pair of trees. There was no point in sneaking up, as she had obviously seen me. Sitting upright, she posed in a three-quarter profile. I raised my camera and started playing with the shutter speed and F-stop. As I speculated about whether I could compose the shot a little better, it occurred to me that my time was probably short. I snapped off a shot, and as I stepped out from cover to try for a better one, she bounded a short distance away to hide by standing in front of a wallaby-coloured tree, which is all of them.

I returned to camp to find that Klarinka was still paddling, and so I rediscovered the sublime joy of dozing on an air mattress on a quiet, shady beach. Drifting in and out of sleep, I pondered who would be crazy enough to want to be responsible for Loch Lomond & The Trossachs National Park. Even though it was Scotland's first national park, it was only three years old. For the folks at—to pick an example—Death Valley National Park in California and Nevada, life is a doddle. Two hours away from the nearest big city, Las Vegas, the park has fully 13,650 square kilometres to accommodate visitors. In contrast, visitors to Loch Lomond & The Trossachs have just 1,865 square kilometres at their disposal. To make things worse, 70 percent of all the people in Scotland live less than an hour from the park, and 15,600 people live within the park itself. Management is particularly tricky because portions of the park are privately owned. Folks at Loch Lomond & The Trossachs National Park are justifiably proud of their huge red deer and roe deer populations, but it probably gets up their noses that they sometimes have to cull animals to keep the population down.

In most nations, national parks make it easy on themselves by making conservation issues the first priority and prohibiting the extraction or exploitation of natural resources. You can hike around Death Valley National Park, but you had better not be carrying a fishing rod. The planners of the park at Loch Lomond & The Trossachs made their lives much more complex by establishing two of its four statutory aims to "promote sustainable use of natural resources of the area" and to "promote sustainable economic

and social development of the area's communities." Farming? Why
not? Forestry? Let's talk about it. Fishing? Go ahead. Indeed, Loch
Lomond is home to nineteen types of fish, making it one of the most
important sites for freshwater fish in Britain. Regrettably, four of
those species are introduced.

When Klarinka got back from her sojourn, I told her about my
limited luck in finding wallabies. She responded by saying "Oh, yes.
I saw five drinking from the water's edge just around the corner."
Some folks are just luckier than others, I suppose. We managed a
fire, but it required a lot of blowing to keep it lit. Our supper was
garlic with pasta. A bottle of whisky that I had brought along was
a big hit.

As night began to fall, we went for another paddle, this time a
circuit of Inchconnachan. Klarinka spotted a wallaby on the beach
of the first embayment. She has good night vision, resolving shadows and shapes that I couldn't. A little further north, she spotted
a second wallaby. At the top end of the island, in the last of the
day's light, we came across a wonderful assemblage of small bats
foraging for insects. I leaned as far back in the boat as I could,
and watched them zoom overhead, skimming down to the water, a
metre or two from my head. Back at our campsite, we found three
more wallabies rooting around, and I suspect that they were eating
campfire ashes.

In the middle of the night, I woke to the loud, harsh cries of
birds, and managed to convince myself that they were Capercaillie, the world's largest game bird, native to Scotland but very rare.
They had been hunted to extirpation in Scotland in 1785 and
reintroduced from Sweden in 1837; they were now in peril of
becoming extinct again. The name Capercaillie is derived from
Gaelic for "horse of the woods." In all likelihood the calls came
from insomniac shorebirds, not Capercaillie.

FOR OUR LAST DAY on Loch Lomond, Klarinka and I had planned
a paddle to Inchmurrin. It was an obvious destination. The largest
inland island in Britain at two and a half kilometres long, it has

a lovely walkway running from the northern peninsula through oak and birch woodlands and along a grassy ridge, and down to the pier at the south end. If I squinted, I could probably ignore the vast thickets of introduced rhododendrons. Inchmurrin was named after St. Mirren, a sixth-century Irish-born priest. Mirren is patron saint of the Scottish town of Paisley, and of football clubs with three or fewer premiership cup titles. The island has reportedly been visited by Robert the Bruce (after an inglorious defeat in battle); King James VI of Scotland (a.k.a. James I of England); Mary, Queen of Scots; and Isabella, Countess of Albany, exiled after witnessing the execution of her father, husband, and two sons. Sir John Colquhoun was probably even less impressed with the island than Isabella, having been murdered there in 1440. Klarinka and I could take the opportunity to see the ruins of Lennox Castle, where the Earl of Lennox brought his family to escape the plague in the fourteenth century. If we weren't careful, we might stumble across the Scottish Outdoor Club, a naturist group entrenched on Inchmurrin since the late 1940s. The winds had come up overnight and the waves looked a bit tricky, but I was game for anything.

We squeaked between Inchconnachan and Inchmoan, then between Inchmoan and Inchfad. The winds grew stronger, and I had increasing difficulty paddling in a straight line. I got a lot of suggestions from Klarinka. These were along the lines of "lengthen your stroke," "hold your paddle higher," and "paddle harder," any of which, I felt, would have tipped me into the drink. I was tenser than I generally like to be, particularly on water.

Using what were, apparently, my inconsiderable paddling skills, I did my best to follow Klarinka as we zipped across to a landing on the western shore of Inchcailloch to consider our options. While resting, I hauled out my guide to the islands of Loch Lomond and discovered that Inchcailloch (Gaelic for "Isle of the Old Woman") was named after St. Kentigerna, a Christian missionary, possibly Irish, who set up shop on the island with her brother and her son early in the eighth century. For 500 years, the church built on the island and dedicated to St. Kentigerna's memory was the site of worship for the faithful on the mainland, who finally twigged in 1670 that rowing out to the island was an unpleasant way to spend every Sunday morning.

I could stall by reading a book for only so long. We gave up on the planned longer paddle to Inchmurrin and aimed for lunch at the village of Balmaha on the loch's eastern shore instead. If the weather was cooperative, the winds would die down over lunch, and we could paddle back to Inchconnachan. I tied down my hat with its idiot straps and settled into the task of paddling against the wind to Balmaha.

The Oak Tree Inn, named after the 500-year-old specimen on its grounds, has a fine restaurant complete with linen tablecloths and cloth napkins. The staff were pleased to serve us lasagna and cheese macaroni despite our rather grubby appearance. As we sat on the deck, I resisted the temptation to get plastered. Klarinka had no objection to me paying for lunch.

We walked back to the water's edge to judge the wind and waves. They were worse. With uncustomary civility, Klarinka waited for me to state the obvious. Rather than push on, it would be far more prudent for me to stay behind and leave Klarinka to paddle back to Luss, get the vehicle, and drive around the south end of Loch Lomond to pick me up. To this point, it would have been comforting to hear a diplomatic expression like "The waves might be a little too much for you." Instead I got the rather more hurtful expression: "You aren't a strong enough paddler for these conditions."

Off went Klarinka, leaving me sitting on a beach, feeling like hell, like a quitter, like an inferior being. As I sat beside my beached kayak, I thought back and was sure that I had never said that I had done more than "a bit" of kayaking.

A couple of hours later, Klarinka drove up. After tying the spare kayak to the roof rack, we proceeded around the south shore of Loch Lomond to offload at Aldochlay. In the calmer, protected waters of the loch's west side, we had no difficulty paddling out to Inchconnachan to pick up our gear; no wallabies saw us off. Back across to Aldochlay, we stowed everything, and Klarinka's body language told me that everything I had stowed would have to be repacked as soon as I was out of sight.

Klarinka pulled her vehicle into a parking lot a couple of blocks from the Balloch train station. She didn't get out to give me a hug. She didn't even turn the engine off. In fact, she left her car in gear as I unloaded my belongings. Her "Goodbye" was simultaneously perfunctory and definitive. She roared off.

I stood on the train platform and pondered the nature of probability. Red-necked wallabies had beaten the odds by persisting on Inchconnachan. Nine out of ten introductions fail to produce a self-sustaining population. Wallabies had, however, joined the ranks of the majority of introduced species by failing to become a pest. They hopped around the island, browsed on vegetation, and looked cute. Perhaps it was time for me to examine something more horrid. I needed a creature whose introduction had resulted in the gnashing of teeth. It had to be something ugly and gooey and wet. Something like an oyster.

CHAPTER TWO

Universal Oysters

REASON NUMBER TWO FOR INTRODUCING A FOREIGN SPECIES: BECAUSE WE RAN OUT OF SEAFOOD.

REGRETTABLY, THERE IS NO GOOD WAY to explain morris dancing. In its place is my rather feeble attempt. Somewhere back in the mists of time, British villagers would gather for general silliness in an attempt to ensure a good harvest or to put an end to bubonic plague or to cure marital fidelity. They would don funny folk costumes and dance funny folk dances to the general derision of more sober-minded members of the community. Luckily, the tradition virtually died away until regaining its popularity in the 1960s and '70s. I attribute this to recreational drugs. Today across the width and breadth of the United Kingdom, town squares are filled with people with bells strapped to their knees and streamers attached to their elbows, waving white handkerchiefs and smacking stout sticks, recreating early fertility-inspiring dances to the accompaniment of drums, pipes, and accordions, while being scoffed at by people trying to complete their weekend shopping.

While on a short holiday in Kent, my dear wife, Lisa, and I decided to celebrate May Day by travelling to the seaside community of Whitstable to see a performance by the Oyster Morris Dance Troupe. The whole affair was scheduled to kick off at ten

o'clock, but by ten thirty most of the troupe was in the local water-
ing hole, downing pints of ale. Whatever else might be said about
morris dancers, they are not a temperance group.

Whitstable is well known for its oysters, which have been harvested from its shallow waters for more than 2,000 years. When
the Romans set up shop in Britain, they exported Whitstable oysters to all corners of their empire. Charles Dickens wrote frequently
about oysters on that part of the coast. Indeed, Whitstable is so
proud of its oysters that it hosts a week-long Oyster Festival in late
July, highlighted by the Official Landing of the Oysters, followed
by a Blessing of the Oyster Waters, and an Oyster Parade featuring
delivery of oysters to local pubs and restaurants by the Lord Mayor
of Canterbury. And despite millennia of harvesting, populations of
the oysters of Whitstable are doing just fine.

On the east side of the North Sea, things are not so rosy. A once
lucrative oyster fishery had long since been fished out, and in its
place was a foreign oyster with designs on universal domination.
Lisa and I were on our way to see it.

HOLLAND IS A TINY PLACE with an awful lot of people. Less than
half the size of South Carolina, the country has managed to cram in
over 16 million citizens. After their border disputes settled down in
1839, the Dutch realized just how little land they were dealing with
and decided to get some more. However, they found themselves
completely surrounded, sandwiched between Germany to the east,
Belgium to the south, and the ocean everywhere else. The Dutch did
not see much potential for expansion by conquest, and so the solution was obvious, at least to them—they would just have to convert
a chunk of the ocean to dry land.

According to writers who weren't around at the time, land rec-
lamation began in the region as early as the eleventh century, or
maybe the fourteenth century, or perhaps the seventeenth century.
Without the technology available today, the enterprise really didn't
get ramped up until about 100 years ago. Before then, a wild and
turbulent arm of the ocean, the Zuiderzee, sliced a mighty swath

through the heart of the Netherlands. As far as the Dutch were concerned, the Zuiderzee was just going to have to go. Consequently, in 1932 they built the Afsluitdijk barrier dam, which stretched from the northern tip of North Holland east to Friesland, leaving a much tamer body of water, the IJsselmeer, to the south.

It then became a simple matter of dredging some ditches, using the earth to build a bunch of dykes, and pumping out the water. As a result of all that terra-forming, the Dutch managed to create a whole new province, the Flevoland, and expand the size of Holland by 10 percent. All of this mucking around did not come without consequences, of course. With several mighty rivers flowing into the IJsselmeer, the whole region turned from salt water to freshwater in about three years. If you were an ocean-dwelling creature caught on the wrong side of the Afsluitdijk, you were pretty much out of luck.

Lisa and I were rather fond of accepting invitations to weddings in exotic locales that required us to travel further than any other guests. Of course, we were working on the assumption that the invitations were genuine, and not a matter of the happy couple assuming that they could politely invite us, safe in the knowledge that we were unlikely to travel halfway around the world to attend.

We had met Sabine Muth, known to her friends as "Bini," an obstetrician/gynecologist from Germany, while we were living in Glasgow. We met her beloved Arjan de Roy soon after. We had become friends so quickly that we had been invited to their wedding. The celebration was to be held in Stavoren in northern Holland, quite close to a site of oyster invasion.

Although Stavoren is a remote and tiny community, finding it proved to be reasonably straightforward. It was largely a matter of getting on a train at Amsterdam's Schiphol airport and then making a series of random changes to trains that seemed to be going from somewhere to nowhere. A lot of other folks seemed to be going nowhere, but we managed to secure a small wedge of standing room in the atrium at the end of a carriage where luggage is normally stored. With our backpacks at our feet, we were held in place against the sway of the train by the sea of humanity around us, including eight youths drinking cheap lager from cans. This meant that we got to listen to their prattle, mostly in English, and frequently had to shift ourselves and our bags to allow the beer-fuelled young people to make trips to the toilet.

The ringleader made reference to his home, asking us: "You've heard of Amsterdam?"

"No, we have never heard of Amsterdam."

"What?"

"Biggest city in the Netherlands; place where our airplane landed; relaxed attitudes toward recreational drugs and prostitution . . . nope, we've never heard of it."

Wanting to show that he wasn't as silly as he seemed, the fellow tried to guess where we were visiting from.

"I'll give you a hint," I said. "It isn't England."

"France? Germany? Spain?"

"*Bonjour, Guten Tag,* and *Hola,* but no, none of those."

"Russia?" He was doing his best.

"Look, I'll give you another hint. I am speaking English, but we are not American."

"Australia? New Zealand?"

"And I have a big red maple leaf on my backpack."

"Then it must be Canada." He congratulated himself by opening another can of lager.

We were lucky that so many residents of the Netherlands speak English. Before leaving home, I had failed to purchase a contemporary Dutch phrase book, and so had to rely on a rather antiquated one picked up at a flea market. It was entitled *How to Get All You Want When Travelling in Holland,* and was clearly designed to meet the needs of those who were determined to make arses of themselves while travelling. The words "please" and "thank you" did not appear anywhere in the book, although I am assured that such phrases are used in Holland. I suppose a lot of the suggested phrases could have been used with greater effect in a generation earlier than mine. These included such gems as: *Wanneer komen we bij de grens?* (When shall we arrive at the frontier?); *Ik wou graag een bolhoed en enige paren zijden kousen* (I want a bowler hat and some silk stockings); and *Kruier, geef deze pakjes in bewaring. U krijgt een fooi* (Porter, put these parcels in the cloak-room. I will give you a tip). If all else failed, the pushy traveller could always fall back on *We gaan zeker ons beklag indienen bij de Spaans Consul* (We shall certainly complain to the Spanish Consul). It is hard to believe that travellers ever required expressions like *nu mijn haarpunten afschroeien* (now singe my hair) or *mijn nagels moeten geknipt worden* (my nails require cutting). To my way of thinking, the most appropriate response would be *Snijd eigen verloekte vingernagels.*

I had read that the Dutch have become very fond of outdoor sex. From the window of our train, this seemed entirely unlikely. Periodically we could see wooded landscapes that hoped to grow up to be forests. Otherwise, we saw very low-lying, canal-dissected pasture and crop land, with no relief in sight. It was pretty straight shot to the horizon. I couldn't imagine where one would have a discreet pee, let alone engage in prolonged shagging.

IN OUR QUEST FOR OYSTERS, Lisa and I were joining a strange new fraternity off limits to most. I found an 1881 document by Ernest Ingersoll describing the peculiar language used by those in the oyster industry. He told of bateaux, brogans, bugeyes, and cunners in which men would row to the oyster beds. They harvested oysters in all shapes and sizes, from blisters no bigger than a 25-cent piece to long slender stickups and coon-heels, to fancies and saddle-rocks of the highest grade. Writing of industrious men, Ingersoll described crackers, shuckers, and stabbers who opened oysters and transformed into hookers when harvesting sponges in the off-season. When shells have been opened and the contents removed, the offal left behind is called rim or gauch. Finger stalls are rubber or cotton gloves worn for protection while shucking oysters. Proggers scratch out a pitiful living on the oyster beds without real application to the task, and ten-fingers go one better by stealing the oysters of other men.

I cannot claim to have ever cracked, shucked, or stabbed an oyster. As a vegetarian, it is unlikely that I will do so anytime soon. However, in the interests of a complete story, I looked up how to do so in case you ever decide to have a go. I consulted a 964-page treatise on marine and freshwater products by Roy E. Martin of the National Fisheries Institute in Arlington, Virginia, and *The Joy of Cooking*.

First, ensure that your oysters are still alive. If they don't close their shells when handled, toss them away to avoid food poisoning. Then use a small hammer to chip a piece of shell at the margin to make it easier to insert a knife. Cut the muscle that holds the two sides of the shell together. Alternatively, you may choose to insert the knife into the shell's hinge and twist. At this point it is best to engage a friend to drive you to hospital to have your thumb sewn back on. Before departing, ask your friend to put your oysters in the refrigerator, where they will remain fresh for up to three days.

Upon your return, if you haven't lost your taste for shellfish, wash your dried blood off the knife and cut the fleshy bits from the shell. Check for particles of shell and sand, and place the flesh back in the deeper half of its shell, resting on ice. You will be pleased to know that the juices that oozed out of the oyster while cutting it open, known as liquor, can be strained and then poured over the meal before serving. I am told, although I can scarcely believe, that etiquette now requires you to swallow the oyster whole. Enjoy your meal.

ON SOME LEVEL, the wedding celebration suffered from its own success. Bini and Arjan are friendly and affable enough as individuals, and are even more engaging as a couple. Between them, the happy pair amassed a guest list of 200. To their surprise, most of this throng wrote back to say that they would be delighted to be part of the happy day in Stavoren, which promised to swell the population of the small town considerably. Beyond us, the guest list included friends from Belgium, Germany, Denmark, Switzerland, France, Sweden, the United States, and Scotland.

Bini had planned the day to within an inch of its life, and had made it clear that nothing good was going to happen to anyone who dared to show up late. There was to be a general welcome at noon, complete with pre-sailing drinks, followed by a boat trip on the IJsselmeer departing promptly at 12:30 p.m. Anyone who was late would be required to swim to the boat.

A furious wind had turned the great freshwater sea to foam, and so we sailed up and down the Johan Frisokanaal instead. Two boats were needed to accommodate all of the guests. It must have been down to some Dutch naval regulation, but having boarded one boat, we were absolutely not, under any circumstances, permitted to jump between boats, so just forget it, cowboy.

Wedding celebration day was also Nationale Molendag (National Windmill Day), on which about 600 of the nation's 1,000 windmills were opened to the public. Surprisingly, no one that I spoke to on the cruise seemed to know this. It was also Landelijke Fietsdag (National Cycling Day), but I didn't bring this up, fearing that the other guests would take me for one of those know-it-all trivia freaks. The canal was orderly, tidy and straight, with some very straight and tidy locks. By Canadian standards, the wedding party itself was far too tidy and straight. In Canada, a group like this would soon have descended to throwing beer glasses into the canal and peeing over the rail, and I briefly contemplated holding up my end by mooning passengers on a passing sailboat.

The day's celebrations continued at de Potvis, a restaurant named after the sperm whales that were hunted in the region in the past. Not itself a behemoth, the restaurant was clearly not designed to serve as many people as Bini and Arjan counted among their friends. The venue might have been able to seat us all if we had been able to spread onto the patio, but a cold wind and drizzle kept us inside. I ran out of small talk rather quickly. I faced the difficulty of speaking to persons struggling to use English as a second (or third or fourth) language, while trying to smother my embarrassment at speaking only one. I spoke with a teacher, a computer programmer, a bioengineer, an investment banker, several retirees, a dental prosthetics specialist, and a startling number of gynecologists. I asked one of them what made somebody decide to become a gynecologist. She said, "It's mainly about the babies." "So, you don't wake up one morning and decide that your life doesn't have enough vaginas?" Her glare reminded me that I am not nearly sufficiently genteel to be European.

PARTY TIME WAS OVER. It was time to seek oysters in the Wadden Sea. Stavoren, also known as Starum, is in the *súd westhoeke* region of Friesland, also known as Fryslân. To the residents of Holland, also known as the Netherlands, everything is known as something else. Getting to Stavoren isn't difficult. Getting away from Stavoren is a lot more challenging. Our target was the island of Texel in the Wadden Sea, where Lisa and I were to find Pacific oysters, also known as Japanese cupped oysters. Without a car, we were forced to take what was disparagingly referred to as the "tourist route." This meant a ferry from Stavoren to Enkhuizen, a train to Hoorn, another train to Heerhugowaard, another train to Den Helder, and then a ferry to Texel.

The Netherlands is not a really big place. Even so, we got to see an awful lot of water and this was contaminated by an incredible assortment of introduced aquatic species. These include clawed frogs from Africa, water ferns from Brazil, Pacific crabs from Japan, round gobies from Russia, tubenose gobies from Germany, slipper limpets from the U.S., pond turtles from Italy, Wels catfish from Hungary, and soft-shelled clams from Canada.

The Wadden Sea is 500 kilometres of coastal waters stretching northeast from Den Helder in the Netherlands, past Germany, and on to Denmark. It is a region of low-lying islands, sandbanks, and mud flats, and long recognized as home to incredible biological diversity, making it a sought-after refuge for citizens looking for an unspoiled corner of Europe. Those with a commercial mind think of it as an important nursery for edible North Sea marine life.

In the 1800s, the Wadden Sea had a thriving oyster fishery based on the native European oyster. But, as so often happens, the harvest was a bit too zealous, and the fishery collapsed. Over the years attempts were made to find ecological replacements for the native oyster, including the American oyster and the Portuguese oyster, but these efforts met with failure. Then came the new kid on the block.

In biology circles, the Pacific oyster has a rather nasty reputation for being where it shouldn't be, including the Wadden Sea. Around sixty countries have reported it in their coastal waters, and it has become well established in at least twenty-four. In countries including Australia, Canada, Chile, and the Netherlands, the Pacific oyster is considered to be invasive, having a negative impact on the ecosystem and/or the economy.

The Netherlands has long been a seafaring nation, and Pacific oysters have probably been arriving in the Wadden Sea for centuries, attached to the hulls of ships. For reasons not fully explored, these oysters didn't establish themselves. Then they were introduced intentionally in the hopes of re-establishing the oyster fisheries where their American and Portuguese counterparts could not. The Pacific oyster followed a pattern typical of the establishment of introduced species; their numbers remained low for a protracted period before rapidly growing in quantity and distribution. Today there are more than 60,000 tonnes of Pacific oysters living on the Wadden Sea's tidal flats. Thirty years after first being reported as a self-sustaining species, their numbers in the Netherlands show no evidence of levelling off.

Pacific oysters are filter feeders, extracting plankton and organic material from the water with great efficiency. We are most familiar with them in their adult form, with two hard shells hinged along one side. But like others of their kind, very young Pacific oysters first spend three or four weeks as tiny free-swimming larvae before settling down to mature. When first establishing themselves in an area, Pacific oysters settle on a hard substrate, such as blue mussel shells. Once the oyster population is established, young oysters are perfectly capable of settling on the shells of older oysters. They require about two years to reach a size worth eating. They don't stop there, living as long as thirty years, during which time they grow to forty centimetres in length and more than a kilogram in mass. In places, they can grow to a density of between 500 and 1,500 individuals per square metre.

How bad are Pacific oysters in the Wadden Sea? There may not be much of an oyster fishery left in the region, but native blue mussels are still harvested. In places, oysters have overgrown blue mussel beds, creating difficulties for that fishery. Oyster numbers are up and mussel numbers are down, but it has proved difficult to draw a direct line from cause to effect and rule out coincidence. Blue mussel beds are fundamental for biodiversity in the region, providing a home for myriad marine life. It is not yet clear if oyster beds will provide the same foundation. The Pacific oyster is now a dominating species on Wadden Sea tidal mud flats and may, in the future, profoundly alter the ecology of the region.

France harvests about 150,000 tonnes of Pacific oysters annually. However, this is a fishery based on cultured oysters that are harvested when they are small. Wild Pacific oysters are not attractive to the consumer. They develop in huge clumps, grow so large as to be unpalatable, and come to the table covered with barnacles and other encrusted sea life.

AMONG THE COUNTLESS PROBLEMS associated with cellular telephones is the fact that I don't have one. Moreover, when you try to call a cellphone from a payphone, you need to shovel in coins at a furious rate. So when Lisa and I discovered that some feeble-minded city planner had put the end of the rail line in Den Helder on the opposite side of town from the ferry that would take us to Texel, we had to call my contact, Norbert Dankers, on his cellphone to tell him about the delay.

Almost as soon as the call was connected, the payphone started to beep to tell me that my 50 cents had been used up. As Norbert began to give me instructions to the ferry terminal, I dug out a €1 coin, and stuffed it into the hungry slot. "Look for a big town square then BEEP BEEP BEEP." Another euro. ". . . Go straight ahead until you see BEEP BEEP BEEP." By this point, I was out of

€1 coins, and the box then proceeded to ignore the parade of other coins I stuck into it, choosing instead to beep at me until I hung up.

The ferry to Texel was big and zoomy, and decorated in all the latest designer colours. After a twenty-minute ride, we found Norbert waiting for us with a van from the Royal Netherlands Institute for Sea Research. Norbert explained that the ferry was a little more crowded than normal because the region had been visited by its first humpback whale in 300 years, and folks were flocking to the region to see it.

With a grey beard and wire-rimmed glasses, Norbert is a classic example of a field biologist. Three years from retirement, he had a face that showed the effects of many mornings spent in a bracing wind. However, as a resident of the Land of the Super-fit Citizen, he cycles ten kilometres to and from work every day. Not satisfied with this, he trains once a week with a cycling group to improve his speed. That is before his training to run half-marathons.

In Norbert's office at the Institute, we were joined by Rob Dekker and Gerhard Cadée, both with an interest in introduced species and the way that these creatures fit themselves into the local food web. They began filling us in.

When considering the potential impact of introduced species, they explained, it is important to assess whether or not local species are suffering from the intrusion. The intruder might be finding its own little niche and simply fitting in. Are Pacific oysters messing things up for the local fauna? Mussels are generally between 30 and 40 percent meat, and the rest is shell. In some regions where Pacific oysters have become very abundant, the meat of mussels has fallen to 18 percent.

Not all the mussel beds in the Wadden Sea have been taken over by oysters. However, as with all such things, it is hard to predict what the eventual outcome might be. In other regions, attempts to remove them have cost €30,000 per hectare. If an effort were made to try to control oysters in the Wadden Sea, we were told, it would probably require ten full-time ships.

Lisa and I heard that once Pacific oysters have grown to full size, and after they have reached reproductive age, they are very stress-tolerant. They can deal with low salinity, and it takes exposure at low tide at $-10°C$ to kill them. Lisa admired the shell of a particularly crenulated oyster that Norbert said was the result of the chemical tributyltin (TBT), an anti-fouling agent painted on ships' hulls to discourage barnacles and other nasty hitchhikers. TBT didn't kill Pacific oysters; it just made their shells more ornate.

Much of the Netherlands is either created or transformed landscape. Islands like Texel are just about the last bit of unaltered area of their type—naturally created and constantly moving sandbanks. We heard that the North Sea is overfished, but as it's a marine environment, people cannot directly see the damage and so have trouble imagining the scale of the destruction. In contrast, the coastal portions of the Wadden Sea are exposed at low tide; you can see the area, and so people become involved in its preservation. There is interest in having the Wadden Sea established as a World Heritage Site. The region is generally thought to play an important ecological and economic role and is recognized as an important nursery for North Sea fishes.

THE FELLOW WHO CHECKED US in to our hotel in Den Burg was the very model of a company man. As he waved his shaven head at us hypnotically, he explained that the hotel restaurant was a fine place to dine. "It can be put on your bill!" We said that we would probably find something to eat in town. He went on to extol the virtues of the hotel's bar, explaining that the tab could be put on the bill. "Well, that sounds nice," we said, even though it didn't. We asked about our options for renting bicycles. "I can make a reservation for you and put it on your bill." Lisa asked for alternatives. He responded: "Rent a bicycle or rent a car." We allowed him to make the bicycle reservation and put it on our bill.

"I am sure that you will want this guidebook. It has everything you will want to know about Texel. It has maps."

"I have good maps."

"It has a tide table for Texel."

"I downloaded a tide table for Texel."

"It has everything," he claimed. Lisa asked if he had an English version.

"No, just Dutch and German."

"But we don't read Dutch or German."

"I can put it on your bill." After that much sales effort, I let him put it on our bill. If Lisa hadn't been with me, I suspect he would have offered to find me a prostitute and put her on my bill.

In the town's main square, we found a nice little restaurant that served pancakes and the products of the Texel *bierbrouwerij*. On offer was Texels Amber and Texels Goud, but I settled on a Texels Witbier. It was close enough to vile as to be quite refreshing. Lisa pointed out that the restaurant's music system played nothing but mid-'70s one-hit wonders. We watched the parade of cyclists, from pre-schoolers through advanced seniors, with not a helmet in sight. As a young boy, I probably would have donned a wig and called myself "Brenda" before I would have put my leg over a girls' bike, the type with no cross-bar. On Texel, there was no obvious "thing" about a man riding a girls' bike.

THE DAWN PROVIDED BEAUTIFUL SUNNY SKIES and no wind. Slathered in SPF 20 sunblock, Lisa and I set off for the bicycle rental shop. This was pretty brave of me. The last time Lisa had got on a bicycle, about fifteen years earlier, she had swerved out of control and run me down. Growing up in rural Alberta, surrounded by gravel roads, Lisa had never come to terms with pedal power. But, she explained, she would have felt foolish trying to get around Texel any other way. It was going to be transportation the way the locals did it or nothing at all. She had been worried about having no control and swerving into the path of oncoming Dutch seniors. But once she got over trying to grip the handlebars too hard, she developed a mastery of her two-wheeled beast and was left with a sense of personal accomplishment. "I even managed to signal twice without going out of control." She used the expression "KaPEEba" to indicate what the crash would have sounded like, and I resisted the temptation to ask what part of the collision would have made that sound.

We set out from Den Burg along scenic and perfectly flat bicycle paths, past Oosterend, along a nasty detour for road construction near Oost, and on to the Lancasterdijk that separates the low-lying parts of the island from the Wadden Sea. The dyke was given its name in commemoration of the crew of an Allied Lancaster bomber that crashed there in WWII.

We reached the sea about an hour before low tide would expose the oysters, and so watched shorebirds foraging on sea life left behind by the receding waters. Adjacent fields were filled with lapwings, spoonbills, and avocets. We also watched a rich cross-section of the island's residents and visitors cycle by. Many of these cyclists were considerably older than us, and were probably pedalling further. If I were to move to Texel, I suppose I would have to begin a diet of muesli and mega-vitamins just to keep up.

Lisa and I leaned back on the Lancaster dyke, soaking up the sun, eating almond pastries and waiting for the sea to recede. We didn't really know what a Pacific oyster bed might look like from the shore, but big black smudges were being revealed at the water's edge some hundreds of metres away. We walked across the tidal flat, trying to choose a route to the biggest smudge that would be least disturbing to the birds foraging on what the outgoing tide had left behind.

As we proceeded, the smudges revealed themselves as patches of oysters. Shoal beds, they stretched a couple of hundred metres. Ugly little devils. Rob had told us that they are unappealing to eat because they are too big to swallow in one gulp. They were grey, corrugated, rock hard, and cemented to everything else in sight. In turn, everything else was cemented to them, including barnacles, snails, and red and brown algae.

You have to give Pacific oysters in the Wadden Sea a high score on the yuck scale even before getting to the squishy bit on the inside. They would probably be best described as beautiful when covered at high tide. Lisa claimed to be surprised that there weren't more of them, given the big hype. Nasty-Pacific-oysters-as-far-as-the-eye-can-see sort of thing. But it was clear that if they continued to spread, occupying more and more of the intertidal zone, Pacific oysters would become an ecological force to be reckoned with.

We played in the sea for about an hour, collecting particularly nice examples of each shell type we saw, after ensuring that their owners and everything attached to them had died. On that day, it seemed that being a biologist was an excuse to splish-splash in the water, get muddy, pick up dead stuff, and get paid for doing it. It was an excuse to be a four-year-old child without an authority figure hovering over you. Standing in any one spot too long was ill-advised, as black organic ooze crept up from under the clean tan-coloured sand and engulfed our feet, making the whole experience that bit more delightfully gross.

We cycled south along the coast to a second spot that Norbert had recommended and watched as the sea retreated further from land. As it did, it exposed more indistinct black smudges, but much further out. I contemplated whether I had seen enough oysters for one day or whether I should tromp out to this next group. One ugly oyster is pretty much like another, right? But my conscience got the better of me. First, I had come a very long way to see Pacific oysters, and surely more was better than less. Second, I knew that Norbert would ask me whether I had visited both sites. And so, with Lisa reclining on the dyke, I set off across the sands.

Or rather, I set off across sands covered everywhere by five centimetres of sea. No matter what my route, each step submerged my sandals and toes, but not my ankles. There seemed to be no way to get around flocks of birds taking advantage of the low-tide bounty. There were lots of gulls, plenty of raucous oystercatchers, with a handful each of turnstones, ducks, and geese, accompanied by endless shorebirds that even the most devout birdwatcher doesn't try to identify.

Patches of oysters became larger and more common as I got further from shore. I stepped over and around beautiful patches of red, brown, and green algae, and avoided stranded jellyfishes, knowing that their dying remains can still sting. I marvelled at tiny transparent comb jellies and strained to see minuscule transparent shrimp that could be found most easily by spotting their shadows.

And after more than twenty minutes of walking, I got to a really substantial oyster bed. It was as ugly as the biggest one at the first site, but without the fetid black ooze underfoot. But I found that I couldn't stop there. Like a magpie drawn to a broken metal watch-strap, I walked further and further out, following oyster beds that turned into oyster reefs, reaching upward from the sand. In spots, cormorants roosted on the oysters, drying their wings in a crucifix posture.

Then I remembered that along parts of Canada's east coast the tide comes in faster than a person can walk. I checked my watch and then the tide table in my pocket. The tide was returning, and I was more than a kilometre from shore. Checking the tide table again, I found that, where I was standing, the sea would reach almost exactly the crown of my head. No real need to worry though, as I had only a thirty-minute walk to shore and the tide would require six hours.

It had taken several decades, but I really felt that I was getting the hang of working for a living. Like everyone else, I had survived plenty of jobs that were less than entirely appealing and barely paid the bills. I had washed trucks, filled oxygen cylinders, unloaded empty beer bottles from trucks, and scraped bakery floors. But on this day my life as a biologist was transcendent. As the sea slowly recovered its oysters, Lisa and I watched the sun shining off clouds to the east, making a stunning reflection in the wet sand. Lisa was in such a good mood that she indicated that she would be willing to eat an oyster if it would help my narrative. I explained that it wasn't part of her job description.

CHAPTER THREE

The Attack of the Killer Rhododendrons

REASON NUMBER THREE FOR INTRODUCING A FOREIGN SPECIES: BECAUSE I NEED TO REPLACE THE TREES I CUT DOWN.

WHEN IT COMES TO BIG, BOLD, AND BEAUTIFUL FLOWERS, it is hard to beat a rhododendron. You also have to give them big points for variety; there is something like 1,000 recognized species, supplemented by all manner of hybrids. Colourful and showy to a fault, they have a wealth of admirers. In Victorian Britain, there was no shortage of adventurers willing to travel to eastern Asia and risk their hides in order to collect new species of rhododendron and bring them back to England. This troupe included such luminary botanists as Joseph Hooker, who brought back about thirty species, and the aptly named George Forrest, who hauled home an astonishing 300 species. Today, rhododendron fanciers' clubs are found everywhere the plant can be cultivated. Rhododendrons have even been named the state flowers of Washington (*Rhododendron macrophyllum*) and West Virginia (*Rhododendron maximum*).

And this is all well and good, because most species of rhododendron know how to sit still and shut up. But at any large party, there is always one guest who doesn't know when to stop drinking or when to go home. In the world of large and showy flowering plants, that unruly guest is *Rhododendron ponticum,* sometimes called the common rhododendron, which is native to parts of southern Europe and the Middle East. The great ancient oak forests of Ireland, Scotland, and Wales are under attack from this pushy introduced monster. Despite being a big and blustery plant, it was largely unknown in Ireland until the mid-1900s. But from then on, its destructive ways were well understood by anyone who loved oak forests. The plant has even been given an Irish Gaelic name—*ródaideandrón.* I was off to a national park in Ireland's southwest to find it.

Rhododendrons are not the only botanical import to the Emerald Isle. According to Sylvia Reynolds of Ireland's National Botanic Gardens, almost as many alien plant species have been uncovered in Ireland as there are plants native to the country. Although humans have been bringing new plants to the British Isles since Neolithic times, the last two centuries have seen a rapid acceleration, with 920 human-introduced plant forms arriving in Ireland. One of the most influential plant additions to the country was the potato, and I was determined to find a few of those too.

My only previous trip to Ireland had not gone entirely well. I had travelled to Dublin to examine a stuffed Labrador Duck, and despite trying with all my heart to love the country, I had found Dublin noisy and crowded, simultaneously uncivilized and overly civilized. On this return trip to Ireland, I promised myself that I would steer well clear of large cities, stick to tourist-approved venues, drink only in the most highly regarded pubs, and lodge in only the friendliest hostelries in the land.

Arriving at Shannon airport, I had my first and only pleasant surprise of the day; at no extra charge, the car rental agency had upgraded me to a much bigger vehicle. "Big" is, of course, a relative word. By North American standards, this car was a tiddler, but I was pleased to see that my backpack fit in the boot, and my legs fit under the steering wheel.

My newly purchased travel guide to southwestern Ireland used less than flattering terms to describe Limerick City, which, "at first sight has something rather drab about it." The guidebook suggested that visitors to the city, despite the community's recent face-lift, wouldn't find anything much cheerier on the second, or indeed any subsequent, viewing. But unless your destination is the tiny community of Newmarket-on-Fergus, travelling from Shannon to anywhere else in Ireland requires a dissection of Limerick.

And High Holy Almighty, what a trip it was. I could deal with being on the wrong side of the road, and managed the stick shift in my left hand like a professional, but the roads were far too narrow for driving habits developed on mighty North American thorough-fares. For the first time—but certainly not the last—I wished that I had insisted on the smaller rental car. I had navigation notes for the best route through Limerick on the seat beside me, but they proved entirely useless as I repeatedly spotted street signs too late to make necessary lane changes. I eventually gave up on my notes and started looking for signs for route N20 on the assumption that it would eventually lead me to the N21 and south through the wilds of County Limerick.

I SUSPECT THAT THERE IS NO WAY to fully appreciate the history of Ireland without understanding the impact of potatoes, known as *práta* in Irish Gaelic. To understand potatoes in Ireland, you have to understand Sir Walter Raleigh. This is a challenge all by itself; even straightforward details like the year of his birth and the proper spelling of his surname are not beyond debate. Some authorities claim that when Raleigh returned to the British Isles from one of his expeditions to North America, perhaps his 1587 trip, he brought spuds back with him. Others claim that Thomas Hariot should get the credit for introducing potatoes to the Old World. Some of those who favour the Raleigh story give him credit for planting potatoes at his Irish estate at Myrtle Grove, Youghal. Others claim that the first cultivation of potatoes in Ireland occurred at Castle Matrix when Raleigh turned them over to Lord Southwell. I was not due to travel anywhere near Myrtle Grove, but my rhododendron adventure was going to take me close to Castle Matrix, and so I conveniently chose to believe that this was the site of the potato's first cultivation in Ireland.

Potatoes grew better than just about any other crop in the stony soils of the Emerald Isle, and soon came to completely dominate the diet of Irish peasants. Potatoes contain little protein, and in centuries past, in order to meet their nutritional needs some folks consumed between four and six kilograms of potatoes each day. Putting this much faith in just one crop is a pretty risky thing. One bad harvest is going to leave you rather hungry. One total crop failure and you and your family are going to starve to death. This is exactly what happened in Ireland in the mid-1840s. A parasitic water mould known as *Phytophthora infestans* causes late blight of potatoes, and in one week in the summer of 1846 the blight destroyed virtually the entire Irish potato crop. Between famine and emigration, the population of Ireland fell from 8.5 million to 6.5 million in just six years.

The community of Adare lies southwest of Limerick, and Rathkeale lies southwest of Adare. If my guidebook was to be trusted, Castle Matrix could be found just southwest of Rathkeale, although I was damned if I could find it or anything that looked, sounded, or tasted like it. I couldn't find a single helpful sign. I began to wonder if all the signs come down in the off-season, or whether the lack of useful signs was a way to get tourists to stop at convenience stores to ask for directions. I stopped at a convenience store, but when I asked the young fellow behind the counter about Castle Matrix, he just gave me a big shrug. As I reached the door on the way out he called, "Not from around here." I don't know if he was referring to me or to himself.

After my failure to find Castle Matrix, I mistakenly trusted my guidebook when it suggested that I might want to travel to Ballingary and from there find the hillside at Knockfierna, site of a well-preserved famine village. Before the famine, Knockfierna was home to 1,000 people. Only 300 remained after. A heritage group had developed a park to commemorate those persons lost to the famine, with restored dwellings of the former residents. But all of this came to nothing for me, because I could find neither evidence of Knockfierna nor anyone to point me in the right direction. On the road to Ballingary, a fellow in a grey Land Cruiser tucked in behind me and tailgated me for the next five kilometres. As we approached the town, I slowed down for schoolchildren, and the Land Cruiser took the opportunity to zoom by me. The driver also took the opportunity to give me the finger.

In a last-ditch effort to find something linked to the potato famine in Ballingary, I headed for the local churchyard. I was hoping to find graves of people who had died in or around 1846. Many of the headstones were too new for persons carried off by the famine, but a few stones had been rubbed nearly smooth by time, hosting a thick crust of lichen. James Reidy had prepared a headstone for his wife, Mary, who died on March 23, 1910, at the age of seventy-four. Hence, Mary would have survived the famine as a young girl.

In three ways, southwest Ireland is like Prince Edward Island on Canada's east coast. Both spots are populated by people of Irish ancestry. People in both regions are really big on cultivating potatoes. Finally, in both places it is assumed that everyone knows where they are, and knows how to get to where they need to be. If you can find a road sign in southwest Ireland, rest assured that it won't be helpful. Three roads leading out of Ballingary were signposted to lead to Newcastle West (An Caisleán Nua), my next destination. I took the road with the newest-looking sign. At a crossroad a bit further along, a sign indicated that I could get to Kilmallock by turning left, but gave no hint of how to get to Newcastle West. I turned right.

This was probably a mistake. About ten kilometres later, I spotted a gigantic broken curb jutting into the road the instant before it tore a hole the size of a €2 coin in my front right sidewall. I kept control of the car and pulled into a quiet side street.

Before leaving Shannon airport, I had paid the rental agency a lot of money for the best possible car insurance and the promise of roadside assistance. In the hope that I could get someone

else to change my tire, I set off to find a public telephone. Coming
to a crossroad, I found a sign that told me I could turn right for
Limerick or left for Tralee. Still no indication of how I could get
to Newcastle West, and no telephone box in sight. I hailed a fellow pedestrian, only to be told, "I don't speak." To Canadians in
particular, or as a matter of general principle? While I was hauling
the flat tire off my rental, a big white lorry pulled up, and the driver
stuck his head out the window. He asked me if I had a puncture,
and I thought for a moment that he was going to offer to help me
put on the spare. Instead, he looked the car up and down, told me
that new cars aren't supposed to get punctures, and drove off.

When I finally found Newcastle West and my hotel, I called
the rental car agency's roadside assistance hotline. I was told that
my super-duper, extra-costly, truly special, all-inclusive insurance
package included everything except tires. If the car had gone over a
cliff, they would have been straight out with a replacement vehicle,
but I was on my own when it came to the punctured tire.

Of all the towns in southwest Ireland, I had chosen to spend the
night in Newcastle West because of an entry in my guidebook that
described Duggan's Pub on Bridge Street as having a fine selection
of beer. Trying to walk off the tension of the day, I followed street
signs toward the town centre, reasoning that Bridge Street would
have a bridge, that a bridge would cross a river, and that a river
would be a good place for a town centre. When I found Duggan's
Pub, a sign above the door proclaimed Frank and Kathy Duggan as
Proprietors. A big metal gate barred the entrance, and the welcome
mat, buried under competing levels of dirt and junk mail, hadn't
welcomed a drinker in quite some time. My guidebook was clearly
in need of an update.

I am told that the Atlantic Ocean's Gulf Stream carries warm
water north from the Caribbean to the coast of Europe, keeping
Ireland unusually warm for its latitude. I am also told that some
experts fear that global climate change brought on by greenhouse
gas emissions could cause the Gulf Stream to stop flowing. On a
cool and drizzly evening in Newcastle West, it was hard to believe

that the Gulf Stream hadn't already come to a screeching halt. As I trudged back to the hotel, I stumbled across Newcastle West's Famine Cemetery. Now little more than an overgrown field twice the size of a tennis court, it is the resting spot for locals who had perished in the famine following the potato blight.

I HAD BEEN TOLD that the Ring of Kerry around the Iveragh Peninsula was beautiful beyond belief, and that no trip to Ireland's southwest could be considered complete without its circumnavigation. It should be just the place to find my first rhododendrons. My guidebook suggested that, without detours, the 180-kilometre road around the Ring of Kerry could be driven in three hours. This might be true for a professional driver in a Ferrari with racing suspension if the road was closed to all other traffic. I began to suspect that the woman who had written the guidebook had never been to the Ring of Kerry. Or indeed, to Ireland.

The roads were twisting and painfully narrow, and I found I could afford only brief glimpses of the hills around me. Dairy cattle that dotted the hills were befriended by a smaller number of sheep. Stone houses, stone bridges, and stone walls were constructed from pickings of the stony soil. I needed a break, and pulled over at a wayside rest stop populated by an elderly gentleman who offered to take my picture with his donkey. I declined, and stared out over the hills, which were decorated in a thousand shades of green, punctuated by periodic flashes of blinding golden-yellow gorse bushes.

The donkey, his handler, and I were soon joined by two tour buses, which disgorged their passengers to share the view with us. The visitors were all from New Jersey, and I indulged in my hobby of offering to take their photos with their cameras. Over the next ten minutes, the photo groups got bigger and bigger, and I had to step further and further back to get everyone in. I bumped into the donkey.

Highway officials in Ireland are an optimistic lot. They seem to have no reservations about posting 100 kilometre per hour speed-limit signs in spots where that kind of velocity existed only in dreams. I had trouble averaging 50. White lines had been neatly applied to the road, but wherever it became too narrow for two lanes of traffic, the lines simply trailed off into the adjacent field. It didn't help that touring cyclists lurked around every corner, and where no footpath existed, trail walkers tromped the middle of the road.

I got my first good look at rhododendrons as I approached the community of Waterville (An Coireán), toward the far western reaches of the Ring of Kerry. Waterville knows full well that it is a resort town, and has no pretence about being anything else. It is the sort of place that you might want to visit for a week during the worst weather of the off-season. You could walk the whole town in your first two hours, confident in the knowledge that you had absolutely nothing else to do for the remainder of your stay but rest.

I was particularly keen to see palm trees and fuchsia plants promised by my guidebook. Both were introduced to Ireland, and both were beneficiaries of the Gulf Stream's warming influence. I found a few palm trees, but a lot more palm bushes, mainly in front of the Butler Arms Hotel. After two hours of walking up and through and around Waterville, I had seen not a single fuchsia.

I searched for famine victims in the churchyard of St. Michael's and All Angels, but found none. I did, however, find a lot of Huggards, some of whom had survived the potato blight, including

> Elizabeth, wife of Richard, died Dec 21 1904, aged 80;
> Martin, son of Thos. died 17 Sept 1896, aged 88;
> Mary, died 23 Sept 1896, aged 86;
> and Rebecca, died 9 December 1879, aged 40.

Only then did it occur to me why I was likely having such trouble finding the headstones of anyone who had died in the famine. So rapid was the crop damage brought on by the blight, and so reliant was the populace on potatoes, that people in this part of Ireland died so quickly that the survivors were unable to keep up with the niceties of formal burials and fancy headstones. There were probably the remains of a lot of famine victims in mass graves. After giving thanks for my life of abundance, I sat on a stone wall and ate my grocery-store lunch of French apple lattices, individually wrapped cheeses from Denmark and Holland, and apples from Brazil.

Rhododendrons became more common as I drove further around the Ring. At Sneem (An Snaidhm), I found them growing in abundance, first as roadside hedges, and then in bunches at a newly constructed Garden of the Senses. Away from this bit of tranquility, the south half of the Ring of Kerry was so rugged that almost every precious chunk of dry flat land had been snatched up for houses. Homes that hadn't made a reservation early enough were left clinging to rocky slopes.

Before leaving Canada, a colleague with Irish roots had insisted that I visit Staigue Fort. The fort is four kilometres up a single-cart track, at the top of a deep gorge, next to a sweet spring. Dating from the early centuries CE, Staigue was one of the largest and finest of Ireland's pre-Christian stone forts. As befits a stone fort, the walls, six metres tall and four metres wide, were made entirely of stones with not a brick or dab of mortar in sight. Chinks between boulders were filled with stone flakes. The fort has not been properly excavated by archaeologists, but that hasn't stopped experts from speculating that it had been built by a wealthy landowner or chieftain in need of great security. At one time, the fort presumably housed wooden buildings or tents, but those were long gone. The interior wall provided nine sets of switchback stairs to the wall tops. My guidebook told me that it was "fun to climb to the top," but a big, official-looking sign asked me to "PLEASE KEEP OFF THE WALL TOPS BY ORDER OF THE OFFICE OF PUBLIC WORKS." I was serenaded by the bleating of sheep and the laughter of four German visitors who hadn't paid the €1 trespassing charge requested by the farmer who owns the field.

After settling in to my bed and breakfast, I wandered the streets of Kenmare (Neidin) as evening fell. My search for a good meal gave me further reason to doubt the accuracy of the guidebook. It suggested that I was in for a "big treat" at a vegetarian restaurant on Henry Street. Having walked the length of Henry Street three times, I can state categorically that such a restaurant doesn't exist. Thinking that I must have purchased a horribly out-of-date guide-book, I checked the publication date. It was one year old. Then I checked the book's back cover and found that I had paid $26.95 too much for it. The town's church bells rang the supper hour. Settling on a pizzeria, I was surprised, but not pleasantly surprised, when my vegetarian pizza arrived with more sausage than crust.

On my post-dinner stroll I found Kenmare's neolithic stone ring was right where it was supposed to be, peering down on the River Finnihy. At the centre, one really big stone was perched neatly on some smaller stones. This was surrounded by a ring of fifteen stones of various sizes, with a diameter of about seven metres. A circle of cedars had recently been planted outside the ring, and they should be quite impressive in about thirty years. Just down the hill, three sheep got into a bleating match.

NOT SO MANY KILOMETRES out of Kenmare, the N61 reaches mountainous country where sheep pick at miserly grass beside deep gorges. As everywhere else in the southeast, the road was narrow and twisting, and as I approached the pinnacle at Moll's Gap I felt the first twinges of motion sickness.

On the far side, I stopped at a pullout at the south end of Muckross Lake to settle my stomach. I found a sign indicating that the region had suffered a recent outbreak of *Phytophthora ramorum*, another parasitic water mould and the causative agent of sudden oak death. The sign explained that *Laburnum*, an introduced, yellow-flowered tree, and *Rhododendron ponticum* were particularly vulnerable to attack by this parasite, so that neither species should be taken from the park under any circumstances to avoid spread of the disease.

With plenty of time before my scheduled afternoon meeting with a rhododendron expert, I went for a hike along an asphalt path by the lake. I tried desperately to ignore the lady squatting immediately beside the path to pee, and was almost as successful as she was in pretending she was squatting to look at moss.

I could not ignore the small rhododendron plants popping out everywhere along the path. They didn't look particularly nasty or dangerous. The trail took me to Dinis Cottage, once a hunting lodge, later a tea house, and now under renovation. The cottage was surrounded by huge, beautiful rhododendron bushes. As the asphalt path ended, a dirt trail beckoned me forward to where I found small rhododendron plants growing as epiphytes on the branches of oak trees, receiving better light than they would on the ground, but taking nothing away from the oaks. I felt relieved that, despite persistent recent efforts to eliminate rhododendrons from the park, I was able to spot a few.

Further north in the park, I stopped for a hike at Torc waterfall, where the constant crash of water tried to drown out the voices of woodland birds. Past the falls, I got my first real sense of the killer heart of *Rhododendron ponticum*. Growing in the form of a densely matted bush, but reaching three times my height, leaves survived only as a cheap crown at the top. Under the tortured rhododendron canopy, no light reached the ground, and no plants of any sort grew. Here and there an old sessile oak tree was holding its own against the newcomers, but the next generation of oaks was nowhere in sight.

There are ever so many reasons why this particular rhododendron species is such a horrible pest in Irish oak forests. Their seeds are tiny and in a good wind can disperse a kilometre from the parent plant. It is likely that the seeds are also carried on fur and feathers. The moderate climate of southwest Ireland must remind this rhododendron of home, because once the seeds settle down the plants grow rapidly, and they are tolerant of the region's slightly acidic soils. The plants contain toxins so that deer and sheep won't eat them. These rhododendron plants grow so densely that they prevent virtually all light from reaching the ground. It isn't that they kill mature oak trees, but rather that they keep new seedlings from light, so that as the forest ages, recruitment of new plants is impossible.

Just how bad was the situation for the oak forests in Killarney National Park? I had lined up an expert to tell me. Chris Barron is an education officer with the Killarney National Park Education Centre. He had generously agreed to take me to spots in the park that were heavily infested with rhododendrons and where clearance efforts had removed them. Finding rhododendrons was easy, but finding Barron was going to prove a bit difficult.

That morning, a lady at the Kenmare tourist information office had assured me that the Killarney National Park Education Centre was in Killarney town (Cill Airne), at the north end of the park. I shouldn't have trusted her; she also told me that Kenmare's stone circle dated back to the eighth century, while standing beside a display indicating that the circle was over 3,000 years old. After following a series of "i" signs to the tourist information centre in Killarney town, I was assured with absolutely no doubt or uncertainty that the Killarney National Park Education Centre was situated in the park at Muckross House, back south along the road I had just travelled. I was unable to conjure up any surprise when a young employee at Muckross House assured me that the Killarney National Park Education Centre did not exist.

Much to his credit, this young fellow skipped his coffee break to take me to the office of someone who had heard of Chris Barron and had a directory with Barron's cellphone number. At a pay telephone, I tried again and again to complete the call, only to be told by a mechanical voice that the call was impossible as dialled. I managed the impossible when I realized that Barron's cellphone number counted as an international call.

"Chris?"

"Yes."

"It's Glen."

"Glen who?"

"Glen Chilton . . . The biologist from overseas . . . We were going to meet today to talk about rhododendrons . . ."

"Oh. Was that today?"

"Yes. Is it a bad day for you?"

"No. Where are you now? Muckross House? I'll meet you there at half-three."

Barron is an ecologist by training, and his car reflects it. It is a bit ratty, which is a perfect situation when you spend your day jumping in and out with muddy boots. The car was decorated throughout with bird feathers, seashells, sea urchins, and an assortment of outdoor clothing. Barron had earned a university graduate degree in Wales for his studies of rhododendrons. Most field biologists come to be very fond of their study species. Not so Barron. He hates rhododendrons, and hates the grazing sheep that wander illegally into the national park from surrounding areas. Barron's wife was also a biologist who had just finished a major report on rhododendrons in the region. Barron's brother also has a job eliminating rhododendrons, demonstrating that eradicating introduced species can be a family affair.

Barron explained that the rhododendron situation in Killarney National Park is not a simple one. It is clear that the original sites of infestation were Dinis Cottage and Muckross House, and that rhododendrons were first planted there about 150 years ago, probably for their ornamental value. At the time, some spots in the region had been cleared of their oak trees, and therefore had poor natural cover. Recognizing that rhododendrons grew very quickly, landowners had probably planted them for their shelter value. Today Muckross House has some monster rhododendrons with trunks the size of my torso, but these are a different species of rhododendron, not nearly so invasive. A big patch of *Rhododendron ponticum* in front of Muckross House, a potential source of seeds, had been eliminated some years earlier.

At one time, Ireland was almost entirely blanketed by forests. Today, it is considered to be Europe's least-wooded nation, and preservation of remaining oak forests is a very high priority. A management plan survey completed in 1990 showed that 75 percent of forest sites in the 11,000-hectare Killarney National Park were infested with the nasty type of rhododendron. Now, after twenty years of clearance efforts, major chunks of the park have been freed from its grip.

In that period, three forms of control had been tried. The efforts of contract workers didn't work as well as was hoped, possibly because of a lack of follow-up to make sure they had done the job properly. Attempts to control rhododendrons by park staff also didn't work. For a spell, rhododendron duty was seen by park personnel as punishment for stepping out of line. More successful are the efforts of a non-profit group called Groundwork operating out of Dublin. Groundwork started off in 1981 as a small collection of Irish students with an environmental conscience. Willing to tackle an assortment of environmental challenges in Ireland, their chief mission is the elimination of rhododendrons from oak forests. Through three summer months, visitors from around the world sign on for one- or two-week work camps, dedicating themselves to rhododendron Armageddon. Volunteers stay in a hostel in Killarney National Park and travel each day to the site where their attentions are most needed.

Because winds in the region generally blow from the west, and rhododendron seeds disperse long distances in the wind, clearance efforts proceed from west to east. The slopes of Torc are among the most heavily infested, but as the region was cleared of its oak trees many years ago, it is not the highest priority for rhododendron removal. In those regions where oak still stand, they continue to provide viable seeds, and an area can establish a new generation of oak even after forty years of rhododendron infestation. With luck, the seeds of other forest plants are still sitting dormant in the soil, waiting to germinate when conditions are right, or perhaps they will blow in from other forested regions. If so, the oak forest community may be able to re-establish its former glory and complexity.

To get rid of rhododendrons, the first step is to cut them down or dig them up. Then you wait a year or so for the plants to try to grow back, and kill the new growth. The site needs to be revisited every few years to kill new rhododendron shoots. Many years must pass before an area can be declared free of the noxious plants. Barron explained that burning the chopped and uprooted rhododendrons would seem like an ideal end to them, but environmental legislation prevents that. Instead, the dead plants are woven into massive fences that resist decay and act as a barrier to grazing deer and sheep.

According to Barron, dried rhododendron wood burns really well. Since it is illegal to take rhododendron wood out of the park, cut wood piles up. Driving from one locale to another, we passed a fellow filling the back of his car with rhododendron logs. When Barron slowed down to have a good look, the fellow jumped into his car and sped off.

As we wandered hills close to the highway, Barron pointed out the remains of abandoned "lazy beds," where the scant earth had been pulled into hilly rows suitable for growing potatoes many years before. I spotted the bones of a largish mammal. "I hope it's a sheep," said Barron. It seems that removing rhododendrons is only half the battle in restoring oak forests. Deer and sheep might not eat rhododendrons, but they are perfectly willing to chow down on young oak seedlings.

These bones were not from a sheep, but from a Sika deer, another introduced pest. According to its promotional material, Killarney National Park is home to Ireland's only remaining wild herd of native red deer. The genetic integrity of red deer is threatened by hybridization with Sika deer. Barron explained that hybridization is less of a problem than generally claimed. The local population of red deer is genetically pure, and the Sika deer are the most genetically pure anywhere outside of Japan. The two do not hybridize in the park. They do so further to the east, and hybrid populations are moving toward the park, but that is a concern for future generations of conservation biologists.

I WANTED TO CONTRAST the difficulties brought on by rhododendrons in the oak forests of Ireland, Wales, and Scotland with the beauty of ornamental rhododendrons growing peacefully where they were planted. In my last act of rapidly dying faith in my guidebook, I aimed for Annes Grove Historic Irish Gardens. These gardens were said to be awash in rhododendrons of every description, collected from all over the world. This sort of gardening seems to me a demonstration of belief in the acts that survive us; young rhododendrons are planted with loving care in the certainty that their best floral displays will come long after the gardener has died.

Travelling east from Killarney, my first great trick was to navigate the narrow streets of Mallow. Not ever such a big town, Mallow certainly has big traffic problems. Delivery trucks are longer and wider than any street in town, where they clog any sensible vehicular progress. The road system was well signed to take me back to Killarney, but not so keen to show me how to move forward. I found no fewer than three signs willing to send me off in what I knew was the wrong direction. All three were the sort of temporary plastic sign that normally read "Real Art Sale This Saturday at the Airport Holiday Inn" or "Jim's Landscaping: No Job Too Small!!!" At first I thought the misleading signs might have been printed and erected by someone with a poorly developed sense of humour. On my third trip down the main street, I concluded that they had been put up by the Town Council in the hopes that weary travellers would eventually need a restaurant or a hotel. Or a mortician.

Halfway between the towns of Mallow and Fermoy (Mainstir Fhearmuighe), Annes Grove Historic Irish Gardens should have been easy to find. The gardens' website indicated that once I got to Castletownroche, I was to turn left at Batterberry's Pub and then follow the signs. I found Batterberry, but it was a grocery store, not a pub, and it wasn't at an intersection. I also found a butcher shop offering a free turnip with every piece of bacon purchased. I spotted a pub called Dany's, and since it was at an intersection, I turned left.

The gardened estate has been in the family of Arthur Grove Annesley for more than two centuries. I was greeted at the entrance by a delightful lady who gave the impression she felt more at ease in her rubber boots than she would in stilettos, and felt closer to God's heart in a garden than anywhere else on Earth. Cats circled her feet. Explaining that I had come to Annes Grove to see the rhododendrons, I was told I had arrived at exactly the right time. Although they had lost some of the larger blooms to a late frost, I was assured that at this time of year "the rhododendrons go off like firecrackers!" I told her I would keep my head down and wear protective eyewear. In exchange for €6, I was given ticket No. 008466, a descriptive brochure, and instructions to proceed to the car park "six or seven kilometres down the way." It was two kilometres. Perhaps my host hadn't fully come to terms with the metric system.

The gardens are described as "a supreme expression of gardening in the Robinsonian manner," which, I gather, means an amalgamation of native and exotic plants with little concern for formality. This was a spot without pretension, without artifice, and without any other visitors. In a walled garden rich in small surprises, I was greeted by the din of birdsong. Backswimmers dodged patches of duckweed in a water feature, and low topiary showed the results of loving attention. I wandered past cedar, magnolia, and arbutus, skipped between patches of bamboo and carpets of ivy, and slipped by a couple of skulking Ring-necked Pheasants. A few steps later I found a couple of shotgun casings, and wondered if they had been used to nab a pheasant for a traditional Christmas dinner.

I can imagine some visitors complaining that there is nothing to do at Annes Grove. There are no interpretive signs, no labels, no interactive displays, no café, and no gift shop. To me this was part of the site's great joy. All alone, I was reluctant to tread too heavily, and even the click of my camera's shutter seemed thunderous.

But click I did. The previous day's encounter with *Rhododendron ponticum* hadn't even hinted at the variety available in the world of rhododendrons. From twiggy saplings through vast shrubs and on to towering trees. New words will have to be coined to describe the range of colours and hues of rhododendron flowers, all vying for the attention of pollinators in the dappled morning light. I was surrounded by tiny flowers in small bunches and huge flowers in enormous displays.

Then I traipsed down the hillside, through a bog, and on to the Awbeg River, which was in no special hurry to get anywhere. I spotted trout (*breac*) lazily holding their position in the current. They were brown spotted fingers against the brown rocky riverbed, and as they twisted they provided silvery flashes from scales on their backs. I took them to be rainbow trout, one of about a dozen fresh-water fish species introduced to Ireland.

I started to envy the trout. Before departing Ireland, I still had to find lunch in Castletownroche, and would then have to face a five-kilometre tailback at Fermoy brought on by roadworks. Inter-change construction at Cork city (Corcaigh) meant that all of my road maps would be useless. I would then have to navigate the streets of Kinsale (Cionn tSáile), never designed for vehicular traf-fic, and battle for the one parking spot that hadn't already been nabbed, before searching for Ireland's best-hidden hotel. The next morning I would face a hellish delay brought on by crushing fog at Cork airport, requiring travellers to catch coaches to connecting flights in Kerry and Dublin. In contrast, with the least flicks of their tails, trout in Awbeg River could remain in one spot, facing the cur-rent, and have everything of value float downstream to them.

CHAPTER FOUR

The Last of the Mynas

**REASON NUMBER FOUR FOR INTRODUCING A FOREIGN SPECIES:
BECAUSE I WANT TO TAKE MY PET ALONG WHEN I LEAVE HOME.**

I HAD A ROMANTIC VISION of what it would be like to engage in a quest for Crested Mynas in Vancouver. My wife, Lisa, and I would drive west out of Calgary on a crisp early autumn day and head for the Rocky Mountains in our steel-grey Land Rover, completely ignoring the fact that to drive a Land Rover we would have to steal one. We would stare in rapture at stands of larch, with their needles turning gold against the backdrop of rich green lodgepole pine. We would drive through the southeastern mountains of British Columbia, marvelling at the early snow in Rogers Pass, all of it piled neatly at the side of the road. Because it was a romantic vision with precious little regard for reality, the town of Golden wouldn't be blanketed in fog, the vegetation around Kamloops would be verdant, and all of the glacial motorhomes would have gone back to Saskatchewan. Arriving in Vancouver, we would seek out the Crested Myna in the ancient Douglas-fir forests of Burnaby, Richmond, and New Westminster. Hundreds of mynas would dart to and fro, singing sweetly, and engage us with their plumage of gold, azure, and flame, and their precision aerobatics.

Life is rarely as attractive as my romantic visions. First off,

Crested Mynas are not multicoloured, unless "multi" means two, and "colour" means black and white. To get a sense of Crested Mynas, imagine a crow that came out of the clothes dryer a little smaller than it went in, or a starling that had never heard of Jenny Craig. Dab a little whiteout on its wings, allow it a really bad hair day, and you have got a Crested Myna. Although they are technically songbirds, it takes a great leap of imagination to describe their shrieking, screeching utterances as songs.

Second, whatever majestic Douglas-fir forests once existed on the Lower Mainland of British Columbia have long since been cut down and replaced by hoards of high-rise apartments, fast-food restaurants, and noisy highways. Not that it really mattered; as I was about to see, Crested Mynas in Vancouver have never been really big on beautiful habitat.

Finally, I knew that Vancouver Crested Mynas, the only population in North America, had been in steady decline for quite some time. What I hadn't realized was just how close they were to local extinction. Word came to me through Vancouver contacts that if I wanted to see Crested Mynas, I had bloody well better hurry up, as they weren't doing very well at all. And so, instead of a lovely autumn drive through the mountains with my wife, I found myself in a boarding lounge at Calgary International Airport, looking out the window at a Boeing 737–700 surrounded by a February snowstorm, while trying to ignore the promise of freezing rain.

THE CRESTED MYNA is endemic to China, Vietnam, and a few of the smaller and potentially more dangerous nations in Southeast Asia, where they are presumably doing quite well, thank you very much. As far as anyone knows, they were brought to Vancouver as pets by Chinese immigrants in the 1890s. But nothing remains captive forever. When it comes to mynas in Vancouver, some people imagine an accidental escape, while others speak of an ornery ship's captain or an insane customs agent who intentionally let them go. My own pet theory is that a couple of birds outlived their owner, and the family, growing tired of their raucous din, tossed them out to fend for themselves. In any case, one or possibly two pairs of mynas managed to establish themselves in the wilds of metropolitan Vancouver in the dying years of the nineteenth century. Considering the City of Vancouver itself wasn't incorporated until 1886, mynas must surely have some claim to landed immigrant status.

From these humble beginnings, the randy little beggars managed impressive population growth. No one undertook a really good population estimate at the time, but at the mynas' peak there may have been as many as 20,000 individuals in four city blocks of Vancouver. They roosted in sufficient numbers that residents in the affected neighbourhoods protested about the great mounds of myna faeces they had to wash off their cars each morning. Mynas went on to establish a breeding population in Nanaimo on Vancouver Island, and another in Seattle, Washington. Unlike the population in Vancouver, these did not persist. They tried to set up shop in Victoria in 1946, but ran afoul of a little shotgun-aided population regulation.

And then, for reasons not fully explored, the myna numbers went into something of a tailspin. By the 1960s, they were down to a few thousand, then to a few hundred in the early 1990s. An extensive survey by members of the Vancouver Natural History Society in 1999 revealed just five individuals. As my flight left the tarmac in Calgary, there were thought to be only two Crested Mynas remaining on the entire North American continent. I was off to find them.

How hard could it be? Vancouver has an area of 113 square kilometres, and two Crested Mynas sitting side by side occupy approximately one one-billionth of that area. I gave myself a 50/50 chance. There was a 50 percent chance that I wouldn't be able to find one, and a 50 percent chance that I would be able to convince myself that I had seen one, even if I hadn't. At the very least, it would be a chance to visit my family and give them further proof of my bird-related insanity.

I had been told that the best spot to search for the remaining two birds was the slightly dishevelled warehouse district south of False Creek at the intersection of 1st and Wylie. Mynas had been known to nest in a building occupied by Maynards Auctioneers and to roost in a building across the street occupied by Best Facilities Services Ltd. These buildings had the advantage of having lost some of their bricks. The owners had never replaced the bricks, giving the mynas access to the space behind. Instead of occupying one of the many beautiful parks in Vancouver and surrounding communities, Crested Mynas had decided to make their last North American stand in the sort of neighbourhood even a mugger might shun on a foggy night but for the security provided by the local constabulary one block south and the police dog training centre one block north.

When i was a child, my mother explained to my teachers that I was "sensitive" and had to be handled gently. Even now, I think that my mother feels that I am at risk of being mistreated by a cruel world. Therefore, when I told her about my journey to find mynas in a beaten-up warehouse district she was more than pleased to tag along to take care of me.

As I peered out through the windshield of her Honda Civic at the grey February drizzle, I could swear that a myna was sitting on the power line just above the car. It was black, just about the right size, and if I squinted, I could see a crest and some white on its wings. When I got out of the car for a better look, the bird transformed itself magically into one of the few hundred European Starlings that I was to see that day. Well, that would have been too easy anyway.

Mynas are non-migratory. When they set up shop, they don't wander very far afield, and so we had a pretty small area to cover. We walked the alleys, and twitched at every starling or crow that flew by. Local bird experts had instructed me to kick dumpsters where mynas might be feeding and shake bushes where they could be roosting. This stirred up only House Sparrows. The area has probably never had designs on being posh. There was an automobile axle repair shop, a windshield repair shop, offices of a radio station, and a dealer of concrete garden gnomes. I spotted starlings, robins, crows, sparrows, and gulls, but not a single Crested Myna.

After about an hour, another myna hunter showed up. He told us that he was from Toronto, in Vancouver on business. As a bird-watcher, he couldn't resist the thrill of the hunt. After thirty min-utes of walking and twitching together, the insistent drizzle turned to a very convincing downpour, and our new friend from Toronto gave up and drove away. What a wimp! Five minutes after that, my mother drove off in search of a coffee shop. My own mother! A quitter! Didn't she realize the importance of this quest?

I wasn't crestfallen. I wasn't disheartened. I may have been just a teeny bit bored. I noticed that Maynards was having an End-of-Season-Clearance Event. King- and queen-size duvet covers were going for $24.99, and a dressing gown would set you back only $30. If you could see past the February rain with optimism, you might be in the market for a summer halter top for $10. The bras and panties were probably flying out the door at $10 and $5, respectively. I couldn't imagine what an auction house was doing with scads of ladies undergarments. Perhaps they had previously been worn by someone famous.

The workers at Maynards gradually trickled in to work. They knew all about the mynas. After all, people from all over North America had been flying to Vancouver to see them for years. The workers seemed bemused that people would spend a perfectly good Saturday morning standing in the rain looking for some stupid birds. One of the employees stood behind me making loud "chirp! chirp!" noises. The workers might have felt themselves consid-erably less foolish than I, but I felt I had the ultimate revenge. I was enjoying myself on a Saturday morning. They were emptying garbage cans at a warehouse. Further, when I go to work, nobody makes me wear a purple pinafore with the company name on it and auction off cheap panties.

It started to rain harder, and the day's best myna-spotting time had already passed. I didn't want my efforts to be a complete waste, so when my mother returned from her coffee hunt I suggested that we check out some of the spots in Vancouver that had been asso-ciated with the Crested Myna in decades past. First we drove to

Sir Guy Carleton School, which had, according to local myna lore, housed large wintering flocks as late as the 1960s. It is a grand old monolith of a school, with the sort of crevice-rich gothic architecture that roosting mynas loved and that frightened the High Holy Hell out of five-year-old children on their first day of school.

Having seen the scary school, I suggested that we try the neighbourhood around Carrall and Cordova streets, which had, half a century before, been the epicentre of Vancouver Crested Myna activity, with a cast of thousands assembling in midwinter. Buildings in the area had been described to me as elaborately corniced. Although I have no idea what a cornice is, it sounded ideal for a Crested Myna. "You know that's right downtown?" my mother asked. It seemed an odd question. "Are we in a hurry? I thought we had the whole day free," I replied. "Oh, we do, we do," came her response in a voice that sounded as though she knew something important that I didn't.

We got to the indicated intersection and I jumped out of the car with my camera bag, ready to get a few shots of the building facades that had made the neighbourhood so popular with mynas. My mother stayed in the car and immediately locked the doors. It was then that I realized that I might have stepped into the wrong sort of neighbourhood for a guy in dress slacks, a mountaineering jacket, and a camera bag full of expensive gear. The neighbourhood was falling to the wrecker's ball, but not nearly quickly enough. Oh well, how bad could it get? After all, there was a gaggle of eight police officers across the street. As I walked toward a likely looking photo opportunity, the police officers jumped on an uncooperative gentleman, tossed him into the back of a van with no windows, and drove off. This left me without any backup.

With no disrespect to the perfectly nice people who live and work in that district, I figured that I might be in some kind of trouble. A dishevelled-looking character shuffled toward me. He seemed to be able to focus on me only if he used one eye at a time. "Nice-looking camera." "Uh, yeah" was the only really appropriate response I could think of, composing and focusing as quickly as I could. "How much is it worth?" he asked. Oh Lord! In a scene straight out of the film *The Omega Man,* a small crowd of zombies started to form around me. I snapped a quick photo of an old building, any old building, repacked my camera bag, and walked smartly back to the car, trying to hold my shoulders in a way that suggested that I might be tougher than I actually am.

My mother was laughing to the point of choking. Perhaps her laughing would save me the trouble. She was still laughing fifteen minutes later, barely able to navigate her car. She had spent a chunk of her working life in a government office building just a couple of blocks away. Unlike her innocent son, she knew that the neighbourhood had the worst reputation for violence in western Canada but had chosen not to tell me. I hope that she is still laughing when it occurs to her that I will get to choose the retirement complex that she will eventually have to live in.

IT WAS A TIME TO CALL IN a big gun. Brian Self is a head bird guru with the Vancouver Natural History Society. Hearing that I had come up empty on Saturday, he enthusiastically offered to have a go with me on Sunday. As my mother and I set off for our second trip to the warehouse district, the skies were peeing down, but by the time we arrived it had settled into a light gullywasher. To show our enthusiasm, we arrived fifteen minutes before the appointed time. Even so, Brian had arrived fifteen minutes before that, no doubt hoping to find the birds and be ready to point them out the moment we stepped out of the Honda Civic. To that point, his efforts had yielded exactly zero mynas.

Brian was my perfect image of a bird enthusiast in Vancouver in February. Imagine the character Gilligan, played by actor Bob Denver in the mid-'60s sitcom *Gilligan's Island.* Age Gilligan by about forty years. Give him a grey beard and a ponytail. After all, the castaways were bound to have run out of razor blades and broken all of their styling scissors after four decades on a tropical island. By this time, Gilligan was probably in need of eyeglasses and would have figured out that a raincoat, rain pants, and stout rubber boots were more appropriate for a tropical island. They were certainly perfect for Vancouver on a rainy February morning, even though the well-worn canvas hat was still part of the ensemble.

Brian and I spent ninety minutes walking the same streets and back alleys that I had covered the previous day. Mom remained behind in the car, promising to watch the warehouse buildings for likely looking birds. Like me, Brian has developed the endlessly valuable talent of being able to walk almost silently, even in rain pants. Also like me, he had a twitchy gait and spoke in sentence fragments as an endless stream of starlings flitted by, each requiring a quick scan with binoculars. He pointed out spots in alleys that had been favourite foraging spots for mynas before a new coat of blacktop had replaced the previous cracked and weedy surface.

We covered all of the likely spots twice, with an increasing sense that we were probably out of luck. Brian spoke about suspected roosting sites further to the south, but he didn't seem wholly con-vinced. Only once did he allow that maybe the Vancouver birds had shuffled off this mortal coil, passing away quietly in a crevice in an old building. Even so, after following the comings and goings of mynas for many years, he wasn't in a big hurry to write them off.

Ask any four bird enthusiasts in British Columbia why their Crested Mynas went into a tailspin and you will get fourteen and a half different theories. Mynas really like fruit and insects, but the foraging opportunities afforded by Vancouver in its earlier days no longer exist; a lot of agricultural land has been turned over to urban sprawl. Railways eventually figured out that spilling grain was not particularly cost-effective, so that source of myna food was cut off. Some people suggested that horse droppings had been an important source of food for mynas, now lost. I would like to sug-gest that if mynas hadn't been able to find anything better to eat than horseshit, they may all have committed suicide.

The neighbourhood around the Cambie Street Bridge has its fair share of fast-food restaurants. Brian felt that one of the best ways to find mynas was to kick open-topped dumpsters, where they had the opportunity to forage for discarded French fries.

Perhaps the Crested Myna was another unfortunate victim of the fast-food industry.

It also seemed that mynas had never really figured out that Vancouver was colder, damper, and generally more miserable than their native Southeast Asia. The concept of paying a lot of attention to their eggs and chicks in cold weather completely evaded them. When heating costs were low, buildings in Vancouver were poorly insulated, so there was abundant opportunity to breed in the comparative warmth of cracks and crevices. When heating costs rose and buildings became better insulated, myna reproductive success fell.

Everyone loves a scapegoat, and in the bird world the European Starling is one of the favourites. Also an introduced species, numbering in the uncounted millions in North America, starlings expanded into the Vancouver region in the 1950s. Ecologically similar to mynas, starlings were likely competitors for limited food and cavities in which to nest.

I am not convinced by any of this. My favourite explanation for the myna decline is a little more technical. If the North American population was founded by just one or two pairs, then every myna would have been involved in consanguineous matings for over a century. It wouldn't have taken too many years for all mynas to be virtual clones of one another. Their contingent would have been so incredibly inbred, so horribly genetically impoverished, that they may have just run out of steam. For Crested Mynas in North America, the gene pool had become a little too shallow.

There is an odd legal angle to the Crested Myna story. If these birds had been native to North America, or if they had arrived there under their own steam, when their population first started to decline they would have received the full protection and support of the governments of Canada and British Columbia. At the very least this would have involved protection of the mynas' favourite haunts (here I envision a lot more dumpsters), allowance for suitable feeding opportunities (perhaps in the form of tax incentives for burger joints), possibly a captive breeding program, and probably a program of translocation of mynas from the Orient to supplement their impoverished reservoir of genetic variation. Instead, they represented members of an invasive species, introduced to North America by humans. Hence, when their population went into a tailspin, the species was absolutely and completely screwed. When all was said and done, it appeared that the Crested Myna had had its day in North America.

I HAD TRAVELLED a couple of thousand kilometres to see the last North American Crested Mynas, and despite my best efforts I had been completely shut out. That isn't really much of a story, and a bit depressing. But then I got a lucky break. I heard a rumour about a Crested Myna held in a wildlife recovery centre north of Vancouver on the Sunshine Coast. My older brother, Reagan, lives on that part of the coast, and I put him on to it. He called back a few minutes later, explaining that he had found the bird, and that its keepers would be willing to see me.

Surely there is a special place in Heaven for people who devote themselves to the aid of distressed animals. If so, then Clint and Irene Davy will be strolling through passport control at Heaven's gates while waving heartily at sinners. Sick and injured animals are presumably not the only things in Clint and Irene's lives, but they represent a pretty good chunk of it. They operate a wildlife rehabilitation centre out of their home just off the highway that runs up British Columbia's Sunshine Coast. There may be a type of injured animal that they would turn away, but I cannot imagine what sort of beast it would be. Perhaps a three-legged skunk with tapeworms.

One animal that they had not turned away was a Crested Myna that they had named "Morris" . . . as in Morris the Myna . . . as in Morris Minor . . . as in the car. I am not a real big fan of puns. In anticipation of my visit, Clint and Irene had dug through their files to find out exactly when Morris had come to live with them. It was May 31, 1986. Morris had been brought to them as a youngster, along with a sibling that had died shortly afterward. The Davys had been living in Richmond, on the mainland, at the time, and when Morris was healthy enough to release, they had been advised against doing so by folks at the Vancouver Natural History Society, who reasoned that with the Crested Myna population dropping so quickly, Morris could do a lot worse than to live out his life in captivity. Although there is little data available, the record for longevity in a Crested Myna in North America appears to be that of a banded individual who held out for eleven years and two months. Morris was demolishing that record.

Although other rescued birds were put safely away in cages, Morris flew freely in the Davys' "bird room." He was particularly keen to perch on a tree branch toward the ceiling, out of the reach of the strange person who had just arrived to invade his world. It wasn't hard to lure him down, though; I just had to extend my left arm with a mealworm on my palm and then look away as if I wasn't the least bit interested in him. Morris had beautiful shiny feathers, a clean vent and nostrils, and clear eyes. Clint and Irene put Morris's great health at such an advanced age down to good nutrition. He was given an endless supply of grapes, bird seed, mealworms, and dog and cat food. He was noisy to the point where at times it was impossible for us to hear each other speak. There was an air of superiority about Morris. But then, I suppose he had a reason to feel a bit lofty. As far as I or anyone else could tell, he was the only representative of his species for many thousands of kilometres, and he wasn't likely to ever see another bird quite like himself.

ALL OF MY CONTACTS in Vancouver promised to stay on top of the story and to let me know if Crested Mynas were seen again. If a few weeks went by and none of the 4 million eyes in the area spotted one, I felt it was pretty safe to consider them extinct in the wild in North America.

And then, exactly two weeks later, I was roused from my well-deserved Saturday morning lie-in by a long-distance telephone call from my younger brother, Ross. "Weren't you looking for Crested Mynas?" I explained that I had been, and asked him why he felt it necessary to wake me up to confirm a rather minor detail. "There is an article in this morning's *Vancouver Sun* that I think you might be interested in."

According to the article, a Vancouver store for bird enthusiasts had a strange visitor in mid-February, exactly the same time I was searching for the last of the Crested Mynas. Employees of the store guessed that this fellow was in his fifties and said that he spoke with a German or eastern European accent. He claimed to have found the bodies of the last two mynas at the warehouse location. General speculation was that one bird had been hit by a car while foraging on the street, and that the second individual kept returning to the spot until it was also struck and killed. The folks at the bird store asked the mysterious stranger what he had done with the corpses. He claimed that he had buried them together in a quiet spot in Stanley Park. Even though they didn't get the gentleman's name or contact details, employees of the store were inclined to believe him.

There were no further sightings of mynas in Vancouver, and it seemed safe to assume that the species was represented in North America by Morris alone. As healthy as he was, he couldn't last forever, and passed away in September of 2007. In a way, Morris was an icon of the changing face of North American avifauna.

CHAPTER FIVE

The Curse of the White Guys

REASON NUMBER FIVE FOR INTRODUCING A FOREIGN SPECIES: BECAUSE MY PREVIOUS CROP GOT WIPED OUT BY A DISEASE.

In the first muzzy moments after waking, I could make absolutely no sense of the world around me. Lisa was on the other side of the king-sized bed, which virtually guaranteed that I had not died and gone to hell. Instead, it started to look as though I might have landed in Heaven. I spied a package of anti-malarial tablets on the bedside table, and so assumed that we were somewhere tropical. Wherever it was, we had gone in style. The room, five-stars or close to it, was decorated in dark wood and brass. Over the dull hum of a ceiling fan I heard the crash of surf, and after retrieving my eyeglasses I spied palm trees. Wherever we were, it was very exotic. All I needed now was a good book and a nice cup of tea.

When it comes to an easy-reading book, it is hard to beat the Sherlock Holmes stories by Arthur Conan Doyle. When Doyle got tired of writing about the great detective, he turned his attentions to a dazzling array of other short fiction—dazzling mainly because it is so blindingly awful that even undergraduate students of Eng-

lish literature are not required to read it. As evidence, I offer up
the short story "De Profundis," written by Doyle in 1892. In "De
Profundis," a man dies at sea from smallpox and his body is tossed
overboard by his shipmates. A couple of weeks later, his corpse
pops to the surface just as his widow sails by. She spots her husband's corpse an instant before it is devoured by a passing shark. To
me this is a shockingly bad storyline.

However, in "De Profundis," Doyle also wrote about the production of tea in Sri Lanka, then called Ceylon, and is frequently
quoted by persons proud of that industry. He wrote,

> Those were the royal days of coffee-plantation in Ceylon,
> before a single season and a rotten fungus drove a whole com-
> munity through years of despair to one of the greatest com-
> mercial victories with pluck and ingenuity ever won. Not often
> is it that men have the heart when their one great industry is
> withered to rear up in a few years another as rich to take its
> place, and the tea-fields of Ceylon are as true a monument to
> courage as is the lion at Waterloo.

It is a shame that such a good quotation comes from such an awful
piece of piffle.

I had been drowning in tea since childhood, but I really didn't
know much about the life of tea before it hits the hot water. And so,
when the opportunity came to attend the wedding of friends on the
island of Sri Lanka, coupled with a trip to see tea in a field instead
of just a cup, I couldn't resist.

Charu Chandrasekera has enough personality for three people.
She has deep copper skin and broody eyes, and I have never seen
her in a mellow mood. When she arrived at the University of Calgary to begin graduate studies in medical physiology, the match
between Charu and her supervisor was gritty, bordering on incan-
descent. After consulting with a graduate student advisor, Charu
was directed to speak with my wife, Lisa, a little further along in
her graduate degree. Knowing many of the pitfalls, Lisa helped

Charu avoid some of the nastier ones. Charu came to think of Lisa as a big sister, and me as a big brother by extension.

Charu eventually took up with fellow Sri Lankan Chaminda Basnayake, who was working toward a Ph.D. in engineering. Chaminda has an unfair advantage over other males; he is impossibly handsome, but in a boy-like unthreatening way. Chaminda saw Charu in all of her moods and loved each of them. The fullness of time saw them married in Prince Edward Island, but something was left unfinished. The marriage wouldn't be quite complete until it was solemnized by a wedding in Sri Lanka. And we, as honorary brother and sister, were invited.

DON'T BOTHER LOOKING for a direct flight to Colombo from anywhere else you might be because there isn't one. Instead, Lisa and I took a flight to London, followed by a long layover in Heathrow's Terminal 3. We then made a jump to the United Arab Emirates. The departure lounge for the flight to Abu Dhabi was, by far, the most boisterous I have ever encountered. It was a carnival of shouting—one passenger to another, through cellphones, and at the television screen broadcasting BBC One sports highlights. When the call came for passengers in the first three rows to board the plane, almost everyone rushed the gate.

Lisa and I couldn't afford tickets in the Diamond Zone, or even the Pearl Zone. No precious or semi-precious stones for us; we were to be seated in the Coral Zone, but judging from the stampede of kittens that tried to get on the plane ahead of us, it was a misspelling of "Corral Zone." The flight began with a prayer in Arabic. I was praying that the flight attendants would manage to keep the kittens in line without having to throw any of them out.

At Abu Dhabi International Airport, the gentleman attending the X-ray machine that scanned our luggage passed the time by burning his hand with a confiscated cigarette lighter. We faced a fourteen-hour layover. As pretty as the airport is—based on a blue desert-flower motif—no one would want to spend fourteen hours there, so a travel agent had arranged for us to spend the layover in a local hotel. We were rounded up and handed from agent to agent in a tentative way that suggested that this sort of arrangement had never been tried before. Eventually we found ourselves on a bus to the hotel.

At an intellectual level, I had always realized that the United Arab Emirates is in the desert. I have been to deserts before, but somehow I wasn't ready for the full enormity of the desert that blankets this part of the planet. Once away from the well-watered, tree-lined avenue from the airport, the world was sand. Not scrubby vegetation clinging to the ground wherever it could find a bit of water, but sand. Great mounds of the stuff as far as the eye could see. We rolled past small communities composed of identical white houses in the style of Scottish castles. Each community had its own mosque, but not a lot of chlorophyll-based life forms.

Poor Lisa. As I caught some sleep, she came to terms with gathering nausea, probably the result of the inflight meal, which had contained a lot of garlic, which Lisa's stomach doesn't tolerate. Instead of sleeping, she stared up at the orange sign on the ceiling, which indicated the direction of most holy Mecca.

And so after my first, very brief, trip to the Middle East, we faced a jump across the Indian Ocean. As we approached Sri Lanka, we were told that "Health regulations require spraying of the air before landing. We will be doing this shortly." There was no mention about what the spray contained. DDT? Arsenic? Lemon-scented furniture polish? We were advised that, should we wish, we could cover our mouths and noses with handkerchiefs. Who carries a handkerchief anymore? Lisa and I did our best with tissues but were the only ones to do so. Flight attendants marched up and down the cabin emptying aerosol spray cans, discharging what smelled like hair spray. Perhaps this was Sri Lanka's contribution to ozone depletion. It all led to bouts of sniffing and coughing. I'll bet the rich snobs in the Diamond Zone didn't get that sort of treatment.

Airport arrivals always remind me of cattle ramps at livestock auctions, with each new arrival getting the undivided attention of the assembled throng. This applies to Colombo International more than most. Behind a barrier on the right as we passed customs were thirty-six eager chauffeurs, each holding a placard with one or more surnames. As Lisa and I glanced toward them, all thirty-six cards went up, like thirty-six chicks begging for a meal. On our left, behind another barrier, were 250 people awaiting the arrival of friends and family. The scene was very orderly, particularly for four thirty on a hot and sticky morning. In Colombo, waiting had become a spectator sport.

There was no sign of Charu and Chaminda, so we took the opportunity to have a little look around. There was a sprinkling of Christmas decorations, including what can only be described as multicoloured disco balls. We found a very liberal air-conditioning unit to stand under. Time passed without any evidence of our friends. We had slept just a few hours in the past forty-eight, and the heat and humidity were washing over us like an incoming tide. The grind of endless bodies was starting to make me dizzy. What does this country look like after it has woken up?

And then our hosts arrived, their faces full of joy and welcome. They reclaimed their cab, and we headed from the airport, through Colombo, and south toward our hotel in the community of Mount Lavinia. We got little more than impressions in the predawn light, but those exotic scenes made my eyes dance. Even at that ungodly hour on a Monday morning, buses were disgorging workers at garment factories. It was raining and some people had umbrellas; the remainder didn't seem to care about getting wet. Traffic was crushingly heavy, with an equal mixture of buses, minivans, commercial trucks, three-wheeled taxis, motorcycles, and bicycles. Few of these vehicles had headlights. Pedestrians were shown no mercy. Stray dogs showed no mercy. I felt swelling motion sickness for the last thirty minutes of our seventy-minute journey. I needed a cup of tea.

THE ISLAND NATION of Sri Lanka was not always renowned for its tea. In the mid-1700s, Dutch interests were making a good return on the harvest of cinnamon growing wild in the forests around the city of Kandy. Following a decline in cinnamon revenue, investors turned to coffee, whose cultivation peaked at about 15,000 hectares in 1845.

But in 1869, a plantation superintendent named Donald Reid noted that things were going awry for the coffee plants near the community of Gallola. Coffee rust, a type of fungal parasite, was damaging the crop. Under the right conditions, some fungi can wipe out a crop in a matter of weeks. Destruction of the coffee industry by the rust was less rapid. Even so, within five years of its appearance, every coffee-growing district in Ceylon was infected, and within ten years the yield had declined from 4.5 hundredweight per acre to 2 hundredweight. The industry went into a spiral, and dead coffee trees were exported to Great Britain for use in furniture.

But when British capitalists arrived in Sri Lanka to make their fortunes from the cultivation of tea, they found that Sinhalese labourers interested in the new endeavour were hard to come by. Locals had their own interests. Investors didn't have to look far to find workers. Just next door on the Indian subcontinent were millions of Tamil agricultural workers who could earn far more in Sri Lanka than they could at home. As the competition for the services of labourers in southern India rose, so too did local wages.

And it has been all about tea ever since. In 1967, D. M. Forrest described tea as the lifeblood of Sri Lanka. At the time, tea represented two-thirds of the country's export revenue, and, directly and indirectly, was responsible for a massive portion of the country's wealth. Sri Lanka was, said Forrest, the only country in the world whose economy relied on the harvest of tea.

AFTER A BATH, a nap, and a posh lunch that included a gin and tonic but no tea, Lisa and I were gathered up by Chaminda and Charu. Their wedding was to be at our hotel, the most popular spot for luxurious weddings in Sri Lanka, six days hence. I got the impression that not every detail was going exactly according to plan, but what wedding for 260 guests ever goes exactly according to plan? Charu was fretting and reportedly had been for several weeks, first in Canada and now in Sri Lanka. This had caused her to lose weight, and while she was still a beautiful woman, we all hoped that she would lose no more.

We piled into a hired car and our driver aimed for the heart of Colombo, travelling north along Galle Road, probably the busiest street in the country. Lisa needed to be fitted for her dress for the wedding. She had decided to forgo Western garb and had opted for a traditional sari in the style of the region around the city of Kandy. Charu had earlier chosen a length of material, but we stopped at a fabric store to make sure that there wasn't something Lisa liked more. Nothing could have suited her better than the maroon and gold material that complemented her hair and complexion. In a shop two doors down, Lisa was measured up and was assured that the completed sari would be waiting for her in a few days. The shop was only a few metres deep but was awash with employees. Chaminda said that the establishment had a good reputation, and that on a busy day it was impossible to get anywhere near a mirror.

Back on the street, our driver earned himself a 150-rupee fine for running a red light. By itself, the small fine was not enough to be a strong deterrent, but paying the fine required spending most of the day in a very long and lethargic queue at a police station. Vehicles all seemed to be equipped with seat belts, but absolutely no one used them. The blare of horns was nearly deafening, and in the traffic ballet they were clearly the most important piece of equipment on any vehicle. The city offered a constant and varied opera of smells. Some were spicy and pleasant; others less so. Lisa described it as discovering a previously unused sense.

Far off the main road, we waited in a courtyard while a beautician shaped Charu's eyebrows in preparation for the wedding. The courtyard was awash with butterflies, ferns, and garden gnomes. On either side of the alleyway was a ditch carrying away water filled with human waste. While wandering up and down the alleyway, Lisa became the centre of attention. Young children and old ladies wanted to touch her face to see what white skin felt like. No offence was intended, and Lisa took none. Curiously, no one wanted to touch me.

In Colombo, no vista fails to be filled with people or punctuated by evidence of celebration. It was hard to tell which decorations had been erected for Christmas and which were in general celebration of living in Sri Lanka. Among the endless parade of shops along the Galle Road, I spied World O' Bangles, Rickshaw Pasty Shop, Fertility Well Woman Centre, and the Shine and Shine Restaurant, which offered fried rice, fried noodles, and devilled chicken; I can only imagine what special behaviours chickens might have when possessed by Satan. I am not certain what lectures are like at the Colon Tech, but when it comes to bowel movements, I like to keep things simple.

Tuktuks, strange little boxes with two-stroke lawnmower engines, were everywhere. These three-wheeled motorized scooters serve as taxis over large portions of Asia. Among the most popular models in Sri Lanka are the Super RE, the Super RE Salon, the Super Edition, and the Super Sport. I mentioned to our driver that I had yet to spot a woman piloting a three-wheeled taxi, and he indicated that out of many thousands of drivers in all of Colombo only three women were registered to pilot these craft. It quickly became apparent that in the crush of traffic there was a hierarchy. Buses outrank trucks, which in turn outrank minivans. Next down the list were cars, which bully tuktuks, which outdo motorbikes, which push aside bicycles. The only thing to outrank a bus is a sufficiently large mass of pedestrians.

Back at the hotel, Lisa and I joined the happy couple for an elegant dinner on a deck overlooking the crashing Indian Ocean. Our food included spices that my tongue had known only in dreams, and fruit that must have still been on the tree when we entered the dining room. Tea was on offer, but in the heat of the late afternoon I couldn't resist a beer, Three Coins, which was almost entirely acceptable.

As we wound down, I asked Charu and Chaminda what they loved most about Sri Lanka. They said that though they had lived in Canada for many years and were at home there, they both felt as though they most belonged to the country of their birth. For them, Sri Lanka had a sense of place. Even though they were scheduled to return to Calgary so that Charu could defend her doctoral dissertation, and although they were likely to spend the next portion of their lives working in Canada or the United States, they felt that their hearts would eventually draw them back to Sri Lanka.

IN THEIR 1931 BOOK on the production, harvest, and processing of tea in Sri Lanka, E. C. Elliott and F. J. Whitehead had a lot to say about tea plants. They explained that tea, *Camellia sinensis*, is an evergreen plant of the Camellia family, native to China and northeastern portions of India. The hardy plant flourishes in Sri Lanka from sea level to just over 2,000 metres, surviving a wide range of soil and climate types. Whatever else a tea plant might be willing to cope with, it needs a minimum of 150 centimetres of rain per year, roughly the same quantity received by Baton Rouge, Louisiana.

A tea plantation is all about tea bushes, but this is not the form the plant takes outside of cultivation. In their natural state, tea plants are sturdy forest trees, growing to ten metres. This wouldn't make for an easy harvest by small-statured women, so the plants are routinely pruned to a height of about 100 centimetres. And the plants live on year after year. Despite the establishment of new plantations and the need to replace dead plants, in 1965 it was estimated that 70 percent of tea plants being harvested in Sri Lanka were over eighty years old.

Tea is so valuable that the best cultivation practices have long since been worked out. Here are a few things you will need to know to grow a hectare's worth of tea plants. Each plant requires a little more than a square metre of ground, resulting in about 1,450 plants to the hectare. Plants mature to the point of plucking in two years in the low country, but require at least four years of growth in the cooler highlands.

There are many grades of tea, largely based on the size of the leaf fragments that remain after processing. These include Broken Orange Pekoe, Orange Pekoe, Pekoe, Souchong, and Dust. You don't want Dust; you want Broken Orange Pekoe, which is derived from the smallest and youngest leaves and looks a bit like small chips of wood.

WHILE SETTING UP with the hotel's cashier, we were approached by a gentleman who asked, "Are you Glen?" I always feel a bit unnerved when strangers in foreign countries know my name. The man doing the asking was middle-aged and well-dressed, and sported a neatly trimmed greying beard. This was Lincoln De Silva, our driver and tour guide for the next three days.

Lincoln had a number of important things working in his favour. First, his use of English was impeccable. Not only could he define words like "impeccable," but unlike me, he could probably spell them without looking them up. It was immediately evident that he was a superior driver, managing to navigate the chaotic and perilous streets of Colombo without running anyone over. He had developed a love of Sri Lankan birdlife, and could either identify every bird or make something up quickly. As we left the capital, Lincoln pointed out Open-billed Herons, White-chested Kingfishers, Indian Pond Herons, and both Cattle and Indian egrets. Best of all, Lincoln could take us to see tea. Not in-a-bag tea, but growing-in-a-field tea.

Lincoln proved to be a wealth of knowledge about his homeland. We learned, for instance, that rice had been introduced in antiquity to Sri Lanka from the Far East and had long been a staple of the diet of most residents. New varieties were being developed to best suit local growing conditions by the Rice Research and Development Institute. In a land without winter, rice farmers had been able to harvest two crops a year. New varieties with shorter growing periods meant that a farmer could get an additional crop each year, even if the rice was of slightly lesser quality and got a somewhat lower price at market.

I told Lincoln that the verdant hills reminded me of my image of Eden. He explained that some people believe that Adam and Eve had been set down in Sri Lanka at a site known as Adam's Peak. It wasn't only Christians who revered the site. Buddhists know the spot as Sri Pada, and believe that a large impression in stone at the peak represents the footprint of Buddha as he departed Earth for Paradise. Others feel the footprint might be that of Lord Shiva or of St. Thomas. Spying the cross hanging from the car's rear-view mirror, I asked Lincoln if he was a Christian. Only 6 percent of Sri Lankans are Christians, lagging behind Buddhists (70 percent), Muslims (8 percent), and Hindustani (7 percent). "I am," he said. I asked him if he thought that the hilltop in Sri Lanka might really be the Garden of Eden. He said, "I haven't travelled much, so comparison isn't easy, but yes, I think it could be."

The road climbed to Kandy. It had been constructed by the British in the 1860s under the direction of a Major Skinner, who was described in Sri Lanka as "The Father of Roads." After the roadway had been completed, a linear community sprung up along it. Lincoln explained that this has happened throughout Sri Lanka. Even though we had gained considerable altitude, Lincoln told us that we were not yet in "Hill Country," but rather "Up Country." "Verdant," "lush," and "fertile" were insufficient adjectives to describe our surroundings. The last road to our hilltop hotel was steep, steep, steep, but provided the most magnificent view of Kandy. The incessant honking of horns far below did nothing to diminish the experience. The windows and doors of our hotel room carried a warning: "Beware of Monkeys."

After dinner at the hotel, Lincoln drove us to the Kandyan Arts Association Hall, a modest facility but covered against the driving rain. For about $3 each, we got to take in the cultural show. After the Sri Lankan national anthem was broadcast through cheap speakers, the evening's performances of the Traditional Kandyan and Low Dances began. We were mesmerized. Dancers were accompanied by percussionists, who slammed away on traditional drums for the better part of an hour. In their turn, men and women performed elegant dances with exotic names like the Pooja Dance, the Cobra Dance, Panteru Netum, and Mayura Vannama. The young women were delicately seductive, the young men were brutally athletic, and the costumes were enchanting. A banquet of flying insects, drawn by the stage lights, was picked off by a parade of small bats throughout the performance.

As the proceedings drew toward the finale, Lincoln led us to the concrete stage steps so that we would have an unimpeded view of the evening's grand climax—fire dancers who drew flaming batons across their bare chests and tongues and walked across braziers filled with red-hot coals. All of the young people involved in the evening's production were amateurs and had not had the joy of performance sucked out of them by professionalism. On occasion, a dancer might fall out of step with the rest, but each had the self-conscious smile of the person who is truly enjoying the movement and being applauded for their efforts. Lincoln explained that this troupe was managing to revive dance traditions that might otherwise die out.

To close out the evening, we were driven to a hill overlooking Kandy. Music and singing drifted from below. Kandy, a World Heritage Site, is a true wonder. Its population is variously given as 100,000, 120,000, and 190,000. On that particular night, just ten days before Christmas, those people were not generating a lot of light, and I had to remind myself that not every community feels the need to light itself up like Los Angeles.

My ANTI-MALARIAL DRUGS were working, at least at some level. I awoke from a dream in which I was dreaming. In my dream's dream I was flying, and in my first-order dream I wondered if that was evidence of mental instability.

It was still raining heavily as we checked out of our hotel in Kandy, and a troupe of monkeys had taken refuge in the roof of the reception hall. Employees of the hotel tried to drive them away by enthusiastically bashing the corrugated metal roof with long plastic poles. The monkeys were very good at appearing utterly unabashed.

Shortly after 7 a.m., we arrived at the Sri Dalada Maligawa, the Temple of the Tooth. The tooth, an incisor, was taken from the Buddha's funeral pyre in 543 BCE. Nine centuries later, during a period of unrest in India, the tooth was secreted to Sri Lanka. Surviving periodic attempts to destroy it, the tooth remains a revered object.

For reasons not fully explored, the receipt for our admission bore the expression, "May triple gem bless you." In the endlessly ornate temple, Lincoln proved indispensable, pointing out things that we could not possibly have noticed otherwise and keeping us from making some unholy faux pas at the sacred site. First we passed through portals—one for Lisa and one for Lincoln and me—for a really good frisking. We then deposited our sandals, a necessity before entering any holy site. As we had been instructed, we were dressed respectfully in long-legged trousers and covered upper arms.

Lincoln then showed us the spot where, in 1998, a bomb was detonated in an attempt to disrupt celebrations marking the anniversary of Sri Lankan independence from Britain. We were shown the site where an elaborately decorated elephant was led at times of celebration. We saw examples of long-forgotten artwork revealed from under plaster by the bomb's blast. We visited a room with many representations of Buddha, gifts from Buddhist nations around the world. We passed the vault in which the most holy relic resides; at this point we spoke in hushed voices so as not to disturb the prayers of the reverent. Even so, seeing us, the faithful gently pushed Lisa and me to the front for an unobstructed view of the vault. I felt humbled by the generosity of spirit.

As we drove to our next stop in Kandy, Lisa spotted a large plastic Spider-Man on the side of a building under construction. Lincoln explained that this was a dummy figure designed to divert the evil eye from the building during its construction. I had to wonder what Stan Lee would think. The night before we had seen a sign at the cinema in Kegalla advertising *Spider-Man 2* and *Night Call Nurses,* "Strictly for Adults!" I hadn't realized that *Spider-Man 2* was such a naughty film.

Heavy rains continued, but we felt that we could not possibly miss the Peradeniya Botanic Gardens, established shortly after the occupation of the region by the British. There were two reasons why we needed to visit the site. First, recent research by Philip Hulme of Lincoln University in New Zealand had shown that botanic gardens were responsible for half of the world's nastiest plant invasions. It seems that botanic gardens are poorly guarded vaults. Indeed, Peradeniya was responsible for the invasion of five of the world's thirty-four most obnoxious introduced plant species.

Second, the site had played a big role in the introduction of tea to Sri Lanka. Writing in 1905, Henry Cave explained that the Peradeniya Gardens had been involved in the testing of many agricultural possibilities and was intimately tied to Sri Lanka's agricultural prosperity. The country's first documented shipment of tea seeds arrived at Peradeniya in December 1839. A field in the Rambodde Pass was planted with tea in 1842, but the first commercially successful tea operations appeared about forty years later.

Lincoln explained that the gardens were one of the few places where he was not licensed to be a guide, as they had their own specially trained guides available for hire. Having taught university-level botany, I explained that Lisa and I would manage on our own.

Among the most fabulous imports under cultivation was the sandbox tree, native to tropical America, whose sign indicated "Latex is poisonous; may cause blindness." We spied the candle tree, native to Central America. We had already seen this plant in several places on our travels around Sri Lanka, and with its very long and robust seed pods, it was an easy spot.

One of the gardens' most outstanding residents was a Java fig. Native to India and the Solomon Islands, it was first introduced to Sri Lanka in 1861. This particular specimen was a little over 100 years old and had a massive spread of branches looking something like a giant squid. A plaque explained that the total spread of branches was 2,420 square metres.

At this point, an eager employee of the gardens trotted across the grass to join us.

"Hello," he said.

"Hello," we responded.

"Java fig," he continued.

"Yes. So we gather."

"Two-thousand-square-metre spread."

"Or perhaps 2,420 square metres."

It was a slow tourist day at the gardens, and he was clearly keen to be engaged as our guide, but we were more interested in a quiet, contemplative stroll with an opportunity to gawk. I didn't need to stand in front of a tree whose plaque told me that it was a cinnamon tree, only to be told "This is cinnamon!"

"You go under fig!" we were told.

"Well, yes, perhaps we will just a little later. Thank you. Goodbye." I suppose that the proper thing would have been to slip him a 100-rupee note and ask him politely to leave us, but I made the mistake of assuming that he would just get tired of us. Five minutes later, Lisa and I found ourselves staring at a group of seventy-five sleeping flying foxes hanging from the branches of a tall and nearly naked tree. I spied our guide-wannabe racing toward us, on an intercept path.

"Bats!" he shouted. "You go this way now!" he said, gesturing down a path to the left.

"No, thank you. We are going to go this way," gesturing down the path he had just walked, for which he could not possibly have a reason to accidentally bump into us.

Half a century earlier, Cuban royal palm trees had been planted to create a majestic row known as Royal Palm Avenue. This took us to a Guinean cannonball tree, whose fruit looked suspiciously like cannonballs. My absolute favourite specimen in the collection was a stunted, anaemic little tree, a yellow saraca from the Malay Peninsula. Despite being planted on December 9, 1961, it had gained no height whatsoever. It probably does much better in Malaya. It was my favourite because it had been planted by Yuri Gagarin, a Russian cosmonaut, just seven months after he became the first human to be launched into space.

WRITING IN 1905, Henry Cave described the harvest of tea. "To such an extent does practice accelerate the action of eye, brain, and the march of nimble fingers, that it is difficult for the uninitiated to believe how carefully chosen is each leaf or shoot. Plucking is the most important branch of the tea-planter's business, and requires careful teaching and constant supervision."

Only the youngest and most succulent of the leaves are used in the manufacture of tea. The younger the leaf, the better the beverage, such that harvest for a particularly delicate batch may involve only the shoot's two youngest leaves. As many as four leaves can be plucked, but it will result in a coarser beverage. Each plant rests for only eight or nine days before being plucked again. After a year or two, the tree is subjected to a merciless dismemberment, with branches lopped until the plant appears beyond hope. And yet, in just a few weeks, it will recover to the point that it is ready for additional harvest. The harvested leaves are dried, rolled, fermented, dried again, and then sorted into grades by the use of giant meshes. More than three-quarters of the product's initial mass is lost in the process.

But who was actually responsible for all of the work? In 1931, Elliott and Whitehead estimated that 800 Europeans supervised the work of at least 300,000 Tamils and 50,000 Sinhalese. They went on to explain that, at the time, eighty-five tea estates were owned by Sinhalese interests, thirty-eight by Tamils and Mohammedans, and 1,175 by Europeans. The vast majority of land under cultivation for tea was owned by Europeans.

For many years, Tamil workers did not receive a formal wage for their efforts on the plantations, securing only indirect benefits such as food and housing, medical treatment, and a measure of education for their youngest children. On January 1, 1929, minimum wages for immigrant Indian workers were established by the government of Ceylon. Men over sixteen years of age were to earn the equivalent of 54 cents US per day; women over fifteen received 43 cents. Each child over ten earned 32 cents. Overtime earned a factory worker an additional 7 to 10 cents per hour, and those plucking tea leaves beyond the required ten hours received 1 or 2 cents per pound of leaf.

In all, a man working as a tea-plant pruner six days a week, with his wife and their two young children all plucking leaves, could earn as much as 38 rupees in a month. At the current exchange rate, that is about 40 cents. Even allowing for inflation, is seems like a lot of work for not a lot of cash. If the wife picked an additional

345 pounds of tea by working overtime, and the older child 115 pounds, the family earnings might be as high as 45 rupees. Yippee.

The wages board also established prices that could not be exceeded for the sale of rice to the workers. Deducting the cost of rice issued to the family of four would reduce the 45 rupees to 27. Additional food, clothing, cooking utensils, and oil could be expected to drain an additional 13 rupees per month, leaving about 15 cents—what amounted to less than $2 per family per year.

Beyond working conditions and wages, life on the tea plantations must have been vile. Among Tamil labourers, upwards of 50 percent of infants died. According to Elliott and Whitehead, sources of mortality included poor nutrition and improper clothing of newborns, failure to thrive because of ill health during pregnancy (particularly caused by hookworm and sexually transmitted infections), and insufficient care provided by the mother because of illegitimacy or the demands of a family already large.

THE PREVIOUS DAY we had been climbing out of Colombo for Kandy. Now we continued to climb out of Kandy. A great deal of rain had caused waterfalls to flood and had hacked up the road badly. Given the country over which the road ran, I suspect that the engineer who had agreed to oversee construction from Kandy to Nuwara Eliya had fallen into deep despair when he first arrived on site. A new and massive project to widen the road seemed to be proceeding mainly under human toil without any heavy machinery. Lincoln suggested that the project would take forever to complete.

At one of many hairpin turns, Lincoln slid to a stop and used one of his favourite expressions: "Oh yeah!" He had spotted a coucal, a beautiful bronze-backed bird. Foraging beside it was a Common Bulbul, both common and rather drab. I hit the jackpot when I spotted, just a few metres away, a type of red-capped woodpecker known as a Greater Flameback. It was the sort of bird that children draw using all of their crayons.

At an elevation of 1,160 metres, we stopped at Ramboda Falls, where someone with great faith in architecture had created a restaurant that clung to the hillside by its fingernails. The establishment had a great view of two waterfalls and undulating green hillsides. Over lunch, we swapped stories and jokes. Lisa spotted a lovely sensitive plant, probably *Mimosa puidca,* whose leaves fold up when touched, proving a favourite among children. Lincoln explained that a newly introduced species, *Mimosa pigra,* was proving to a nasty invasive pest in Sri Lanka.

Having achieved sufficient altitude, we were now in the region of finest tea cultivation. Lincoln stopped the car at a tea plantation so that Lisa and I could follow a small trail through the plants, over a steep hilltop, and down the other side. The tea plants were knee-high. Although plants are given no opportunity to get taller, their trunks get thicker and thicker over the years, and they reminded me of bonsai. Tea leaves are picked by women only. Most of them are barefoot, and their back-mounted collection bags seemed incredibly heavy. We were told that men do even heavier work like pruning the plants and fertilizing the fields.

A little further along the track, Lisa and I took a tour of the Mackwoods/Labookellie Tea Estates. This was one of the earliest commercially successful tea operations in Sri Lanka; brothers Solomon and Gabriel de Worms planted tea seeds here in 1867. A teeny woman with a matching voice told us about the stages involved in processing tea. I was hoping to get the gory details about the history of tea harvest in Sri Lanka, but instead we heard about times and temperatures required to process the leaves. We were told that the word "pekoe" is derived from "Peking." We heard that plucked leaves are subject to drying, rolling, fermenting, drying, and sorting. A couple of Australian lads on the tour joked that their favourite three-step process involved drying, rolling, and smoking. Four neatly stencilled signs told us that

> If you are too hot, tea will cool you.
> If you are too cold, tea will warm you.
> If you are excited, tea will calm you.
> If you are depressed, tea will cheer you.

We arrived in Nuwara Eliya in mid-afternoon, leaving us about three hours of daylight to explore the community of 25,000 residents. From the car, many of the buildings seemed more suited to an English seaside town, presumably a hangover from Sri Lanka's colonial period. Unfortunately, the heavens were attempting to drown the unwary, so we had an excuse to sit quietly in our magnificent hotel, relaxing, dining, and digesting all that we had seen. For me, the highlight of the day had been the sense of honour at being admitted into the Temple of the Tooth. I asked Lisa for her favourite impression of the day. She replied: "The monkeys were fun." You have to love a childlike enthusiasm that never dies.

THE MORE I INVESTIGATED the history of tea in Sri Lanka, the more I was shocked by the blatantly racist comments that older books contained. My shock probably has more to say about my naïveté than anything else, but it was abundantly clear that the people who worked the tea plantations in the early days did not get a lot of respect from their managers.

It is hard to imagine a time when the word "coolie," implying someone who works very hard for very little pay, was anything other than a pejorative. Even so, it seems to be derived from the Tamil word *kuli,* implying a hired servant. Its application to the tea plantation workers of nineteenth-century Sri Lanka was probably proper usage.

In Cave's 1905 treatment of the issue of management of tea plantation workers, he explained that the weight of tea plucked by each coolie was noted, and "laziness thus detected brings a fine of half pay and in many cases a taste of the cangany's stick." I have no idea what a cangany is. Nor does the unabridged *Oxford English Dictionary.* Apparently he, she, or it hits people with a stick. Cave went on to write, "The Tamil coolie in Ceylon may be a shocking barbarian in point of intellect and civilisation as compared to his British master, but making allowances for his origin and opportunities he is by no means an unfortunate or contemptible creature." That must be the weakest compliment of all time.

Not content with insulting the workplace behaviour of Tamil workers, Cave went on to insult their religious beliefs: "Their inborn inclination to saami worship, with its weird demon rites of the most debasing type, holds them in awe of the supernatural. . . . But if we can realize the extreme ignorance of the coolies, the basest forms of religious worship and the barbarous forms of amusement which they practice will not surprise us."

Just eighty years have passed since Elliott and Whitehead wrote, "In their own peculiar way the Tamils are a cleanly people. . . . The moral standards of the cooly are low; polygamy is practised among them and sexual relations are often free and easy, with the result that disease is rife. . . . With all their faults and failings it is generally admitted that Tamil coolies are unrivalled in their own sphere, and provide the finest coloured agricultural labour to be found in the tropics."

Offering a minor compliment in one paragraph, Elliott and Whitehead took it all away in another:

Many of the Tamils employed on Tea Estates come of the depressed classes or untouchables, Pallan, Pariah and Saikli. . . . Most low caste coolies . . . are thriftless and seldom . . . even appear to try to secure a higher standard of living in Ceylon itself, for as long as they can cover the cost of their weekly rice ration . . . they are content to work the minimum number of days. . . . The only way, therefore to ensure their turning out to work at all regularly is to be strict with the issue of rice.

It wasn't just the Tamil workers who Elliott and Whitehead looked down on. In fact, "The ordinary Tamil cooly, male or female, is usually a good-tempered and cheerful individual . . . and will work day after day . . . in wind and rain, and only ask to be knocked off when conditions become really impossible. In this respect they display a great superiority over Sinhalese coolies, who are inclined to make for shelter directly as rain sets in."

WE GOT A VERY EARLY START out of Nuwara Eliya. Even though the trip was only 180 kilometres, it would take nearly six hours to get back to Colombo because of the state of the roads. The word among Lincoln's fellow drivers was that a massive rock had fallen across the road we had travelled the day before, and that mudslides had closed the alternative road to the south. As we departed, the road into Colombo was apparently still open. We crossed our fingers and set off.

When we stopped at St. Clair Falls, we found them in full flood from earlier rain, and brown from all the soil that had been washed away. A little further along, we came across Devon Falls, a clear and gentle lacework of water suggesting that its watershed had received less rain.

We had seen thousands of dogs along the roads since arriving in Sri Lanka. Anywhere there were people, there dwelt dogs. A small fraction of these were well cared for. Mongrels all, they varied in size from a large terrier to a small Alsatian, and the damnably largest portion of them were in rough shape. A very good small-animal veterinarian once told me that most dogs are a good weight when you can feel their ribs but cannot see them. In Sri Lanka, dogs' ribs were visible from a speeding car. They lay at the side of the road, or in the middle of the road, and while drivers try hard to miss them, many are relieved from their earthly misery by being run over. As cars drove by, dogs cowered, with ears and tails down. We saw many dogs trying to eat items that were clearly not food.

A particularly piteous bitch walked up to us at the Devon Falls lookout. In her gaze I saw a message that I knew to be honest. She said, "If you don't feed me now, I will be dead within a day or two." She was so thin that I would have been nearly able to girdle her waist with the fingers of one hand. Her left hind leg was drawn uselessly toward her midline. We had seen this deformity so often that I wondered if it was a skeletal condition brought on by chronic malnutrition. We had nothing to feed her, and I suspect that if we had, she would have wolfed it down and immediately vomited it up.

"You are having a hard life," said Lincoln, and the little thing tried hard to wag her tail without falling over.

We stopped for a late breakfast at a fine restaurant and small hotel near the Kelani River. It must be the perfect place to escape for a few days of quiet in dappled shade. The spot is famous as the site where most of the sequences in *The Bridge on the River Kwai* were filmed.

While we ate, Lincoln told us a quintessential Sri Lanka joke. It seemed that an Air Lanka flight was high over the Arabian Sea when the pilot came on the intercom to inform passengers that he was going to have to ditch the plane because of engine failure. After coming to rest on the water, the plane slowly started to sink, and the pilot instructed all passengers to climb onto the wings. "Swimmers are to climb onto the right wing, and non-swimmers are to climb onto the left wing." A few minutes later, the evacuation had been successfully completed, and the pilot made one more announcement. "For those of you on the right wing, Karachi is due north. For those of you on the left wing . . . thank you for flying Air Lanka!"

THE WEDDING DAY of Charu and Chaminda was to be as full of pageantry and symbolism as any since Charles and Diana's. For those in the wedding party, the day began at 3 a.m. following a brief and sleepless night. Hair had to be coiffed, metre upon metre of robes affixed, and one jewel after another applied. In contrast, Lisa and I had a nice little lie-in until seven, followed by a leisurely and sumptuous breakfast overlooking the ocean.

Guests started entering the Empire Room shortly after ten o'clock. Thirty magnificent columns, each illuminated by endless tiny lights, swept past a balcony, rising up to support a grand dome. The room was festooned with white and gold, including metallic gold sashes over each chair. Lisa in her purple sari and me in my black suit; for an hour we introduced ourselves and shook hands.

Promptly at 11 a.m., the master of ceremonies began his introduction to the event in Sinhalese. Just as he began the English version of the same speech, a cacophony rang out; it was time for the groom's procession. Chaminda and his attendants entered, accompanied by four dancers, two drummers, and someone tootling on a conch shell. Each was dressed in white, black, yellow, and red. Girdled with scarves to make him look fat, Chaminda was dressed as a king, resplendent in a cream wrap and a burgundy jacket adorned with gold. Lisa and I stood to one side, trying to see as much as we could without looking too obvious as the only white people in the throng.

The performers left but returned minutes later to accompany the bride and her entourage. This time the dancers were complemented by acrobats. Charu and Chaminda came together at the front of a raised platform finished all over in gold with strings of white flowers. Charu is a Cancer and Chaminda is a Leo, and an astrologer had decreed that the most auspicious time for the couple to ascend the marriage platform was 11:24 a.m. In ceremonial tradition, attendants kept them from rising to the platform too early. A man providing spoken and sung prayers looked back and forth between the happy couple and his watch.

When the appointed time came, Chaminda and Charu stepped onto the platform and stood between statues of golden swans with interlocking necks. The couple was handed bunches of seven betel leaves, which they then dropped to the ground. Chaminda placed a gold necklace around Charu's neck, bringing her tally to eight. He placed over her shoulders a burgundy vest, and then held a similar vest in front of her. He gave her two rings, and she gave him one. Their hands were tied together and water trickled over them. Several guests joked with us about the complexity of the ceremony, and one said, "Well, I suppose you have to suffer a bit with these things." I think he was referring to the couple.

Then parents and other close relatives were called forward to receive bundles of betel leaves from the couple. Chaminda looked a little overwhelmed, but Charu looked so full of joy that she seemed on the verge of tears. Lisa and I were apparently a little more honoured than we realized, as Chaminda and Charu motioned for us to move to the platform to be handed a bunch of betel leaves.

"Ah, good," I thought. "A chance to really screw things up." We walked forward and stuck out our hands.

"Together," whispered Charu, and Lisa and I put our hands side by side, received the leaves, bowed, and walked away. I thought that we had done pretty well, until I noticed that everyone after us was dropping the leaves after receiving them. I snuck back up to the platform, whispered "sorry," and dropped the leaves so that they could be reused.

At precisely 11:59, the couple descended the platform and lit the wick of an oil candle. They cut their wedding cake and fed each other. Only then did they proceed to a pair of monks in saffron robes to receive a chanted blessing; one of the monks was Charu's grandmother.

The time had come for Chaminda and Charu to meet their family and friends as a married couple for the first time. We were among the first to be invited into the reception line. I preceded Lisa. The bride and groom bowed deeply, and I bowed back. Chaminda brought his hands together in prayer and bowed. I did the same, and offered them my little rehearsed blessing, which was: "I hope that many years of marriage bring you as much happiness as they have brought Lisa and me." I then stuck out my hand to shake Chaminda's. He smiled and bowed again. When I didn't withdraw my hand, he whispered through his teeth, "I'm not supposed to shake your hand." Oops. I bowed again to Chaminda, bowed one final time to Charu, and scuttled off. It will come as a surprise to no one that I have come to think of each new day as an opportunity to embarrass myself.

I HAVE BEEN INVITED to many weddings, but I had never before been invited to join a honeymoon. The opportunity to visit some of Sri Lanka's greatest ancient sites in the Central Province was too good to miss. The initial plan was to leave the wedding with Charu and Chaminda at 3 p.m. and make the three-hour trip to the Kandalama Resort near the rock fortress of Sigiriya with a hired driver. I had visions of sipping gin and tonic beside a pool by six. We were very late in leaving Mount Lavinia, and the ride was much longer than three hours. This came down to a combination of heavy traffic and a crappy road. The approach road into the resort had been nearly demolished by rain, and I was tired and grumpy when we arrived. All of that dropped away as our van pulled up to the facility. There was no front door, and I suppose one isn't necessary in a tropical paradise without plagues of biting insects. Instead, the van disgorged us under a high ceiling. Lisa and Charu were given lotus flowers, and we were led, not to the registration desk, but to a lounge where we were brought fruit drinks. "Oh, and by the way, if you could fill in the registration cards at some point, that would be very kind of you."

Being open to the jungle from which it was carved, the building attracted small insects, which flew towards the lights. These were followed by myriad small bats that worked the hallways. On closer examination, we found that the walls were decorated with small insect-eating lizards.

Despite our late arrival, the restaurant was still open, and the four of us dove into creations exotic and conventional. Salads and curries and soups and breads and all manner of flesh and desserts. Oh, the desserts! I even managed to get a gin and tonic. When we gave up on the day and took to our room, we found it had a bathroom large enough for a family of six. Both the bath and shower looked out of floor-to-ceiling windows over the jungle. Other than odd dreams brought on by the anti-malarial drugs, I slept the sleep of the fabulously rich.

The next morning, after a breakfast as sumptuous as dinner, we set off for the rock-top fortress at Sigiriya. Because there were white people in the van, our driver was able to take us right up to the entrance. Locals had to park much further away. But then we were hit by what Charu called "the curse of the white guys." While Charu and Chaminda were admitted for 20 rupees, Lisa and I were charged 2,000 rupees apiece. We were told that the Sinhala word *Sudda* means "white guy." It isn't terribly derogatory, but it isn't used as a big compliment either. We had no reason for complaint because Chaminda paid our entry fee.

We discovered that King Kasyapa had constructed a bathing facility for his 500 wives on the plain below the fortress. Being a pervy kind of king, he used a hidden portal to watch them all bathe. Being a randy kind of king, he took the chosen wife or wives back through the portal for some less-public action. I was terribly impressed when told that the facility's moat had originally been filled with alligators, and by the sheer scope of the plumbing problems that had been solved 1,500 years earlier.

We began the climb to the fortress. About halfway to the top, a spiral staircase took us to an alcove with rock paintings. In the past there were many more, but today some two dozen semi-naked, larger-than-life celestial nymphs danced across the rock face. Explicitly anatomical, this was pretty racy stuff for a country where topless sunbathing guarantees prosecution. In so restrained a society, it seemed odd that the image of the most buxom nymph with nipples three sizes too large was featured on tourist guidebooks to Sigiriya.

Never a slouch at spotting wildlife, Lisa managed to find lizard after lizard sunning themselves on smooth rock faces. Some were the size of my index finger and decorated in the most delightful metallic bronze sheen. Others were as big as a mid-sized Iguanodon. By this point in the day, all the lizards had warmed themselves to the point where they moved very quickly.

We continued our ascent, mounting a rock staircase between sculpted lion paws. Up and up. We were all clad in sandals, but at points the stairs were too shallow for a good purchase, so we stripped to bare feet. At one point, our progress was barred by a monkey. Charu expressed concern, explaining that they can be really mean little devils. In a rush of testosterone, I offered to go first. I said, "Excuse me, please," and the monkey politely stepped out of our way.

Finally, at 380 metres above sea level and fully 200 metres above Kasyapa's water garden of naughty pleasures, we achieved the summit. Everything else was down, and all of it was lush green forest. I might have felt a degree of pride at having completed so

great a climb on so hot and humid a day, but we had been preceded to the top by many small children and old women, many of
them encumbered by traditional robes. Lisa told me that Duran
Duran had shot their video for the song "Save a Prayer" from this
peak, and I wish that she hadn't. I later looked it up on the Internet.
That's six minutes and three seconds of my life I'll never get back.

Next our driver took us to the cave temple at Dambulla, where
the curse of the white guys hit us again. As Sri Lankans, Charu and
Chaminda were welcome to enter the temple at no charge, but as
foreigners, Lisa and I required 300-rupee tickets. While Chaminda
secured our tickets, we stood in the shade of a Bodhi tree. These are
said to be descendants of the sacred Bodhi tree that overarched the
Buddha as he gained enlightenment. Propagated from cuttings, these
trees are found at principal intersections of many communities in Sri
Lanka. The leaves of our tree rustled very gently in the breeze.

Attaining the temple first involved a climb up a gigantic slippery rock. The day was passing, and getting warmer by the minute, but it wasn't too much of a slog for four fit young people.
Life didn't seem like much of a slog for the monkeys that lined
the trail. The big difference was that the monkeys had the sense
to lie about in the shade. We showed our tickets to a uniformed
guard and left our sandals with an attendant, only to find that the
stone walkway was blessedly hot. Charu and Chaminda showed a
degree of dignity, but Lisa and I hopped around like water sprites.
It was only a minute or two before I could say that the soles of my
feet were well and truly burned.

The site's history dates back more than two millennia, and
a series of five caves contain carvings and other depictions of
Buddha. We entered the cool and shady interior of the first cave.
Inside was a gigantic reclining Buddha that we could see only
after our eyes adapted to the dark. The next cave had Buddhas
on all four sides. Charu said that the twenty-four statues represented the succession of twenty-four Buddhas to date. I discreetly counted the figures. There were only twenty-one, but I
didn't tell Charu.

Each cave ceiling was painted with hundreds of images of Buddha. Chaminda explained that the subtle differences in the hands of the statues and paintings had significance. These were subtleties that he had learned in school but had since forgotten. Following the lead of our hosts, Lisa and I laid freshly washed lotus flowers, stems removed, on a desk in front of a particularly friendly rendition.

Back at the hotel, the remainder of the day was filled with eating, drinking, swimming, and bug-watching. I was the insect king. I found a red-and-black centipede and gave him a wide berth; centipedes bite. I found an orange-and-black millipede with orange legs and was able to pick him up and show him around, knowing him to be a detritivore. I was pleased to stumble across stick insects—not the common-old everyday sort related to bugs, but those more closely related to grasshoppers. It was a classic example of convergent evolution. Finding a red-and-black butterfly bashing himself against a window, I gathered him up and walked him over to a ledge. When I opened my hands to set him free, he fell like a stone four storeys to the ground below. I suppose it must be some sort of anti-predator adaptation.

With the daylight fading, Lisa and I sat on a terrace, drinking gin and tonics, listening to a gentleman playing a recorder on a nearby rock. A small bird flew in, and Chaminda identified him as a *Konda Kurulla*. A little bigger than a sparrow, with a black head with a crest, a grey body, and a white rump patch, the name translates loosely as a bird with hair. Bats and swifts took to the air for their first bugs of the night, and all was right with the world.

VIRTUALLY NO PLACE ON EARTH has avoided the ravages of introduced plant and animal species. Even Sri Lanka, possibly the original Garden of Eden, has been invaded again and again. The Global Invasive Species Database lists 120 species for Sri Lanka, most of them plants. Tea didn't make the list. We rarely think of our crops and livestock as introduced species, even if a large part of our diet is derived from plants and animals brought in from far and wide.

In Sri Lanka, I had seen all the tea plants that a rational man could ever want, but I couldn't remember drinking a single cup of it. I could, however, remember a lot of gin and tonic. And monkeys.

CHAPTER SIX

Paradise Made to Order

REASON NUMBER SIX FOR INTRODUCING A FOREIGN SPECIES: BECAUSE MY OUTHOUSE IS UGLY.

SOMETIMES EVENTS IN LIFE can go spiralling outward from the most trivial of incidents. I had picked up a copy of *Islands* magazine because it had a pretty picture on the cover. The issue had a special feature on Hawaii, which probably happens about four times a year in *Islands* magazine. In its treatment of the island of Kauai, the issue described an upcoming festival in Kōke'e State Park dedicated to an introduced plant species. The Banana Poka Round-up was to feature a parade, live Hawaiian music, face-painting, and lessons on *lei* making. Best of all, I could register for a workshop to learn to make baskets from vines of the introduced banana poka plant. How could I possibly miss all of that?

Regrettably, I missed all of that. The Banana Poka Round-up coincided with a trip I had scheduled to southern Spain to look at endangered ducks. Fortunately, Michelle Hookano at the Kōke'e Natural History Museum promised me that if I could make a trip to Kauai in February she would be pleased to show me around and introduce me to banana poka plants. And so, on the basis of a two-page magazine piece, Lisa and I tore ourselves away from the depths of a Canadian winter and headed for Paradise in a slightly modified form.

I was, admittedly, among the last people on Earth with sufficient money to visit Hawaii who had never actually done so. Almost everyone I knew had been there, and that is exactly the reason why I had never gone. It is also the very reason why Hawaii is knee-deep in introduced species. Everyone wants to go to Paradise, but they want to make it more like home by bringing along reminders of what they left behind. Hawaii is in perpetual competition with Australia for bragging rights about whose landscape has been more thoroughly chewed up by introduced species. Australia has rabbits, cane toads, camels, rabbits, fire ants, foxes, rabbits, pigeons, and more rabbits, but virtually everything in Hawaii has been brought from somewhere else.

Shortly after stepping off the plane at Honolulu airport, I was bitten by our first introduced species in Hawaii—a mosquito. There are no mosquitoes—or indeed any other biting insects—native to Hawaii, and the one that got me was likely *Culex pipiens fatigans*. It was introduced when the ship *Wellington* put in at Maui for water in 1826. Before filling their barrels with fresh drinking water, the sailors tipped out their reserves of stale water, contaminated by the larvae of the mosquito picked up in Mexico. Before the mid-1800s there was no word in the Hawaiian language for "mosquito." It has one now, *makika,* which diminishes Paradise just that little bit.

While waiting for our flight to Kauai, Lisa and I walked to a nearby waterside park, where we spotted a range of lovely birds, including Zebra Doves (introduced to Hawaii in 1922), Spotted Doves (mid-1800s), Red-crested Cardinals (1930s), House Sparrows (1871), House Finches (1860s), Common Mynas (1865), and some lovely little creatures with yellow heads and breasts, splashes of red on their faces, and olive backs, called Saffron Finches (1960s). We also spied several Java Sparrows, which were first introduced about 1865 but didn't become established until their introduction again in the 1960s. They are now trapped intensively for sale as pets overseas. So far, Paradise had revealed nine introduced bird species, and nil native species. Because of introductions, the birdlife of Hawaii is considerably more varied now than before human contact, despite the extinction of more than half of the native species, including the Hawaii Mamo, the 'Ula-'ai-hāwane, and the Kona Grosbeak. Several other native Hawaiian birds are feared extinct, including the Kakawahie, the Maui 'Alauahio, and 'Ō'ū.

THE ISLANDS OF HAWAII have a combined human population of just over 1.2 million. Kauai, the "Garden Island," tucked up in the upper left-hand corner of the chain, has a population of 58,303 but an average daily visitor population of 16,160, which surely also makes it the "Covered-by-Tourists Island." On any given day, every fifth person on the street is a visitor. Residents of Kauai make up just 4.8 percent of the state's population but are responsible for only 2.2 percent of the state's violent crimes. Even so, everyone was keen to point out that the criminals on Kauai target tourists. A guidebook, our hosts at our rental accommodation, our car rental agreement, and even a sticker in the Jeep warned us not to leave valuables in the car, or they would, absolutely, most certainly not be there when we got back.

Hawaii is the perfect place for people who love little factoids. The state bird is the Nene, its tree the candlenut, its flower the yellow hibiscus, and the state fish is the Humuhumunukunukuapua'a, a coral-reef dweller also known as the Hawaiian triggerfish. All of these are native to the islands. The state motto is *Ua Mau ke Ea o ka 'Āina i ka Pono,* which apparently translates as "The life of the land is perpetuated in righteousness." The state song is "Hawaii Pono'i," and the state's four nicknames are Aloha State, Pineapple State, Rainbow State, and State of Utter Confusion.

When we drove from our rented accommodation in Lawai to a grocery store in Kóloa for provisions, we discovered a local protest against the removal of large old monkeypod trees to make room for additional retail development. Monkeypod trees are certainly stately, but they are not native to Hawaii, having been introduced from Mexico in 1847. Surrounding fields supported abundant Cattle Egrets, introduced in the mid-twentieth century to reduce pest insects around cattle, which were, themselves, introduced. In the grocery store parking lot, we spied Moa or Red Junglefowl. With red comb and wattles, feathers of flame along the neck, and jet-black breast, flank, and tail, the cocks seem to fear nothing. Except hens. Moas were the first birds to be introduced to Hawaii by settling Polynesians and do particularly well on Kauai because, unlike other islands in the state, this one has no introduced mongooses to eat their eggs. Kauai had similarly missed a major outbreak of coquis—small, very noisy frogs introduced from Puerto Rico that swarm over other islands in the chain.

Back on our *lanai,* we heard smoochy-smoochy noises, which promised to be the occupants of the adjoining suite, but proved to be house geckos, also introduced, this time from Southeast Asia. Indeed, none of Hawaii's terrestrial reptiles or amphibians are thought to be native. Even so, the state now has five species of amphibians and twenty species of land reptile. It was kind of romantic to sit back and watch Lisa point out one smoochy gecko after another.

MONDAY WAS PRESIDENT'S DAY, so we could not get our official introduction to banana poka plants in Kōke'e State Park until the following morning, giving us the opportunity to explore the south coast of Kauai. Of all the wonderful opportunities described in the guidebooks to the island, the neatest seemed to be the Barking Sands Beach in Polihale State Park, where footfalls on golden sand were said to sound like the barking of dogs. The description of the roads to Barking Sands as "miserable" didn't deter us. We checked and rechecked that our Jeep's rental agreement did not explicitly forbid our travel on the rough access road and set off along Highway 50 on a beautiful sunny morning.

We were instructed to follow the road until it ran out. When it did, we found a sign telling us in no uncertain terms that the park was closed. Permanently. To emphasize the point, the sign was punctuated by a large bullet hole. As we considered our next move, a posh black Nissan with four occupants came beetling along the prohibited road and pulled onto the highway. "What do you think they were doing down that road?" I asked Lisa. "Two young men and two young women? I think *that's* what they were doing down that road."

On our drive back along Highway 50, we spotted two Pueo, a subspecies of Short-eared Owl, which represented our first native birds. Although the owl is native to Hawaii, it is thought that it has done much better since the arrival of the Polynesians, who altered the landscape toward open grassland, making foraging by the owl much more effective. The highway was lined with coffee (introduced) plantations perforating mile after mile of sugar cane (introduced) plantations. Of all agricultural crops, tall, scrubby sugar cane must be among the ten least pretty. Even so, it was prettier than the military airfields and missile firing facilities that also lined the road.

Monarch butterflies were, by far, the most common butterfly we spotted on Kauai. They weren't found in Hawaii until the middle of the nineteenth century, but whether they were introduced intentionally or by accident or managed to disperse there themselves isn't clear. Their establishment followed the introduction of milkweed plants, the favourite food of monarch caterpillars.

At an impressively long stretch of sand at Kekaha Beach Park, we drenched ourselves in sunblock in an attempt to return to winter as pale as when we left. The sand was a beautiful gold colour and completely unlittered by kelp or shells, suggesting to me that the waters around Kauai cannot be very productive. The beach was also almost completely unlittered by other people, surprising for a holiday Monday in February. The few that did join us were trying to boogie-board in the entirely underwhelming surf, or hanging out near their large-wheeled beach trucks. We spotted 'A (a.k.a. Brown Boobies), Ae'o (Hawaiian Stilts), and Kōlea (Pacific Golden Plovers). All were native.

In the evening, we drove to the moaning Spouting Horn blowhole. The area is built up with swank hotels and posh homes. Almost every tourist we came across was making a game of telling every other tourist that they would have had a much better experience if they had arrived just ten minutes, ten days, or ten years earlier. A Minnesotan told anyone who would listen that the blowhole had been blowing much higher just ten minutes earlier. A lady from Texas claimed that the humpback whales had been far more numerous when she visited the previous year. We had a pretty good time of it despite being chronologically challenged. A cow humpback whale was demonstrating to her calf the best ways of showing off to a crowd, arcing out of the water, lying on her back, and slapping the water with her fins, and generally doing the hokey-pokey.

THE KŌKE'E NATURAL HISTORY MUSEUM isn't an easy spot to get to, high on a narrow and tortured road along the Waimae Canyon. As we were on our way shortly after sunrise and most vacationers seem to enjoy a little lie-in, we had the road to ourselves. The route was punctuated with opportunities to pull off and see the canyon in all its glory. Mark Twain apparently described it as the "Grand Canyon of the Pacific." It must be true, because the quote appears on more than 40,000 websites. Strangely, I cannot find a shred of evidence that Twain ever did describe the canyon that way. I'm not even sure that he ever visited the original Grand Canyon. I suppose the canyon is so jagged because it has never been blunted by glaciers. It is a valley of the gnarled digits of a very elderly woman crippled by arthritis. While I kept the Jeep from plunging into the canyon, Lisa spotted a Chuckar and two Erckel Francolins, introduced to Hawaii in 1923 and 1957, respectively.

We were met at the museum by Michelle Hookano. She seemed in particularly good spirits for someone who had just come from a staff meeting. Her raven hair spoke of Polynesian genes, but her blue eyes were so light it made me wonder if she saw the world differently than I did. She is involved in outdoor programs for youth and seemed to be the sort of person who would rather have children playing in the forest than playing video games.

The banana poka, the focus of our visit to Paradise, is one of roughly 600 plant species in the passion flower family. Passion flowers were given their genus name, *Passiflora*, because Spanish explorers of the New World felt that their flowers had signs of the Passion of Christ. The banana poka is native to the cool, moist forests of the Andes in Venezuela, Peru, and Bolivia. At least twenty-five other *Passiflora* species are found in Hawaii. Most of these are under cultivation, but a dozen manage to persist without the help of humans.

The banana poka is a liana, a vine that makes its living by clambering over other plants; the "poka" part of its Hawaiian name refers to this inclination to climb. In South America, the species is comparatively rare, with insects and other pests consuming its flowers and fruits. In the absence of the predators, parasites, and disease that keep the banana poka populations in check at home, densities in Hawaii greatly exceed those in South America. In Hawaii, the banana poka is capable of growing so densely that it sometimes creates a curtain of vegetation, running roughshod over forests, pastures, and farmland. It can be so thick as to inhibit the germination and growth of native seedlings. By covering the host tree, banana poka plants decrease their host's ability to photosynthesize, and compete with the tree for nutrients in the soil. In a storm, the banana poka can break its host's branches or even topple the supporting tree. A perennial, individual banana pokas may persist for as long as twenty years.

The plant has a sneaky trick that makes it all the more noxious. Unlike many other plant species, an individual can fertilize itself, and so a single individual can found a population even in the absence of friends. The banana poka blooms throughout the year, its pink flowers hanging like medallions from the vine; it was introduced to Hawaii for its ornamental value. An oft-repeated story claims that the original introduction was made by someone trying to cover an unsightly outhouse, although the story may be apocryphal.

The plant was first introduced to the Pu'uwa'awa'a region of Hawaii in 1921. Another introduction came in 1928 in Honua'ula. Infestations spread so rapidly that they eventually coalesced into one continuous population.

The infestation of Kauai began in 1923. The plant now covers something like 520 square kilometres of Hawaii and Kauai, an area greater than the combined surfaces of the countries of Barbados and San Marino. Hawaii's Department of Agriculture considers it to be a "Noxious Weed for Eradication or Control Purposes"; given all of the capital letters, it seems they take the plant rather seriously. Besides Hawaii, the banana poka has also been introduced to Mexico, South Africa, India, Sri Lanka, and New Zealand, although it is only in Hawaii that it has become a serious pest.

Given its name, it is not surprising that banana pokas produce edible, elongate yellow fruit. Each fruit contains as many as 200 seeds. The seeds have hard coats, allowing them to pass unharmed through the digestive system of the creature that eats them. Seeds are then deposited in a fertile situation. Feral pigs are the single most important dispersing agent, and the highest pig densities often correspond to the highest banana poka densities.

So what is to be done about the banana poka in Hawaii? Getting rid of the pigs would be a good start. Herbicides are often ineffective and can kill native plants in the community. Control is sometimes possible by chopping them down, which is notoriously labour-intensive for a plant that grows so quickly. Introducing pests from their South America home comes with the risk of damage to other desirable plant species, including the lillikoi, the purple passion fruit whose harvest constitutes a minor industry in Hawaii. To date, the greatest success with agents of biological control has been with a fungus, *Septoria passiflora,* which seems to work best in wetter areas.

Michelle pointed out another interesting biological control method. Some birds are nectar robbers. Birds had discovered the nectar reserves located at the base of the banana poka's flowers, and by gaining access to the nectar by poking a hole in the flower, and therefore not fertilizing it, were keeping the plant from producing seeds. "The birds are nailing it," she said.

Banana poka eradication efforts in Kōke'e State Park have been so effective that when park personnel need to collect vines for the

Banana Poka Round-up, volunteers have to search backroads in four-wheel drive trucks. Luckily, Michelle spotted one of the vines draped over a tree in a nearby meadow.

However, other forces are continuing to spread the plant. When ripe fruit drops to the ground, pigs eat them, dispersing the seeds. Pigs didn't swim to Hawaii, of course; they were brought by Polynesian settlers. These were followed by black-tailed deer and goats, which quickly proliferated and spread. All three mammals are hunted legally in Kōke'e State Park. Michelle explained that pigs can be hunted throughout the year with dogs and knives. I thought I had misheard, and asked for clarification. She claimed that an Airedale–pit bull–Labrador retriever cross is trained to grab and hold the pig while the hunter runs up and kills it with a knife. Was she teasing me?

According to the Kauai telephone directory, she wasn't. Wild pigs can be hunted with dogs and knives in, for instance, Hunting Unit C, year-round on Saturdays, Sundays, Mondays, and state holidays, at a rate of one pig per hunter per day. Hunting Unit C must really hate wild pigs, where they can also be dispatched with rifle, muzzleloader, handgun, bow and arrow, or sustained teasing.

I suppose I can see why locals are so eager to kill pigs, aside from the opportunity to eat their yummy, yummy bits. Pigs in Hawaii now number more than 100,000 individuals. They root in the soil for grubs and worms, leaving depressions that fill with rainwater and become breeding opportunities for mosquitoes. They eat the fruit of introduced plants like the banana poka and Brazilian strawberry guava, spreading their seeds.

Banana poka were not the only exotic plant species we spied growing around the museum's buildings. Michelle pointed out Chinese fir, introduced around 1804. Hoop pines were brought from Australia around 1880. We saw loblolly pines, California redwoods, Monterey cypress, Italian cypress, Mexican cypress, and two species of eucalyptus.

After thanking Michelle for her time, there was nothing for it but a hike, and in all of Kauai, this was the place for it. Michelle suggested that to see native birds the best spot was the Alaka'i swamp, the highest-elevation swamp in the world. We continued up to the end of the road and found the Pu'u o Kila Lookout. At more than 1,200 metres, looking out over the Kalalau Valley, it seemed that we had come to the end of the world. The swamp is the result of past volcanic indigestion and 350 days of rain a year. Even though we were fortunate to be visiting on one of the other fifteen days, the red mud trail was slick, preventing the vast majority of visitors to Pu'u o Kila from leaving the car park. A missed step put Lisa on her backside and covered our *Birds of Kauai* book, purchased thirty minutes earlier at the museum's gift shop, in red slime.

Our perseverance was rewarded. We had left the mosquitoes below us and entered a fern-filled world of shade trees and mist. Verdant greenness was punctuated by the spiky red flowers of the 'ohi'a lehua tree, whose nectar attracted wonderful feathered creatures. First came the 'Apapane, a crimson-red honeycreeper whose black bill and red wings seemed a suitable costume for a superhero. Then we spied the 'Anianiau, which seemed less like a bird and more like a flying lemon plugged into a car battery. The smallest of Hawaii's honeycreepers, it is found only on Kauai, and generally only above 1,000 metres. A little deeper into the swamp, we spied the Kauai 'Elepaio. I had read about the behaviour of this bird in scholarly papers and expected something a little showier from a native Hawaiian bird. They are grey and slightly darker grey, with bits of tan and two narrow grey bars on the wings, but they earn bonus points for being relatively common and carefree.

THIS LEFT US with a glorious February day to play tourist. Rising very early, we took the Jeep to the region of Poipu, and bounced along rutted dirt cane-field roads to the last of the beaches, Mahaulepu. It was supposed to be one of the best places on the island to see endangered monk seals. We didn't see any. Scrambling up and over rocks of solidified sand, we spotted a pod of thirty dolphins. Then we spied a group of whales bearing down on a school of large fish, driving them up in the air in a mad attempt to avoid being breakfast. And then we spotted something almost as good as a monk seal—a green sea turtle, endangered in anyone's book, lazily swimming by. Liberally slathered in sunblock, I dozed on the beach while Lisa watched the antics of humpbacks for nearly three hours. She also spotted a Wandering Tattler, known locally as the ʻŪlili.

By the end of our brief stay in Hawaii, we had seen nine native bird species. Regrettably, we had chalked up a massive sixteen species of bird that been brought to Hawaii by humans. Most of the plants and insects and all of the reptiles we had seen were also introduced. It all got me thinking about the nature of Paradise. I had to wonder if Hawaii can be Paradise if it hosts so strong a military presence. Can an island be Paradise if its crime statistics look good only in comparison to other islands? Is it Paradise if the only major road is notoriously congested all day every day? Is this Paradise if the shark attack statistics are downplayed by claiming that most fatalities are those paddling surfboards? Hawaii certainly looked like Paradise when we were greeted home by a blizzard.

CHAPTER SEVEN

If God Were a Frog

REASON NUMBER SEVEN FOR INTRODUCING A FOREIGN SPECIES: BECAUSE POOR PEOPLE WILL EAT ANYTHING, RIGHT?

IF GOD WERE A FROG, I suppose He might be a Paradise toad. The sort of creature that only a mother could love, this amphibian has warty red skin with patches of sickly green. Discovered by Harold Braack, whose surname sounds oddly like the call of a toad, it breeds in small spring-fed pools in arid rocky regions of western South Africa. There seems to be something particularly holy about both Mary's frog, known only from Mount Balabag on the island of Palawan in western Philippines, and the Virgin Island coqui, found on the islands of Tortola and Virgin Gorda. Alternatively, the Almighty might be represented in amphibian form by the southern ghost frog. Found in forest streams of the Cape Mountains of South Africa, it has skin the colour of light brown sugar with splotches of slightly darker brown sugar. The bleeding toad sounds somehow biblical; its status of "critically endangered" wasn't helped by the eruption of its favourite home, Mount Galunggung, in 1987. My favourite contender for an all-powerful frog is a globular little yellow mass with red and black spots known as the Holy Cross toad.

In contrast, there can be only one contender for Satan in the form of a frog. So foul and evil a creature that it appears on the

World Conservation Union's list of 100 worst invasive alien species, the American bullfrog is a truly despicable creature when it is
found in the wrong place.

The right place for an American bullfrog is eastern North
America from Nova Scotia south to central Florida and northern Mexico. The wrong place is anywhere else, including China,
Cuba, England, France, Israel, Japan, Russia, and nine countries in
South America. Once established at a site, bullfrogs seem willing
to expand their range rapidly along streams, canals, and irrigation
ditches.

Some frogs are attractive. Bullfrogs aren't. They are green or
brown and always blotchy. A really big one would have a twenty-
centimetre body, with another twenty centimetres tacked on as
legs. A bullfrog that big would weigh in at something approaching
750 grams. The sides of their heads are marked by huge eardrums
and big, bulgy eyes. They have come to me in my nastier dreams.

American bullfrogs have been imported as pets and as accidental tag-alongs with goldfish. However, the introduction of bullfrogs
has been mainly an issue of food. You might try to win your next
Scrabble game with the word "ranarium," a commercial operation
where bullfrogs are raised for human consumption. These facilities
do not require a lot of space and need only a modest initial investment, and have been tried with varying degrees of success around
the world for over a century.

Curiously, it seems that every attempt to raise bullfrogs for food
had an export market in mind. Locals generally seem to prefer
steaks and burgers to frogs' legs. Is it possible that no one really
wants to eat them? Many countries have found that the market was
overestimated, and bullfrog farms sit abandoned. Frogs then sneak
away into the night and cause trouble.

Introduced American bullfrogs have been reported willing to
stuff down just about anything they can fit in their mouths, including native insects, other frogs, newts, fish, and crayfish. Among
the more unlikely items found in their diet are grass snakes, young
mink, small turtles, and ducklings. Bullfrog tadpoles are thought to

compete for food with the larval forms of native frogs, and adults have the potential to transmit diseases to which local amphibians have no natural resistance. Experts in Venezuela feel that the endangered La Carbonera stub-toed toad could be wiped out in months if American bullfrogs were to invade their habitat. Competition with American bullfrogs is most likely to have a negative impact on frog species that are most closely related to them, particularly other members of the same genus. For close relatives, hybridization is also possible. At a time when amphibians are under threat globally, introduced bullfrogs seem to be an additional problem that no one needs.

IT WAS ROUGHLY AT THIS POINT that Lisa and I joined the global transplantation of living organisms by moving from Canada to Australia. Lisa had completed a series of post-doctoral fellowships in the field of biomedical physiology and was poised to become a professor in her own right. It had become apparent that the chances of finding professorial positions in our respective fields in the city of Calgary were remote, and so we began to look at alternatives. Among those was the possibility that I would allow myself to be a kept husband and rely on my spouse for my next meal. When Lisa interviewed for and was subsequently offered an outstanding post at James Cook University in north Queensland, the correct route seemed obvious. At least it seemed obvious to us. When my colleagues found out that I was chucking in a position that was virtually guaranteed for life to move to a hemisphere that I hadn't even visited, their responses were of two sorts. I must be very brave or I must be very stupid.

Australia is covered with introduced species, but it doesn't have American bullfrogs. Of all the places that I might have chosen to spy on bullfrogs, I chose Uruguay for three reasons. First, no one I knew had ever been there. Second, I had recently completed a twelve-session night course in elementary Spanish, and although I had always felt like the most dim-witted student in the class, I wanted to try out some of my new-found knowledge.

Finally, research had just been completed on the invader in Uruguay, and the country's principle amphibian researcher had promised to show me around.

Unless you are a member of the Uruguayan military, you will find it nearly impossible to fly to Uruguay without flying to Argentina first. For me, this meant a flight from Sydney to Buenos Aires, the closest transportation hub to Uruguay's capital city, Montevideo. The Pacific Ocean is really, really big, and our plane seemed in no hurry to get to Buenos Aires. I passed the time by constructing naughty expressions in Spanish using my phrasebook. Nothing I came up with would be naughty enough to get my face slapped. However, I made a mental note not to use the word *coger*. In Spain the verb means "to take" or "to catch." In South America it is a much cruder version of the expression "to have carnal knowledge of." Asking a local where I might be able to engage in coitus with a bus could conceivably get me into a bit of trouble.

Before departing for Montevideo, I enjoyed a couple of free days wandering the streets of Buenos Aires. I found my way to the Cementerio de la Recoleta, populated by the earthly remains of presidents, physicians, Nobel Prize winners, writers, diplomats, and other mucky-mucks. I discovered that coffee culture in Argentina means *café con leche* (coffee with a large quantity of steamed milk), a glass of water, a glass of orange juice, and tasty chocolate wafers. Florida Avenue was alive and electrified late into the evening. Street vendors hawked beaded work, quick portraits, more beaded work, cigarette lighters, and additional beaded work.

Indeed, there was only one great challenge for me in Buenos Aires. In a country full of ravenous carnivores, a good vegetarian restaurant is a rare and precious thing. And so for an evening meal I set off for La Esquina de las Flores (The Corner of the Flowers). When I arrived at the address on Córdoba, I found that my dining opportunity had been replaced by a gaping construction site. Luckily, I had a plan B. The restaurant Rubia y Negra (Blond and Black) on Libertad was said to brew eight varieties of beer.

In its place I found a hairdressing salon. For an instant, I toyed with plan C. Ligure on Juncal was said to serve the best *ranas a la provenzal,* bullfrog legs in garlic, in all of Argentina. Bullfrogs? What an opportunity. Not that I wanted to eat bullfrog legs; most vegetarians don't. But perhaps I could find a fellow patron who had ordered them and could then ask how they tasted. Fat chance.

I had hoped to visit another introduced species before I left Argentina. Just as it had been introduced to Vancouver in the nineteenth century, the Crested Myna had been found in Argentina since 1982. In the hopes of seeing it, I contacted local bird enthusiast Mark Pearman. Although we were not able to dovetail our schedules, he gave me all of the details that I needed to find mynas myself at the Plaza Paso in the city of La Plata, fifty kilometres south of Buenos Aires. Mark warned me about a lack of signposts, awkward exit roads, dangerous ghettos, and general violence and security problems in La Plata. Despite the city's promise of Belle Epoque and Flemish Renaissance architecture, a great natural history museum, and convenient bus service, I decided against a detour to La Plata.

BE ADVISED—on the ferry between Buenos Aires and Montevideo, *turista* class isn't nearly as much fun as it sounds. Bring a book. I hadn't. I tried to keep track of the announcements made in Spanish, and most of them were followed by the same commentary in English so that I could check my translation. The video highlighting the ferry's safety features made disaster look jolly fun. The lifejackets appeared a lot more substantial than the flimsy thing promised on inflight safety videos. Sliding down a chute from the ferry to a waiting life raft seemed like a thoroughly survivable adventure. I had always felt that if an airliner fell from 11,000 metres with me on it, my last concern was likely to be whether my lifejacket had an operating light and whistle.

In the months leading up to the trip, my correspondence with ecologist Gabriel Laufer had been spotty, so I was both delighted and relieved when he approached me outside the customs hall in Montevideo. In a way that I cannot properly articulate, I immediately felt as though I was making a lifelong friend. He shook my hand firmly, tossed my bags into the back of his truck, and we set off for my hotel.

I got an informal tour of Montevideo en route. Gabriel pointed out the building of the university's veterinary school as we passed it. It was, with the support of the government, the first institution to promote the idea of bullfrog farms in Uruguay, and did substantial research on cultivation techniques suitable for the country. Like so many people using English as a second tongue, Gabriel downplayed his grasp of the language, although it seemed lucid and coherent. In explaining why a street, Avenida 18 de Julio, was named after a date, he stumbled when trying to translate the word *constitución* into English. "Constitution," I said. He corrected my use of the word *bambino* ("No, that's Italian," he said), and sorted out my confusion of the words *nombre* and *numero*. We agreed that we would meet early the following morning to travel to a site of bullfrog introduction. We also agreed that Gabriel and his wife, Adriana, would meet me for dinner that evening at nine o'clock.

I was far too excited to sit still, and so after dropping my bags at the hotel, I set off. I wanted to explore, explore, explore. I first selected an *al fresco* establishment on a side street, and taking the advice of a fellow diner ordered melted mozzarella on a thick pizza-like crust. The prices looked steep, until I remembered that the Uruguayan peso was trading at twenty-to-one with a dollar. Compared to prices at home, everything on the menu was dirt cheap. A long string of very young children came to beg at my table, but none were pushy or impolite when I turned them down.

After wandering slowly through the streets of central Montevideo, I came to rest under the shade trees of the Plaza del Entrevero. I spied Rock Doves and very pale House Sparrows, but none of the other introduced birds (European Greenfinches, European Goldfinches, and Common Waxbills) that I had been told to expect in Uruguay. How delightful that some older park users felt free to feed the birds.

A fellow on the next park bench finished off a joint and then quietly picked at his guitar. In an accent that suggested he had spent considerable time smoking joints in the U.S., or watching far too much American television, he said: "So, are you lost in Paradise?"

I replied that I wasn't sure if it was Paradise, but that I certainly wasn't lost. "What about you?"

"No, I live here."

"Does that mean that it can't be Paradise?"

He pondered my question for a minute, gave up, and changed the topic. He had just been to see the Mausoleo de Artigas, crypt of José Gervasio Artigas, a nineteenth-century resistance fighter, in the Plaza Independencia.

"They dug him up, and put him in a crypt with an armed guard. Do you know about him?" I replied that I did. "Well, he's too far from the Earth, you know what I mean?" I said that I did, but I didn't.

"If they scatter me over there," he said, pointing to a spot about twenty metres away, "and it makes the grass greener, then I figure I've done my part."

I wondered if, when he was a baby, his mother looked down on him in his bassinet and said, "I hope that he strives to be fertilizer."

At the appointed hour, Gabriel and Adriana arrived at the hotel, and we drove to a lovely beachfront restaurant. Adriana used English flawlessly, having spent several of her formative years in Massachusetts. Over a full-bodied Uruguayan red wine and a great meal, I learned a lot about the country that tourist bureaus try to ignore. For instance, I heard that the Uruguay economy is sufficiently weak that many families require four or five jobs just to keep moving forward.

University entrance in Uruguay is free—my favourite price for post-secondary education. However, Gabriel explained that this isn't necessarily a good thing; even with free tuition, many qualified people cannot afford books, accommodation, and all of the other costs associated with university life. He suggested that a suitable system would be one of pay-what-you-can-afford, with the revenue generated going to scholarships and bursaries.

At one time, the Universidad de la República was one of the best, perhaps even the single best institution of its kind in South America. However, with a combination of state-of-emergency, suppression of civil liberties, and military government in the 1960s, '70s, and '80s, the focus of the university had swerved wildly to satisfy political ends. Even with a return to proper national elections and social and economic reforms, more than two decades later the university is struggling to return to the ideals of scholarship.

Gabriel had a lot to contribute to my knowledge of invasive species in Uruguay. Just the week before, he said, an exotic jellyfish had been discovered in a freshwater lake. Similarly, a small flock of toucans from Central America had recently been spotted. I heard that eucalyptus trees from Australia and acacias from Africa were grown in many parts of Uruguay, including places of special ecological importance. Gabriel used the expression "green deserts" to explain the impact of the exotic trees on native fauna and flora. We also spoke about skinny-dipping, Canada's second-most-popular spectator sport. Apparently, two weeks earlier an Australian tourist had been arrested in Uruguay for swimming nude.

I am undoubtedly the luckiest man alive. Everyone who has met my wife knows what I mean. It is a tribute to my phenomenal luck that I had landed in Montevideo on the first day of Carnaval. Gabriel and Adriana suggested that we drive over to the all-night parade, the Desfile de las Llamadas, to take in part of the evening's festivities. We had no difficulty finding parking just two blocks from the parade route. Those two blocks were populated with folks smoking spliffs and trees propping up peeing men.

How could I have allowed half a century of my life to pass without taking in Montevideo's Carnaval celebrations? Both sides of the street were packed with as many bodies as would fit. The most fortunate souls hung from balconies overlooking the parade route. Community groups had pulled together to create the most outrageous

spectacle they could. Flag bearers swept impossibly large curtains
in bold and contrasting colours. The crowd was draped in ecstasy
when each flag was dragged over their heads. These marchers were
followed by beautiful women in the skimpiest of glittering costumes;
I cannot imagine how many birds gave their feathers for the head-
dresses. Each group pulsed up the street. The nearly naked women
were followed by drummers, row after row, pounding away on their
huge instruments. No power could keep me from joining in the clap-
ping. I could feel the drumming in my face, in my chest, and in my
hips. Words like "thrubbing" and "orgiastic" came to mind. Some
groups had teams of tango-dancing couples who didn't miss a step
while keeping up with the remainder of the army. As the marching
party swept one way, another small army swam the other, hawking
candy floss, candied apples, glow sticks, and cheap plastic masks.

Well after midnight, I was caught off guard by the large number
of very small children along the parade route. They were outnum-
bered by adults twenty to one, but some of those weaving in and
out of the crowd were as young as three and four. If anyone at
Carnaval had skin whiter or hair greyer than mine, they weren't
making themselves obvious. The mass of jet-black hair and skin
the colour of old oiled mahogany that swept past me and around
me and through me was joyous. I didn't want to leave. I wanted to
grind my life away at Carnaval. However, there were bullfrogs to
be chased.

FOR THE DAY'S EFFORTS, Gabriel deserves some level of canoniza-
tion. We were en route to the site where bullfrogs were first noticed
in the wild, having escaped from a commercial captive frog-
breeding facility. As we passed through and out of Montevideo,
Gabriel pointed out important landmarks and filled me in on recent
Uruguayan political history. In many parts of the world, changes in
the political party elected to govern result in only minor changes in
the day-to-day lives of its citizens. This may be why so few citizens
exercise their right to vote. It is not the case in Uruguay, where lives
change in profound ways after each election, and almost everyone

in the country would vote even if they weren't required to do so by law.

Gabriel was quick to point out that while Uruguayans are politically engaged, they are not particularly nationalistic. The country does not maintain a large military force, and its efforts are directed mainly at peacekeeping and disaster relief. When a military plane roared overhead, Gabriel suggested that it was probably en route to, or just returned from, Haiti, where personnel had been assisting in earthquake relief.

In some parts of the world, ranches and farms are enormous affairs. In the region east of Montevideo, agricultural holdings are much smaller. The spot we were aiming for was the site of one of the first bullfrog production facilities in Uruguay. When it became clear that no profit was to be had from bullfrogs, the site had been turned over to the production of poultry, and there was now talk about getting rid of the chickens and planting tomatoes instead.

We travelled down a series of roads with diminishing width and gravel depth. We arrived at our destination and pulled into a yard, drove down a packed-earth path, and were greeted by a man of considerable years, all of them spent in the sun. There were four others in the yard: a middle-aged man who had dissected a chainsaw into more pieces than I would have imagined; a woman washing clothes in a large pail; a teenager in a Liverpool Football Club jersey; and a shy young boy. We exchanged a happy "*¡Hola!*" and a wave with each of them.

The man in charge told us to expect to see lots of frogs, because the people living at the site heard them croaking every night. He gave us his impersonation. Aside, Gabriel told me that he was dubious, suspecting that they were hearing the calls of two species of native frog. Amorous bullfrogs should sound something like a bellowing cow. Or perhaps a bull.

From the back of his truck, Gabriel dragged out his favourite frog-catching apparatus. It was an aluminum ring a little over a metre in diameter with a loosely strung small mesh net in the centre. A heavy rope allowed the net to be dragged through the water.

It was likely to catch tadpoles, but it might snag an adult or two as well.

We arrived at a promising small lake about forty metres across and covered with a thick mat of duckweed and other floating vegetation. To my eyes it looked like frog nirvana. In turns, Gabriel and I got very wet and more than a bit mucky by lowering, tossing, or otherwise convincing the net to go into the water while the person at the other side of the pond tugged on the rope. After each dredge, we tossed aquatic vegetation aside and looked for tadpoles. None looked back at us. Instead, we got hundreds of tiny silvery fish. After several fruitless attempts, we marched around the margin of the lake, hoping that if an adult bullfrog was resting at the perimeter, it would jump in and make a big splash. We saw no splash. We moved downhill to a deeply flooded field to try our luck there. Gabriel and I dragged a long linear net between us and were rewarded with hundreds of small sparkly fish, but no bullfrogs.

We marched on to another spot, this time a very large circular pond, but after throwing and dragging the big circular net all we retrieved were more fish. Gabriel was clearly disappointed that he had been unable to produce bullfrogs. Instead he showed me the building once used to try to raise frogs for fun and profit. It was constructed of concrete and cinder blocks to a height of about a metre, with a wood and fabric shack above it. It was now used to house chickens. New stock had just arrived, and the operators were keen that they remain undisturbed while settling in. Ever a devil, I slowly peeled back a flap of material and was met by the stares of hundreds of surprised chickens. Not startled, just surprised.

Gabriel explained that when this bullfrog farm had been in operation, to maintain cleanliness in the enclosure, stale water had been periodically pumped out and fresh water pumped in. In doing so, the facility had probably released chytridiomycosis into the environment. This disease, caused by a microscopic fungus-like creature, has been implicated in worldwide declines in amphibian populations, and it could not possibly help the situation for Uruguay's native frogs.

Gabriel had examined a number of sites where bullfrogs had been raised and then abandoned. In his experience, the habitat around the abandoned farm now had either large numbers of frogs or none at all. He hadn't found any sites with an intermediate number. Perhaps after release and escape, small populations either died out or increased very rapidly to the habitat's carrying capacity.

As we were pulling away from the site, Gabriel spotted an elderly couple at the side of the road, waiting for a ride into the nearby community of Pando. Gabriel offered them a lift, and they piled in the backseat. On hearing that we were looking for bullfrogs, they explained that when they had moved to the site six years earlier they had been kept awake each night by the bellowing of amorous bullfrogs. Now they heard none and took it as evidence that the introduced pests no longer inhabited the site.

On the drive back to Montevideo, I took the opportunity to spy on the world outside the window. Scooters and small motorcycles that no one would be caught dead on in North America are popular in Uruguay, and drivers seem to have no reservations about speaking on cellphones while piloting them. Those conversations are unencumbered by safety helmets. The country is one of contrasts, and seemed to have its feet in two very different eras. For instance, it was the government's stated position that every child should have a computer, but we had passed villages where a new roof on the family's shack would presumably be a better way to go.

GABRIEL CONTINUED ON HIS PATH to sainthood by offering to take me to Punta del Este with his family the next morning. It is one thing to welcome a colleague and facilitate his work with a bit of translation, but it is quite another to take that colleague along on a family holiday. How could I possibly say no to an offer like that?

Their seven-year-old daughter, Sofía, was attending a school where English was the language of instruction, and her grasp was already exceptional. Their son, Nicolás, was a couple of years younger and had an incomplete mastery of his second language.

On the road east out of Montevideo, Gabriel drove and I rode shotgun. When I wasn't making myself popular by folding origami cranes for Sofía and Nicolás, Gabriel and I talked about ecology in general and conservation in particular. He pointed out sand dune sites that were threatened by beachfront development and spots where uncontrolled fires had destroyed substantial woodlots. We joked about the bumps that pass for mountains in Uruguay, and about a type of pointy-nosed frog known as Sapito de Darwin because Charles Darwin had first described it. If I have the story right (Adriana was translating bits and pieces of our conversation from the back seat), Darwin's frog is one of the lick-a-frog-to-get-stoned species. We also talked about Darwin's time in Uruguay. The great naturalist toured the region in and around Uruguay between May and November of 1833. Writing about an excursion near Punta del Este, Darwin wrote, "My companions were well armed with pistols and sabres; a precaution which I thought rather unnecessary; but the first piece of news we heard was, that, the day before, a traveller from Monte Video had been found dead on the road with his throat cut. This happened close to a cross, the record of a former murder."

As we approached Punta del Este, we found the region to be a little tamer than Darwin had. We parked at a spot with a grand view of the ocean. It is an enormously popular spot in spring, when southern right whales pass in significant numbers. Looking down at the villas on the hillside, I got the impression that enormous bags of cash would be needed to live there. And perhaps that is what drives Punta del Este ever onward. The seaside is lined with one monstrous high-rise block after another, filled with people who had stopped for a short visit and realized that they and their cash wanted to live nowhere else.

Adriana and Nicolás stopped off at Adriana's father's home while Gabriel, Sofía, and I set off for a walk along the waterfront. We stopped for a snack of seafood and beer. When Sofía asked if I was going to eat any fish, I explained that I don't eat meat. She seemed confused, and so Gabriel stepped in and said, "He's like ET." It had been a while since I had been compared to an alien life form, but I certainly wasn't insulted. Since I had no food in my stomach, the beer made me really loopy, and shortly afterward I tried to make friends with a male sea lion that had hauled himself onto the seawall, probably after losing one too many fights over access to females.

After a delightful lunch with Adriana's father, I set off with the family for Brava Beach, although no one on the beach that day seemed brave enough to go out beyond the crashing breakers in about a metre of water. Even so, the splishing and splashing were great fun. The children played with fist-sized jellyfishes, which I can only assume were of the less toxic variety. The beach was very busy despite the cloudy conditions, and I cannot imagine what it would be like on a sunny day. Punta del Este is one of the most glamorous resorts in South America and the most expensive spot in Uruguay. On this day, some of the bodies were less than absolutely beautiful, being a bit beyond their best-before date. Even so, the party life in the community of 7,500 residents was apparently great. The night-life didn't get started until 1 a.m., and some of the nightclubs served breakfast.

When I took Spanish lessons, I was told not to be surprised by get-to-know-you questions like "How old are you?" or "What is your birthday?" As we sat on the beach, Sofía had a much better question, and one that I had never been asked before.

"Do you like your name?"

"Yes, I do. It means 'valley.' I think it is *cañada* in Spanish. Do you like your name?"

"Yes, but I prefer 'Amelia.'" For the rest of the day, I called her Amelia.

I USED THE COMPUTER in the hotel lobby to search for service times for the Catedral Metropolitana Iglesia Matriz–Montevideo. I found plenty of websites with photographs of the cathedral, and a few describing the building's history, but they were all strangely silent about the times of Sunday masses. I stumbled across a website that offered the times of services of virtually every Catholic church you might have the chance to visit, including those in Vanuatu and on Henderson Island, but it steadfastly refused to tell me about Montevideo. Even if it had, the website had last been updated in 1993, so some changes might have been expected. At eleven o'clock, based on my best guess, I took a leisurely stroll after breakfast along the *rambla* toward the church. I was hoping for a cooling breeze from the sea, but the wind was blowing from the town. I felt it was bringing me the pheromones of sleeping citizens.

The church was warm; air conditioning and electric fans have yet to find this corner of the Christian world. Some ladies had brought small decorated paper fans, and other visitors—me included—tried to be discreet in waving any odd bit of paper. The remainder just put up with the heat.

I was surprised that in a city of over a million people, in a country that is on some level Catholic, fewer than 100 people showed up for the service. Perhaps an incredibly popular minister had said mass the night before. Maybe the church is filled for services throughout the year except during Carnaval. Perhaps the Uruguayan soccer team was playing a long-time rival in the South American Cup final and the game had gone to overtime at 11 a.m. Of those in attendance, I appeared to be the eighth youngest, and that included a family of four and the priest.

I couldn't identify the reading but think that I got the essence of the sermon. Commitment, said the priest, has a big role to play in salvation (*salvación*). Day and night, year after year, we need to be committed (*comprometido*) to our faith. But (*pero*), the world is full of things that might divert our attention. Even if those diversions don't lead to hedonism (*hedonismo*) or Satan worship (*adoración de Satanás*), they can take us away from the commitment necessary to show our love of Christ (*Cristo*). I think that the sermon was a thinly veiled jab at Carnaval-goers and vegetarians.

BUSES DEPART FROM MONTEVIDEO for Punta del Este several times an hour, but if your destination is Punta del Diablo, the choices are more limited. A bus left at 1:00 a.m. without me. The bus leaving

at 1:30 p.m. wouldn't give me much of the day to enjoy the seaside.
And so, less than four hours after watching the New Orleans Saints
win Super Bowl XLIV, I was up again and in a cab to the central
bus station.

Even at six in the morning, the terminal was swarming with bodies
arriving and departing, but my smattering of Spanish was sufficient
to get me on the correct coach. I have come to expect strange happen-
ings on bus rides in exotic foreign lands. On this journey, there were
really only three things notable: (1) Although they were not frequent,
I did spot long and stately windbreaks, consisting of white-barked
eucalyptus trees, originally imported from Australia. They were very
tall and clearly not harvested in Uruguay; (2) I spotted rheas. At first
I thought my dozy eyes must be deceiving me. Like an idiot, I looked
around the bus excitedly to see if anyone else had spotted the giant
flightless birds. But in a bus full of Uruguayans, if anyone had noticed,
no one would have cared; and (3) At a police detachment next to
the highway, near a river crossing, traffic was stopped, and an officer came on board to give us all a good look. I smiled politely as he
passed, but he ignored me completely, walked to the end of the bus,
turned and walked back, and sent the bus on its way. I got no clue as
to what it was all about.

Although Punta del Diablo was once a sleepy little fishing village, everyone I spoke to claimed that it had grown considerably
of late. To me, it still had the sense of the minuscule, wanting to
remain so. The community boasts just 1,000 residents. The bus station is a shack. Most of the community's restaurants are shacks.
The streets are no more than compacted sand, and deep channels
had been created by the previous week's rains. A bulldozer was trying to patch the worst of the damage.

Streets in Punta del Diablo have names, but that has nothing
to do with the reality of the town. There are plenty of signs, but
none of them are street signs. Instead, every intersection, such as
it is—two sandy tracks intersecting—has numerous hand-painted
signs trying to convince the traveller to visit this restaurant, that
cabaña, or this hostel. By the looks of things, Punta del Diablo was

Uruguay's hostel capital. With a map from the tourist information centre, a shack, I made my way to my *cabaña*.

Luckily the rains had stopped, because Punta del Diablo is all about the beach. If you don't like sun and sand, there is no reason for you to be in Punta del Diablo. I wondered what there might be to do in this town if it was raining, and suspected that the principal activity might involve *coger*. I made my way past modest residences to the beach, where I strolled slowly for several hours.

Forget what online descriptions say about being buff, waxed, and tanned on the beaches of Punta del Este—Punta del Diablo is the place to see acres of very nice skin. Punta del Este is for rich bodies. Punta del Diablo is for young bodies, and many of them sported a deep, deep tan to complement their natural pigmentation. By comparison, I was a grub.

On my pre-breakfast run the next day, I spied a hotel (really more a series of shacks) with a miniature golf course. It had four flags, presumably signalling four holes. In all, I spotted forty-two places to get a bite to eat, and six small markets, but not a single school, library, or church. I have to wonder what Punta del Diablo will become in forty or fifty years. Will it be fashionable to replace the tumbledown shacks with posh summer homes for the newly rich? Will backpackers tell stories about how Punta del Diablo was once *the* place for beach parties and cheap digs, or will it fall back out of favour and be washed away with the outgoing tide?

I set off to explore a very long and less populated beach to the south. Kilometres of light brown sand were punctuated by darker brown bodies. I strolled as slowly as I have ever walked, stopping periodically to apply more high-SPF sunblock. The lotion gave my already out of place pale skin an unearthly silver sheen. A little further on I spied two young ladies with skin as white as mine, squinting and blinking as though seeing the sun for the first time. I wondered what snowy place they had just arrived from, and how many SPF points their sunblock could boast.

I picked an open-air cantina on the beach for dinner and ordered a rum and coke and pasta. Ten minutes later I was approached by the only English-speaking member of staff, who explained that there was "only one problem."

"Only one? That's great." It seems that the power to the food preparation area had gone out. I could wait until someone was found to restore the power (perhaps ten minutes, perhaps never), or I could have an *ensalada*. I had an *ensalada*. I was getting sick of *ensaladas*.

When I had arrived at my hotel, I had noticed that there was a telephone in my room, but it wasn't plugged in. When I plugged it in, there was no sign of life. However, shortly after I got back from dinner a note was brought to my room. It read:

> HABITACÍON IV
> Lisa phoned,
> she'd wish to be
> here with you.

When I got home I had it framed.

FOR MY LAST STOP in Uruguay, I needed to travel from Punta del Diablo, in the country's southwestern corner, to Colonia del Sacramento in the southeastern corner—as much as that is possible in a more or less circular country. Before leaving home, I had given thought to renting a car to get from Buenos Aires to Punta del Diablo and then on to Colonia. Thank goodness I didn't. Uruguayan buses are clean, cheap, run on time, and saved me from having to distinguish among traffic laws, strong traffic suggestions, and easily dismissed traffic hints. Leaving behind the sand streets and dirt-poor hippie travellers behind, the bus passed hills and valleys and agricultural fields on the four-hour run back to Montevideo.

The bus was scheduled to get into the capital at 1:00 p.m. Coaches then left for Colonia at 1:30 and 3:30 p.m. When I had purchased my ticket a few days earlier, I was told that the incoming bus was frequently late, and so it was safer to reserve seats for a 3:30 departure. However, *if* I got in on time, and *if* I could find a ticket agent who understood my version of Spanish, I *might* be able to switch my tickets for a pair on the 1:30 bus. When our bus pulled in at exactly 1:00 p.m., I was less than keen on a long wait in the terminal, and tried my gringo Spanish.

When I got to the front of a very long but very quick-moving line, I asked *"¿Está possible ir Colonia la una media en rez de tres y media?"*

"¿Cambio?" asked the lady behind the counter.

To this point, I thought that *cambio* indicated a currency exchange office, but now it was clear that the word just meant "change." *"Si, si. Cambio."* Bless the efficiency of the clerks at the Montevideo bus terminal; I was sitting on the 1:30 coach to Colonia.

As I peered out the window, I played the highway alphabet game, demanding of myself that I get the whole alphabet, including *CH, LL,* and *Ñ,* all in the correct order. *K, V,* and *X* were a challenge, particularly since they aren't Spanish letters, but I managed. Then I tried to get all of the vowels, both accented and unaccented; *A, Á, E, É, I, Í, O, Ó, U,* and *Ú.* Just as highway alphabet got really, really tedious, I spied a sulphuric acid factory. Intellectually you realize that sulphuric acid factories must exist, but you don't really think that someone out there is responsible for making the stuff. I hope that they get paid really well.

After settling in at a cute hotel on the Plaza Mayor in Colonia, I set off in search of adventure. It may be a silly little thing, and not an adventure per se, but I get pleasure out of asking for a package of gum in a foreign language and actually getting a package of gum. A shopkeeper in Colonia didn't disappoint me. I wandered up and down the streets of the Barrio Histórico, the colonial heart of old Colonia, chewing gum, peeping in shop windows, and hopping between patches of shade provided by sycamore trees. Stopping at a tourist information office, I couldn't get any English out of the lady behind the desk, but she told me, proudly, in Spanish, that Colonia had five kilometres of beautiful beaches. She pointed them out on a small street map. A little further along, I purchased green glass earrings for Lisa. I misplaced my hat. I sat on a bench in front of the Comisaría de Policía on Avenida General Flores. I watched as eighty-eight people passed me on motorbikes and scooters. Of these, five wore helmets. Many were barefoot, and most of the rest wore sandals. My favourite group was a family of four who zipped by on a Baccio Cruiser 125. The scooter was piloted by dad, who had their six-year-old daughter between him and the handlebars. Behind them rode mom, nursing a newborn.

After a lunch that was far heavier than anything I would have had at home, I wandered to an information kiosk on the main strip and asked about guided walking tours of the town. I got only as far as "Can you tell . . ." when I was told *"¡No, no, no!"* and a lady further down the line was pointed out. Very cheerful, very friendly—just not English-friendly.

The new lady said, "I speak English . . ." and then couldn't think of the next word.

"¿Un poco?" I tried. A little?

"Poquito," she responded. Very little.

Fearing what I would get if I asked in English, I tried: *"¿Caminata tour en ingles?"* This prompted a flurry of activity and several telephone calls, which frequently involved the word *no,* until the lady stepped outside and asked among the walking-tour hawkers if anyone could speak English. Beatriz Rivas did. She tried to convince me to come along on a two-hour automobile tour of the city, but agreed to meet in front of my hotel at 6:30 p.m. for a one-hour walking tour of the Barrio Histórico.

I wandered over to the Plaza Manuel Lobo and entered the Iglesia Matriz, hoping for some inspiration. It was possibly the warmest, and certainly the least adorned, church I had ever visited. An altarpiece, a few small statues, a couple of paintings behind glass, and big white walls leading to a big white ceiling that would have made Michelangelo drool in anticipation. This austerity is apparently the result of Jesuit influence. After about ten minutes of quiet contemplation, I heard a *boom* as the entrance doors were slammed closed. It was siesta time, but as I appeared to be praying, I hadn't been asked to leave.

Beatriz arrived at my hotel dripping with sweat and enthusiasm.

She walked me to a plaque near the old town wall and drawbridge to begin the tour. She first explained about the complete annihilation of Uruguay's aboriginal people, the Charrúa, as a way of saying that the remainder of the tour was going to be based on the country's history since the arrival of Europeans.

I heard about how Uruguay had bounced back and forth over the centuries between Spanish and Portuguese occupation, with brief incursions by other nations. As we walked, I was shown how to distinguish between historical buildings from the Portuguese period (sloped roofs with tiles) and those of Spanish construction (flat roofs with gargoyles). Spanish streets had sidewalks; Portuguese streets didn't. I saw old buildings still occupied, and others razed to the foundations. Beatriz explained that Colonia's protective wall had stretched across a peninsula from sea to sea, isolating a plot of land about thirty-five square blocks. I heard the names of plants, some native but most introduced, in Spanish and English, and was told which ones had scented flowers.

Beatriz explained that the sun would set at about seven o'clock and that the river would then be beautiful. "Bery romantic!" she said. I wasn't quite sure what she was getting at.

After seeing Beatriz off, and having completed a light dinner, I went for a wander, fuelled by a half-bottle of red wine. It was a warm evening, with only a whisper of wind, but by walking slowly enough I managed not to overheat. The river was bery beautiful and bery romantic, and restaurants were doing a good trade at eleven o'clock. As I entered an intersection on the main street, a fellow on a motor scooter got himself into a fix when, failing to see me, he nearly ran me down. I smiled, stepped back, and waved him through. He smiled back, and called out *"Gracias."* I replied *"De nada."* Strolling down Florida, the quietest back street I could find, I looked up at the Southern Cross imbedded firmly in the Milky Way. I can't say that love was in the air, but life certainly was.

CHAPTER EIGHT

The Perforation of New Orleans

REASON NUMBER EIGHT FOR INTRODUCING A FOREIGN SPECIES: BECAUSE I WASN'T PAYING ATTENTION.

MISERY LOVES COMPANY. This may explain such gatherings as Star Trek conventions, Weight Watchers, and the Republican Party. University students congregate for the same reason—they don't have any money and they don't get enough sleep, but at least they can be miserable together. In many cases, friends made in college become friends for life.

One summer many years ago, having just completed one degree but before starting the next, I accepted the opportunity to teach summer school in order to keep collection agencies at bay. I was sharing an office with Rob Higgins, another impoverished M.Sc. graduate who was also lecturing his summer away. Rob and I would periodically look up from our desks and glance out at coeds frolicking in the glorious sunshine and moan about being stuck indoors.

One day Rob had a tremendous idea. At the end of our teaching assignments, he said, we should go on a long canoeing trip. We could spend two weeks on the Bloodvein River, snaking back and forth across the Manitoba-Ontario border, without contact with the outside world. It sounded glorious, and I agreed in a heartbeat.

Ten days into our trip, we approached a waterfall. Our canoe-trail map was very clear on the subject; to go over the waterfall meant certain death. Less clear was the location of the portage around the waterfall. And so we paddled up to a rock in the middle of the river, close to the falls, knowing that the trail had to be somewhere to the right or the left. Rob hopped onto the rock to try to spot the head of the portage, leaving me in the canoe. "Hold on to the rock," he said as he jumped out.

Well, fine and dandy, but this was a big, smooth, slippery rock with no handholds. I lay my palms flat on the rock and tried to use my fingerprints to hold on. Regrettably, I am not a gecko. As I started to lose my grip, Rob hopped back in, and we backpaddled to put a little more space between us and the waterfall. Strangely, the faster we paddled away from the falls, the closer we got to them.

"Paddle harder!" Rob screamed. He was apparently not in the mood to die.

"I'm paddling as hard as I bloody well can!" I screamed back. Death was not a high priority for me either.

When the inevitable was imminent, Rob called out "Hold on!!!"—only he said it with more exclamation marks.

I am pleased to report that the canoe-trail map was in error. It *is* possible to go over that waterfall without dying.

Perhaps the waterfall incident made us closer, and when it came time to hunt good food, good music, and Formosan termites in New Orleans, I gave Rob a shout.

SINCE OUR CANOEING DAYS, Rob had gone on to teach biology at Thompson River University in central British Columbia and had become something of an expert on ants. In an ecological sense, ants are not so different from termites. Our initial plan was to visit New Orleans during Mardi Gras. It would be a chance to skip a few days of wintry weather, miss a couple of lectures, and get our fill of hedonism. Unfortunately, our termite expert, Jerry Howard at the

University of New Orleans, told us that Formosan termites would be staying pretty close to home in their underground excavations at that time of year. However, if we wanted to see great masses of swarming termites—which of course we did—Jerry indicated that there was another option, but only if we were jazz music fans—which of course we were.

Each year, on the last weekend in April and the first weekend of May, New Orleans plays host to its great Jazz & Heritage Festival, or "Jazz Fest" to those in the know. Spread over seven days, Jazz Fest attracts all of the greatest acts and more than 600,000 jazz fans, and generates more than $300 million in revenue. And by a strange coincidence, $300 million is just how much damage is caused each year in New Orleans by the Formosan termite.

In the United States, these wood-chomping immigrants were first noticed in 1965 in a shipyard in Houston. Our best guess is that they came from Asia to the southern U.S. in wooden packing material on a military transport ship at the end of WWII. Once authorities started looking, it became apparent that the problem was not a local one, with colonies as far away as Charleston, South Carolina. Formosan termites are now found in eleven states, including Hawaii. Their impact is felt most keenly in and around New Orleans.

These termites play it close to the chest for most of the year, hiding and slowly devouring all the wood they can stuff in their mouths. In the spring, when a group has come to maturity, it sends out winged colony members to find suitable spots to establish new colonies. When they do, they infest as many as half of New Orleans' 4,000 magnificent oak trees. Even worse, Formosan termites find their way into wooden buildings in the city's historic French Quarter. Recent study has shown that the problem is now spreading far beyond that section of the city, and the termite population is up, up, up. Global climate change may be making the situation worse; termites like a hot and humid climate, and they don't like frost. To demonstrate the scope of the problem, the New Orleans Yellow Pages have one page with thirty-four entries under the heading "Escort Services." Under the title of "Pest Control Services," I found 121 businesses spread over eleven pages.

In early August 2005, *The Independent* newspaper ran an article entitled "The tiny pest that threatens to gobble up the Big Easy." The piece described the enormous cost of trying to control Formosan termites. Just a few weeks after the article appeared, New Orleans was hit by hurricane Katrina, and those who survived had bigger problems than termites.

OVER BREAKFAST AT OUR HOTEL, Rob said, "I suppose we are the only ones who have no idea what's going on." He meant that we seemed to be the only Jazz Fest virgins in New Orleans. Everyone else on our flight from Houston had been wearing T-shirts from a previous Jazz Fest. Everyone in our hotel was now reading festival programs. Well, everyone gets to be a virgin once.

Rob and I went for a wander in the famed French Quarter. Long the geographical and cultural pivot point of New Orleans, the French Quarter was awash with souvenir shops, restaurants, and street performers. The balconies of many of its two-storey businesses and residences showed off their iconic ironwork railings. Bourbon Street is legendary for its music and vice, but in the uncompromising glare of a Friday morning, it was a woman, past her prime, on her way home from a party that broke up several hours before. I spotted a young fellow in an Orkin uniform filling out a work invoice on the hood of his truck. Recognizing Orkin as a major pest-control firm, I asked him where I might find termites. "Formosan termites?" He then explained that he was more involved in rat and cockroach control than in the management of termites. Even so, if the weather held, he explained, I should have no trouble finding termites, as they swarmed after dark. They needed heavy rains to soften up the ground, followed by a couple of warm days.

I asked if rats were a big problem in the French Quarter. He chuckled at my naïveté and explained that he could kill all ten rats in a building, then come back a week later and kill ten more.

One of the problems is that every building in the French Quarter is attached to its neighbours, allowing rats to have free run. He said that the only way to get rid of the vermin would be to order every building to get pest treatment at exactly the same time. The biologist in me is pretty confident that nothing short of a biblical holocaust could wipe out all of New Orleans' pests.

The streetcar ride along Canal did not take us into the heart of the hurricane and flood devastation, but the neighbourhood we saw was still in pretty rough shape. Many buildings had been reconstructed and their occupants re-established. A lot hadn't been. They remained boarded up and the properties fenced in, even several years after the hurricane. With so many FOR SALE signs, it seemed to me that a property speculator with a few dollars would find easy pickings in New Orleans. Banks, grocery stores, pharmacies, homes . . . even the City of New Orleans City Hall Annex sat empty. But as Rob pointed out, a developer might find every building infested with rats, cockroaches, and termites.

At the Fair Grounds Race Course in Mid-City, Jazz Fest was in full swing. The sensory onslaught was enormous. With eleven stages running simultaneously, we did what everyone else seemed to be doing; we walked the fairgrounds in a counter-clockwise circle, spending fifteen minutes at each stage before moving on to the next one. The air was filled with the expectation that wherever you were headed would be more exciting than wherever you were.

Some acts were great, including the Tulane University Jazz Ensemble, and some were simply outstanding, such as Richard Thompson. Others were peculiar, like Jumpin' Johnny Sansone's Harmonica Review. At each venue, I couldn't help but think how odd young people would find it to see their grandparents bouncing and swaying to a combo of keyboard, base, drums, and accordion. We strolled and ate and drank and stopped to listen, and then strolled some more. When we got to the main stage, we found acres of folks reclining in lawn chairs. "Are they waiting for a shuttle launch?" Rob asked. They were listening to a group called Papa Grows Funk, which was good, but not good enough to deserve the idolatry of many thousands of people. And then we twigged. Most of these people were staking out a bit of turf for the Stevie Wonder concert due to begin in three and a half hours.

Shorts, sandals, wide-brimmed hats, and T-shirts were the order of the day. Many of the shirts proved that their owners had been to an earlier Jazz Fest, or to some other music festival, or to a Kmart. Some shirts were more profound than others. A man gave high-fives to strangers while wearing a shirt proclaiming, "I high-five strangers." "I ♥ dorks" and "I ♥ sailors" were circling the fairgrounds. The shirt of an amply endowed lady told other women, "Don't be jealous." Showing a higher level of self-realization than most of the crowd, one fellow sported a shirt explaining, "I'm not an alcoholic; I'm a drunkard. Alcoholics go to meetings!"

And the closer we got to the performance by Stevie Wonder, the highlight of the day, the more it looked like we were in for a thorough soaking. When the skies finally opened, the crowd cried "Ooooh!" This was no spring shower but a cloudburst that would have had Noah frantically scrambling over last-minute details.

Wonder started on time despite the rain, and settled into a string of less than fully inspired pieces. About thirty minutes in, he performed a preachy little number whose refrain was "I can't believe," which seemed to indicate that he was not particularly keen on hate, crime, American wars overseas, high gasoline prices, and the Large Hadron Collider particle accelerator. The rains continued, and about half the crowd left.

And then a beautiful thing happened. Wonder and his band launched into "Don't You Worry 'Bout a Thing" and "Signed, Sealed, Delivered." The crowd began to sing and dance, and the rain didn't make any difference at all. The band came at us with one hit after another, and everyone seemed to know all the words. Those who stayed to the end left the grounds on a high. In terms of termites, the soaking rain was just what we needed.

THANK GOODNESS FOR TERMITES. Without them we would be up to our necks in undecomposed plant matter. Luckily, termites spend their lives munching away on dead vegetation, saving us the bother of cleaning up every tree that falls. They become a nuisance only when they stop eating the things that we want removed and start chomping on things that we would rather keep. Like our homes.

To be fair, there are only eighty-odd species of termite that do significant damage to buildings. On the downside, that damage is significant, particularly in tropical India, Africa, and Central America. It is difficult to determine the annual cost of termites globally, including building inspection, prevention and control of infestation, and repair of damage, but the figure is somewhere in the billions of dollars.

Thank goodness for anteaters. Without them, we would be up to our necks in termites. With over 2,600 species of termite described, there certainly are an awful lot of them, despite the anteaters. At the more modest end, with an average colony population of just 6,400 individuals, groups of *Microcerotermes septentrionalis* termites are about the same size as the human population of Alajärvi in Finland. The residents of Dilovasi, Turkey, and the residents of a colony of *Cubitermes speciosus* both number about 42,000. At 1,360,000 inhabitants, an average colony of *Nasutitermes macrocephalus* exceeds the population of Benin City in Nigeria by 200,000. Topping the charts at over 7 million residents per community are *Mastotermes darwiniensis* and Hong Kong.

On Saturday, we arrived at Jazz Fest a little later than we had the day before, and the action was well hotted-up. Being the weekend, families were out in full party mode. Even so, this seemed a time and place for adults to have their music fun. In contrast with Friday evening, it was hot and sunny, and while most people had slapped on a hat and slopped on sunscreen, a fair few were going to be tender the following morning.

The Gospel Tent was fairly throbbing, with every seat filled and as many people standing in the aisles as the wranglers would allow. A few folks stood and swayed and spun with their arms raised, broadcasting their faith. Song after song, I'm not sure that I could have held my arms up that long. They were devout and must have had a lot of practice. Rob wondered which lobe of the brain would light up if subjected to a CAT scan during that sort of religious frenzy.

Bottled water was selling for $3, and those in the know were refilling their bottles at slowly dribbling water fountains. While filling my bottle, I fell into conversation with a woman named Audrey. She was New Orleans–born and bred but had moved to South Carolina after Katrina. I asked if she was planning to move back. "The sincere answer is that the longer I stay at Jazz Fest, the more likely I am to take my house here off the market."

We arrived early for a presentation by pianist Chick Corea and vocalist Bobby McFerrin. The tent was packed. Someone had mistakenly given a microphone to an organizer on a power trip, who then started issuing stupid instructions. "No flags. Period. I mean it! Absolutely no flags!"

Thirty minutes after the set was due to start, the duo came on stage and began an agonizingly slow warm-up. McFerrin slapped his chest and sang, "Dibbly-dibbly-dibbly; do-whap, do-whap." Corea pecked at the keyboard like someone in his first typing class. It wasn't a crowd-pleaser. "Spiggety-spiggety; dab-dab-dab." "When are they going to start?" asked Rob. Then it occurred to us that it wasn't a warm-up; this was the set. After three pieces, we left in search of some real music.

We arrived at the Gentilly Stage to catch Diana Krall, one of my all-time favourites. As we waited for the show to begin, Rob and I chatted with Melissa, a social worker from Monterey, California. She started the conversation by asking why I was writing notes; perhaps she thought that I was a reporter for *Rolling Stone* magazine. Melissa explained that she was visiting her crazy aunts and would be volunteering the following day at a furniture-distribution centre for folks rebuilding after Katrina. She wasn't convinced that Rob and I were being honest when we described our quest for termites.

Krall was as spectacular as I had hoped she would be. She wasn't afraid to cover tunes by Fats Domino, Nat King Cole, and Irving Berlin, which seemed to be exactly on track for the fans at

Jazz Fest. She ended her set with "'S Wonderful ('S Marvelous)," which it truly was.

THE FIRST TWO DAYS of Jazz Fest were great, and the whole event is so damned important to the city of New Orleans that the First Grace Methodist United Church was moved to declare, "Blessed Are Those Who Fest." But we still hadn't seen a Formosan termite. We (mainly Rob) had been talking to almost anyone who would talk back, asking them about termites. Some claimed that they ought to be swarming as soon as the sun went down. Others said that we had arrived a month too early. Some said that the French Quarter would be alive with termites, while others directed us to the rather more rundown wooden buildings beyond that. A Voodoo priestess explained that her landlord fumigated her shop once a year and that the state had made a big sweep through the French Quarter, but she confidently predicted that we would still be in good shape. We had seen heavy rains, and the day was now warm and sunny. In May, this is the recipe for swarms of termites.

Back at our hotel, I spied a film crew setting up for a poolside interview with a gospel singer. I spotted some largish insects swarming around the camera lights. Wings . . . a centimetre long . . . brownish . . . They looked like termites to me.

"Rob! Quick! I found termites." Rob grabbed his forceps and a glass vial, and we were off. These termites were the dispersing reproductive form. The camera crew didn't seem to mind us working around them as Rob picked ten termites off their white backdrop screen. It wasn't a lot, but it was a start. The fellow in charge of the microphone derisively referred to them as "Formosans" instead of "termites," in the same sort of way that he might have said "Belgians." The collected termites bashed against each other in the vial, and we feared that they might knock their wings off, so we slowed them down by putting the vial in a coffee cup filled with ice. Later we picked up a small bottle of gin to pickle them.

And a big, happy wave of contentment washed over me. The Jazz Fest had been fun, and we had found Formosan termites; the rest of the trip was a bonus. So we headed down Bourbon Street and into the French Quarter in search of adventure on a Saturday night. It was just after 9 p.m., and the French Quarter was unfolding. Taxis, fire trucks, and cars from the Sheriff's Office competed with revelers for space on the road. Although the night was young, the trendiest clubs were already turning away the unpretty.

Bourbon Street, old and vulgar by day, is the Promised Land of fantasy and excess by night. Jazz spilled out of one club after another and slithered across the pavement. Three groups of people set the backdrop: those who were lapping up the night, those who were terrified of the night, and those who were throwing up into the night. Neon lights filled my eyes. Members of the David Cobb Evangelistic Association of Gatlinburg, Tennessee, promised to save my soul, and Larry Flynt's Hustler Club offered to do the opposite. Every bar in the neighbourhood was happy to put a beer in a "go-cup" so that I could—legally—walk the streets and drink at the same time.

From parties on second-storey balconies, revelers hung over the ironwork offering to throw strings of beads to those who asked. I asked, and soon had four strings around my neck. Then eight. Three ladies at a balcony party tried to get the attention of anyone who would look at them. I looked. They were pointing at the ground, having obviously dropped something. "Where is it?" I asked. "Go forward," they screamed. "Go to the right. Just at your feet!" I found a packaged condom and picked it up. "This?" "Yes. Throw it up!" I am not sure how much fun three women can have with one condom, but they shouted their thanks and blew me kisses.

On our way out of the district, we came across two uniformed police officers. Rob asked them if the street party was largely self-policing. "Noooo, no, no," they explained. "We'll be taking people away all night." Rob asked how early it had all started. "We've been hauling away drunks since five this afternoon."

I liked myself twenty years ago, and hope that I am fundamentally the same fellow today. I liked Rob twenty years ago, and was delighted to find that he was the same fine fellow all these years later. Rob is committed to social justice, but he is just as committed to finding joy in life. He is that rare sort of person who can use the expression "Nice rack" without insulting anyone.

PERHAPS YOU ARE AMONG those smarty-pants orators who make themselves unpopular at parties by spouting minutiae that are of no benefit to anyone. You may, for instance offer such gems as "Termites *eat* wood but are unable to *digest* it without the help of single-celled organisms known as flagellates that live in the insects' intestines." If so, then shame on you. First, everyone knows about the microorganisms. Second, no one cares. Third, it isn't true. Facts are true. Factoids sound as though they should be true, but aren't. The reliance of termites on the flagellates in their guts to digest the cellulose in wood is a factoid, according to Professor David Bignell of Queen Mary University of London. And who are you going to believe, the Internet or Professor David Bignell? The flagellates may help, but all termites have the ability to break down cellulose on their own without the help of microbes. If you want to share wisdom at a party, tell people that termites are more closely related to cockroaches than to ants. At least you won't be spouting a factoid.

Saturday's heat hadn't done much to dry the fairgrounds, and tens of thousands of feet had turned large tracts into the sort of ooze that might spawn life anew. For many at Jazz Fest, the highlight of the weekend would be the performance by Carlos Santana. We arrived at the stage, or rather at the lip of a ditch 200 metres back from the stage, twenty minutes before the scheduled start but found the band already in full flight. We seemed to have achieved the perfect sound balance, and I cannot imagine what remained of the eardrums of people 195 metres closer. Rob and I tried to estimate the size of the crowd and came up with something like 30,000. It was as though the entire population of Braintree, Massachusetts, had stopped by to see the performance.

Given that "Black Magic Woman" had been released thirty-eight years earlier, I probably shouldn't have been surprised that the average age of the folks around us was sixty and that this number was held down by numerous grandchildren. The grey crowd was slurping back cheap, low-alcohol beer and consuming huge quantities of dope. Never has so much marijuana been consumed by so many who were so old. A lot of the music seemed to sail right over the heads of the shit-faced seniors around us, and I was left wondering if they grew their weed themselves or scored it from some geriatric dealer.

While waiting for a pizza in a restaurant in the French Quarter, Rob and I spotted a couple of termites fluttering wildly through the air above our heads. And then a few more. And then a lot more. The New Orleans swarming of Formosan termites had begun in full. To us, they were as delightful as dancing sprites under a full moon, but to the restaurant manager they were pure evil. He dashed around closing windows before any more could enter and attempt to set up shop.

Now closed, the outer surfaces of the windows were covered with termites, presumably drawn in by the restaurant's neon lights. Back on the streets, we found that the termites had a curiously clumped distribution. A termite trap at one corner was well attended, but another just a half-block away had no visitors at all. Termites are not very good fliers, and Rob suggested that a big swarm might indicate a large nearby colony sending out its next generation.

HAVING SEEN TERMITES SWARMING in the French Quarter, the only thing left was to speak with a termite expert. Regrettably, our local contact had been called out of town on family business, and we needed an alternative. Digging through my files, I found a newspaper clipping that made reference to the City of New Orleans Mosquito and Termite Control Board. The telephone directory had an entry for the board, and after a few misdirections I was put through to Ken Brown, a research entomologist. Ken immediately invited Rob and me to join him and his colleague Ed Freytag at the termite laboratory in the USDA building at the north end of City Park.

We were lucky enough to arrive on a day when the laboratory's technician was knocking termites out of infested wood collected from a military base. As he banged bits of wood together, huge numbers of termites dropped out. I gathered that the creatures were going to be used in an exhibition at New Orleans' soon-to-be-opened insectarium.

We were told that the winged reproductives, more formally called "alates," that we had seen the night before included both males and females, not very different in size. However, the specimens in front of us were mainly wingless workers, joined by a number of big-jawed soldiers. In a colony, workers do all the grunt work. Soldiers are about the size of workers but are aggressive. They have teardrop-shaped heads with nasty mandibles and a gland that exudes glue. They use these attributes to defend the colony when threatened. Neither workers nor soldiers stray far from their nests or the shelter tubes they construct of mud, wood, spit, and poop to protect them while searching for food.

Ed said that we couldn't leave the lab without being bitten by a Formosan termite soldier, and so he dropped one each into our hands. As long as we kept the skin of our palms stretched tight, the soldiers had nothing to clamp on to. But as soon as we creased our skin, they grabbed us. This is probably something that you don't want to happen if you are, for instance, a bug, but it didn't hurt us any more than having a hair pulled out.

Ken and Ed were incredibly cooperative, and gave us 25-cent answers to nickel questions. For instance, they explained that, until recently, fundamental aspects of the termites' biology were not well understood, even whether they had a preference for one type of tree over another. We heard that it takes about five years for a termite colony to mature to the point where it is producing dispersing alates. By that point, the house probably has sagging floorboards; when you first notice you have termites, you already have a huge problem. Formosan termites survived two weeks of flooding following Katrina. Those survivors had probably invaded abandoned buildings, and the city was likely to see an enormous increase in the scope of its termite problem.

We learned that the Formosan subterranean termite is only one of nine termite species in Louisiana. The others are bit less obnoxious, and so don't get all the bad press. In fact, Formosans are not the only termites introduced to Louisiana from abroad; they are joined by West Indian powderpost drywood termites. We were provided with an identification guide to the termites of Louisiana and a fact sheet on brown widow spiders, another invasive species. On the general topic of introduced species, we were told that the City of New Orleans was putting mosquitofish into swimming pools of abandoned properties in order to help keep down the mosquito population. I found this a bit strange. Mosquitofish are considered one of the 100 most horrible invasive species in the world. Aliens were being introduced to control other aliens.

And then Ken made us very happy. He said that he could arrange for Rob and me to follow along on a building inspection in the French Quarter the next day.

After leaving the USDA building, Rob spotted a fire ant colony and decided to collect some for his research collection. Another introduced species, they aren't called fire ants without reason. We skipped around to avoid contact with them, but Rob got nipped anyway. "It stings," he said, "like a fine needle dipped in vinegar and pushed slowly into your skin." It made me wonder how he knew what that felt like.

The taxi driver taking us back to the heart of the action was positively loquacious. Various hurricanes during his many years in New Orleans meant that David and his family had been evacuated on six or seven occasions. Each time, they had waited out the storm further inland and then moved back home, but post-Katrina had been very different. By the time of our visit, the city's population had returned to only half its pre-hurricane numbers. Driving south on St. Bernard Street, our driver pointed out homes that were still unoccupied—either rotting quietly where they stood or actively throwing themselves at the ground.

A little later, in a restaurant in the French Quarter, our server, Rebecca, gave us her take on the failure of the world's richest country to help fully restore New Orleans. Even though she understood the need to get the French Quarter back on its feet quickly, there was a lot of resentment that the same sort of effort had not been made on other, more hard-hit districts.

After dinner, we walked the evening streets for two hours and didn't spot a single termite. The swarming was over for now. Perhaps we were lucky to have seen them at all.

AT THE APPOINTED TIME, Rob and I met Perry Ponseti at a two-storey apartment complex on St. Philip Street in the French Quarter, for the building's termite inspection. It was part of the USDA's anti-termite initiative called Operation Full Stop. An inspection is paid for partly by the USDA and partly by the building's owner. Inspections are conducted as frequently as once per year.

The building's resident caretaker was waiting for us. He was the nervous sort, and very keen to please. I suspect that if we found termites, he would feel that the building's owner would find some way to hold him responsible. He insisted that the most recent inspection, made just before Katrina, had found no termites.

"A college education—that's what it's all about!" said the caretaker. He swept the narrow courtyard as we worked along it. He justified every little thing about the building that wasn't in perfect shape, as though we had the ability to lower his wage for the peeling paint and uneven pavement stones.

Perry had been working in the field for nine years, had made hundreds of inspections, and had found active termite colonies in about one-fifth of them. He emphasized that almost every building in the French Quarter had been damaged by termites at some time, and that all buildings were being treated to avoid further damage. Perry explained that Formosan termites stay in the centre of the wood, avoiding the outermost bits, making detection all the more difficult. "What looks like a two-by-four is just hollow, and crushes in your hand." And that is what makes Perry's work so crucial. Caught in time, a building can be treated. Left untreated, a single house can support tens of millions of termites. At this point, the war has long been lost.

The inspection began with the building's exterior. Perry immediately found a doorsill showing evidence of old damage. Perry poked and tapped at the wood to find weak spots, and in suspect areas used an infrared camera to look for spaces in the wood that might represent excavated tunnels. He was particularly attentive to spots where pipes entered the building as possible entryways for termites. One of the great challenges was to distinguish between water damage and damage caused by termites.

Perry was incredibly professional. He had an important job to do and needed to be thorough about it, but he also recognized that he was invading people's homes at a time of day when many were just waking up. At each door, the caretaker knocked and called out, "Mr. Termite Man's here!" If I were Perry, that title would really get up my nose after a while.

One of the building's residents asked if the use of yellow light bulbs would help to avoid attracting swarming termites attempting to establish a new colony. Perry rolled his eyes, made a sad face, and dismissed the idea as often-repeated misinformation. "Nobody should turn *any* lights on," he said. The last unit was inspected and, like the others, found to be free of current termite infestation.

Back on the street, Perry showed us some nifty apparatus used in the war on Formosan termites. In the early days of termite monitoring and treatment, holes were bored through the concrete and down to the earth outside of buildings. There are thousands or perhaps tens of thousands of these holes in the French Quarter, each capped by a metal disk. If inspection of a hole shows evidence of termites, the same hole can be used to apply insecticides.

In years gone by, each hole had to be uncapped and inspected manually. Now a wonderful device is used to speed things up. A piece of paper is inserted between two small wooden slats. Embedded in the paper is a thin metal conducting strip that completes a circuit to a transmitter. If termites find their way into the hole, they chew into the wood along the seam between the slats. In doing so, they nibble through the paper and conducting strip and break the circuit. Inspectors come by with hand-held devices that look like metal detectors used to find coins at the beach. When waved over the cap of a hole with an intact circuit, the device makes the sound *too-too-tee-tee-tee*. But if termites have invaded and broken the circuit, the detector makes the sound *too-too-tee-tee-tee*.

"The Big Easy" may be New Orleans' most frequently used nickname, but I prefer the less common moniker "The City That Care Forgot." It seems to encapsulate the aura that New Orleans residents emanate. Life unfolds, and it is pretty damned special if you just allow it to be. There will surely be a time when citizens of New Orleans will be able to claim that they have thrown off the cloak of Katrina. However, shortly after Rob and I flew home, word came down the pipe that Formosan termites may have been far more destructive than anyone had realized. Professor Gregg Henderson of Louisiana State University published a paper in the journal *American Entomologist,* discussing the possibility that the subterranean termite may have subverted New Orleans' flood defences by weakening expansion joints in concrete floodwalls and excavating soil levees. Katrina was bad. Introduced Formosan termites may have made it worse.

CHAPTER NINE

Through a Great
Undersea Tunnel

REASON NUMBER NINE FOR INTRODUCING A FOREIGN SPECIES: ACTUALLY, IT HAPPENED SUCH A LONG TIME AGO, I DON'T REMEMBER.

MONKEYS ARE LIKELY SO APPEALING because they remind us of us. Looking into the face of a non-human primate is to see a quieter, simpler reflection of ourselves. They have big eyes set in big heads, and gentle and dextrous fingers to gather food and tend their infants. In our closest relatives there is a reminder that we are, after all, just reasonably sophisticated monkeys.

The closer the resemblance of a monkey to humans, the greater its appeal, and perhaps this is why the Barbary macaques have so many fans in Gibraltar. Unlike most monkeys, they have no tails. They move slowly, and when they sit, they do so with rounded shoulders. The skin around their eyes and mouth is nearly hairless, and their inquiring eyes are olive or hazel.

As macaques go, the Barbary is a large and heavily built creature, but at eleven kilograms for an average adult male and slightly less for a female, they have roughly the proportions of a fifteen-month-old infant. Relative to the body, the head is large and set on a short neck, just as it is on a child. The individual variation in faces is considerable. The macaques' hair is thick and shaggy in the most delightful combination of grey, brown, and blond; it is the sort of colouration that stymies hairdressers. The incisors are a bit pointy, but the remainder of the teeth are not particularly scary. All around, they are rather pleasant-looking creatures, and so iconic as to be Gibraltar's national animal and appear on the country's currency. But they didn't get there by themselves.

Landing in Gibraltar is a surreal experience, in part because it is hard to believe that so many flights are needed each day to service a population so small, and partly because of the country's peculiar geography. Two kilometres wide and six kilometres long, Gibraltar is shaped like a really big deerstalker cap with its earflaps laid flat. One flap hangs onto Spain, and the rest of the hat juts out into the Mediterranean Sea. As our plane approached Gibraltar's airport at the north end, I was seated on the port side. On our final approach, with the plane just a few hundred metres above the waves, because of our approach angle all I could see was sea, and I got the unnerving impression that we were going to find out how many of us had been paying attention during the pre-flight safety demonstration. Then, with a small path correction, all I could see was the rapidly approaching peak of the cap, and it looked certain that we were going to crash into the cliff. We didn't. Even so, I am glad not to be a pilot on the route to Gibraltar. Pulling up short would mean a swim in the Mediterranean. Running long would mean pitching into the Atlantic. Technically, it would be the Alborán Sea or the Bay of Gibraltar, but you get the idea.

Despite the presence of army personnel with bullet-proof vests and machine guns at the airport, customs was a quick and pleasant experience. Indeed, Gibraltar is probably the only place in the world with the word "Welcome" on its passport stamp, although I was a little confused by a huge sign that proclaimed THANK YOU FOR VISITING GIBRALTAR—BLAND TRAVEL. Hopefully this was not a comment on the state of tourism opportunities.

IT IS CLEAR from archaeological excavations that Gibraltar has
been occupied by people since people were still Neanderthals.
Much later, the Phoenicians and Greeks had a go at the region.
The Moors set up shop in 711 CE and stayed until the Spanish
came barging in around 1390. Twenty-five years on, the Moors
took Gibraltar back, until the Spanish regained it in 1492. Then the
British took control under the Treaty of Utrecht, and despite a four-
year siege in the late-eighteenth century have held power ever since.
Gibraltar is now a Crown colony working under its own constitution but leaving such matters as foreign affairs and defence to
Great Britain. Today, with nearly 30,000 people crammed into just
6.5 square kilometres, Gibraltar is one of the most densely populated places on Earth. Thirty-three times more packed than China,
fourteen times more crammed than Japan, more densely jammed
than even the Vatican City and Taiwan, Gibraltar gets nudged out
only by Hong Kong, Singapore, Monaco, and Macau.

And yet the population continues to grow, and I found the
region awash in high-rise apartments under construction. A cab
driver told me that the cost of new units was so high that those
already living in Gibraltar had no hope of ever buying one.

I asked around, hoping to find out what drew more and more
people to Gibraltar. I was told that new arrivals were mainly British expatriates who fell into one of two categories. The first group
were pensioners who decided they had lived through one too many
cold and dreary winters in Britain and wanted to live somewhere
exactly like home, only warmer. The second group were wealthy
citizens who had grown tired of paying taxes and moved to Gibraltar for tax relief. Some of these apparently lived in Gibraltar for as
little as two weeks each year to get the benefits of the tax haven. I
was also told that you can drink in Gibraltar at any age, although
it is illegal to provide alcohol to anyone under the age of sixteen.
On Main Street, one shop window after another offered a litre of
hard alcohol for less that £10, although that didn't seem to me to
be enough incentive to emigrate. Cigarettes are free, or so close as
to make no difference, and McDonald's appears to have discovered

a region so isolated that even anti-smoking laws for restaurants haven't found it.

This didn't really seem like my kind of place. There were too many people and not enough serenity. There wasn't a vacant parking spot in sight, and many residents had taken to tootling around on scooters they could park on the sidewalk. These vehicles help make Gibraltar ridiculously noisy, with the sound of their *rin-tin-tin* engines reverberating off concrete offices, apartment blocks, and hotels. The air is filled with exhaust fumes, and the view of Gibraltar Bay from the promenade is completely obscured by an unbroken queue of shipyards, warehouses, docks, and high-rises.

I was counting on finding a bit of tranquility as I searched the slopes of the Rock for Barbary apes. I was also scheduled to make a presentation on Labrador Ducks to the Gibraltar Ornithological & Natural History Society (GONHS). I met my hosts at the administrative offices of the Botanical Gardens.

If Gibraltar is a sea of noise, then the Botanical Gardens are a small harbour of tranquility. I joined John Cortez and Charlie Perez of the GONHS for tea, which they have every day after work while solving all of Gibraltar's problems. These include such puzzlers as where to put all of the new residents, given that every square metre of Gibraltar is already spoken for.

As the time for my lecture approached, it became clear that I was going to speak to a rather small audience. Without being too specific, it was fewer than nine. Admittedly, I was up against some pretty stiff competition that night. According to the *Gibraltar Chronicle,* citizens had a choice of Bingo Night at the South District Senior Citizens Club, Quiz Night at the Cannon Bar, or a meeting of the Gibraltar Psychological Support Group. But the gathering was enthusiastic and laughed at appropriate times. After my presentation, I walked to a pub for a pint. Despite what the pump collar said, I wouldn't have guessed that it was Bass Ale if I had been given fifteen guesses. I got about half of it down while reflecting on what I knew about the wildlife of Gibraltar.

Despite being a minuscule place, Gibraltar has an amazing

collection of fauna and flora. A wide assortment of plants call the territory home, including Gibraltar thyme, Gibraltar restharrow, Gibraltar candytuft (the national flower), Gibraltar saxifrage, and Gibraltar sea lavender. Not all of Gibraltar's plants and animals are thriving. Neither Schreiber's bat nor the soprano pipistrelle are faring particularly well despite fifty kilometres of limestone caves to roost in. A small mollusc, *Acicula norrisi,* is found only in Gibraltar, and although it has never been seen alive, collections of fresh shells from under rocks indicate that it is hiding somewhere. The Gibraltar campion, a cute little perennial with pink flowers and a heady fragrance found on Gibraltar and nowhere else on Earth, was thought to be extinct until a few specimens were discovered in 1994.

For much of the threatened wildlife, the challenge comes down to nasty introduced plants and animals. More than sixty species of exotic flowering plants have become established, and some are considered to be a serious problem, running roughshod over native plants. These invaders include the rooikrans (an acacia from Australia), the stinking sumac (China), the Hottentot fig (Africa), and the prickly pear cactus (Mexico). Black rats have been introduced from India, and goats from Central Asia. Feral cats, found everywhere in Gibraltar and aided by well-intentioned but misguided persons who feed them, are a real pest for young Barbary Partridge and European rabbits.

MACAQUES OF ONE SORT OR ANOTHER have been around for about 7 million years. Some 5 million years ago, the ancestral macaque emerged from Africa and went wandering across the Middle East, Europe, and Asia, diversifying as it went. Today, the group has between twenty-two and twenty-five species (depending on who is counting), all in the genus *Macaca.* They all reside in Asia, except for the Barbary macaque. During the last glacial period, which finished about 10,000 years ago, Barbary macaques ended their residence in Europe and were thereafter found only in northern Africa.

So how did Barbary macaques find their way back to Gibraltar?

There are a number of fanciful explanations, including the possibility of a tunnel known only to the macaques, stretching from Ceuta on the north shore of Africa, thirteen kilometres under the Straits of Gibraltar, emerging on the north side at the series of caverns known as St. Michael's Caves. A little less fanciful is the notion that the macaques were introduced to Europe in the Carthaginian and Roman eras. Many feel that macaques were introduced to Gibraltar by Moors in the eighth century. It is all a bit hazy, and the first written reference to macaques in Spain dates back only as far as 1704. By the time macaques were first described in Gibraltar in 1782, they were already well established.

Well established, perhaps, but not necessarily secure. In the early 1900s, a few macaques were brought to Gibraltar from northern Africa to help prop up a flagging population. Numbers continued to decline, and by the end of the 1930s everyone started to get a little skittish. There is a saying that as long as Barbary apes persist in Gibraltar, so too will the British. When the Gibraltar population of macaques plummeted during WWII, Winston Churchill took a personal interest, directing the British Consulate in Morocco to introduce more. At the end of hostilities, the macaque population in Gibraltar starting doing a little better, and it soon became necessary to control their numbers by shooting some and exporting others to zoos. Until 1980, the population was actively limited to about thirty-five animals. Given the small population size, it probably isn't surprising that the group is starting to show the consequences of inbreeding. Today there are between 200 and 250 macaques in Gibraltar living in six groups, all found in the ninety-seven hectare Upper Rock Nature Reserve.

Estimates of the number of visitors to Gibraltar each year fall between 4 million and 6 million. Most of them step out of their cars or off their cruise ship, take a quick stroll down Main Street, and then bugger off. However, nearly 800,000 tourists visit the Upper Rock per year, most of them drawn by the apes. Guidebooks warned me that every spot with macaques is crowded with visitors, but I hoped to miss all of that by rising early. When I turned over my room key at six thirty in the morning, the front-desk attendant looked as though she had never seen a hotel guest at that hour. The skies were still dark, but I wanted to be on the hillside before any tourists got there. I tucked in behind the Garrison Library, climbed the Referendum Stairs, and ascended a combination of steps and pathways. The hillside was alive with wildflowers.

The Apes' Den is about halfway to the top of the rock, under the cable car line, and despite the name I was a little surprised when I turned a corner and was confronted by a group of six adult macaques, an immature male, and a couple of teeny troupe members. After glancing at me and presumably assessing the likelihood of getting breakfast, most of them returned to looking up at the cable, as though willing it to start moving. I gather their first meal of the day is brought to them by someone on the first cable car run. I pressed on, keen to see the larger group of apes at the top.

Having been fought over for so long, it is no surprise that Gibraltar is littered with the detritus of military conflict. The town has defensive towers, walls, and gatehouses, and the cliffs are perforated by caves and tunnels that harboured thousands of troops during times of war. Even today, many military personnel are stationed in Gibraltar, and the highest reaches of the Upper Rock are still home to the skeletons of cannons and anti-aircraft guns of earlier conflicts. It isn't pretty.

It had been about two hours since I left the hotel, and as I reached the summit, Gibraltar was coming alive. When I looked over the east ramparts and down toward the Mediterranean with its slight matte finish from a gentle breeze, the only sound to reach me was the serenade of hundreds of Yellow-legged Gulls. However, when I peered over the west side and down onto the town, the distant roar of metal on metal from the shipyards and vehicular traffic drifted up to me like acrid smoke. More than two dozen cargo ships sat in Gibraltar Bay awaiting loading, unloading, or repair. I could also see where new land was being created for the next generation of high-rises.

At the top of the King's Stairs, I came across a group of ten apes. A couple were picking at the remains of the repast provided the night before, which consisted mainly of onions, cabbage, and oranges. Everywhere I saw a macaque, I also saw a sign warning that, for their own good, the monkeys were not to be fed by visitors. One pair proved themselves up for a little early-morning lovin'.' She urged him on, reaching behind her to grab his left leg, encouraging him to thrust.

It is truly amazing what you can discover if you are willing to spend enough time in a library. In a 1998 volume on primate sexuality, Alan F. Dixson reported that, during the mating season, adult male Barbary macaques ejaculate an average of 2.28 times an hour, with a minimum refractory period of just thirteen minutes. Females, it seems, are happy to solicit copulations from as many as ten males in a day. According to a 1974 monograph by W. C. Osman Hill, the scrotum of an adult male Barbary macaque is 63 millimetres by 50.5 millimetres by 32 millimetres, and the penis is 40 millimetres long. The baculum, a bone inserted into the penis to make it rigid, is "short and thick." In describing the appearance of the external genitalia of young females, Hill explained that "the callosities are contiguous, with the rima pudendi at the lower end of the intervening sulcus and the clitoris, with its praeputium, projecting below the lower limit of the calloused area." How romantic.

Continuing a little further down the path, I came across a heartbreaking scene. A female macaque sat on the road next to her newborn, its umbilical cord still attached, stone dead. Her head hung as though she had lost the last of her vital spirit. I said aloud, "Oh, God. I am so sorry. I am *so* sorry."

A young macaque joined the scene, and touched and smelled the newborn corpse. The mother allowed the contact. Then an adult male approached the dead infant, and the mother attacked him, screaming with fangs exposed. But then she ran out of steam and lay down flat on the road, face to the ground. The adult male walked over and began to groom her, working systematically from front to back, turning over one bit of hair after another, searching for anything to pick off. The mother would open her eyes for a moment and then gently close them again.

Part of my training as an animal behaviour specialist was to avoid reading too much into the actions of non-human animals. We are taught not to visit the emotions of a human on them. But to claim that this female was not deep in mourning would be heartless. I wanted to toss the small body into the bush so that it wouldn't be flattened by the first passing vehicle, but it probably would have earned me a savage bite, and more importantly, I didn't think I had any right to do so. Gulls would make off with the corpse when the mother was able to tear herself away.

Globally, Barbary macaques are not doing particularly well. Although they formally had a wide distribution in North Africa, they are now restricted to fragmented forests in Algeria (with about 3,000) and Morocco (with fewer than 8,000). Besides those living in Gibraltar, three captive colonies in France and Germany account for 900 individuals, with another 200 spread amongst all other captive groups. In the past twenty years, the world's population of Barbary macaques has halved, with the blame going to all the usual culprits, including habitat destruction from over-grazing by sheep and goats, and predation of young macaques by shepherds' dogs. There is also a large illegal trade in macaques; infants are captured and sold to tourists or to Moroccans living in Europe. More than 300 infants per year are sold in Europe, which represents fully 50 percent of all macaques born in Morocco. In its latest assessment, the International Union for the Conservation of Nature (IUCN) categorized the Barbary macaque as endangered on the basis of its small population, recent population declines, and the expectation that they will continue to decline in number. Six other macaque species are also endangered.

A narrow zigzag path brought me to O'Haras Battery, the highest point on Gibraltar at 426 metres. From there, everywhere was down, and the Mediterranean steps provided a 1.5 kilometre, two-hour opportunity to experience "the peace and tranquillity of this area," as described by one of the signs put up by the GONHS.

Indeed, in more than five hours of tramping, I saw just two other people. Along the steep trail, I was disappointed by the amount of litter—mainly empty water bottles, but with quite a few beer cans and cigarette ends. Frankly, I was surprised that a smoker would have the wind to complete the steep hike.

I WAS WORKING FROM A GUIDEBOOK optimistically entitled *The Best of Gibraltar*. In third spot and earning it the maximum three out of three stars were the Barbary macaques. Back in fifth place, but still managing three stars, was Europa Point, reputedly the southernmost spot in mainland Europe. It isn't; parts of Spain hang lower. But with the sky just beginning to lighten, I set off to see this most splendid spot with the promise of soaring seabirds and cavorting dolphins.

It really is an atrocious dump. Fair enough—full marks for the panoramic view of the Mediterranean Sea, which was magnificent, despite the complete absence of seabirds and dolphins, but the rest of it is really quite crap. It is a small, flat region above some low cliffs, covered in litter. If it was in a mood to boast, Europa Point could brag about its cricket pitch, although it was sloped and gravelled instead of flat and grassy. The spot has a small lighthouse, now automated, that couldn't be visited "By Order of the Corporation of Trinity House." A small tile-covered pyramid at the site explained that the ancients considered Europa Point to be the edge of the world. The ancients must have been a bit thick—I could see bits of Spain to the west and chunks of northern Africa to the south.

I walked to the Shrine of Our Lady of Europe only to find it closed. Our Lady must have had a late night. I walked past the Mosque of the Custodian of the Two Mosques, which serves the needs of Gibraltar's sizable Muslim population. My guidebook described it as a spectacular landmark and provided a photograph to prove it. The photo had benefitted greatly from retouching. Which left me with the point itself. Two billboards offered "conceptualized images of the Europa Point project . . . works to start in January 2008." They were late. From the conceptualized images,

I gather planners envisioned a grand promenade, a children's play area, and a range of shops. At present, there was only one shop, promoting itself as "The Last Shop in Europe . . . Much Cheapness . . . Free Gift With every Souvenir you buy here!" It was closed, a derelict building with broken windows.

In an act of unadulterated optimism, public transit buses pulled up every fifteen minutes. Each arrived, idled for ten minutes while its driver had a cigarette, and then pulled away to be replaced by its successor five minutes later. I saw seven buses arrive and depart, and never saw a passenger. This may be the loneliest bus stop in the world.

And then, amazingly, a fellow outfitted in a yellow reflective jacket came by with a broom, scoop, and garbage bag to have a go with the accumulated litter. Dear God, there was a lot of litter for him to tackle. In places it had drifted into great piles. He carefully swept up cigarette ends and candy wrappers, leaving beer cans, spools of wire, and a discarded industrial-strength cappuccino maker. He left after an hour, and without a reason to stay, I left too.

On the Barbary ape theme, I felt there was one more task that I had to get stuck into. I had already watched the monkeys interact with each other, but I hadn't seen them interact with tourists. So back up the hill I went. Anyone walking to the Upper Rock from sea level is in for a reminder of how "up" up really is. Gravity isn't keen on "up." Since I was on foot, I avoided the £8 toll levied on cars and had to pay only 50p. From Europa Point, a zigzag path took me past a lot of construction sites to the Jew's Gate, so named because of a nearby Jewish cemetery.

I climbed and climbed to St. Michael's Cave, attraction number four in my guidebook and a spot where I was told I would see Barbary apes interacting with visitors. I wasn't interested in a tour of the system of caves and caverns, but I was gasping for a cup of tea. Arriving at the café at ten o'clock, I was told that I was too early for tea. It seemed I was also too early for tourists and so too early for human-monkey interactions. A little further along the track, at a roadside pullout, a plaque explained: "At this spot HM Queen Elizabeth II and HRH Duke of Edinburgh stood and looked out over Gibraltar during their visit to the Rock May 10th–11th 1954." I'd bet that HM didn't have trouble getting a cup of tea.

I walked along the Royal Anglican Way and saw a grand assortment of military leftovers and an awful lot of gulls that screamed and dive-bombed without actually striking me. Several had been holding their bowels all morning and tried to splatter me, but only one managed to do so. It takes a bigger and meaner bird than a Yellow-legged Gull to scare off an ornithologist.

Tracking downhill, I came across a group of eleven macaques at the last turn before the Apes' Den. I sat on a wall to watch them; none had any reservations about plonking themselves down next to me, and when one female took a run at another, I had to quickly vacate my spot to avoid being knocked over. They spent most of their time picking at wild plants and grooming themselves and each other. If a younger individual wanted to be groomed by an older one, it backed into it. Older individuals invited attention by lying in the road and exposing itchy parts. It is no surprise that road accidents are the leading cause of death among Barbary apes in Gibraltar.

For immature apes, the favourite game seemed to be *will-this-branch-hold-me-if-I-swing-from-it?* For the smallest ones, the best game was *what-will-happen-to-me-if-I-stick-this-in-my-mouth?* The oldest individuals have the most expressive woolly eyebrows. Fluttering raised eyebrows seemed to imply interest, whereas slamming them down showed disdain.

I walked to a level spot that served as a pullout for tour buses. Here I met Ernest, the most contented man in Gibraltar. As I approached, he was broadcasting small seeds over a wide area but acting as though he wasn't really supposed to. He told me that he had been feeding the macaques since 1954, first as a member of the military, and now as a hobby.

"Have you ever been bitten?"

"Never!" he said with pride. He explained that the troupe at the top of the Rock was inclined to be a bit aggressive, but not this group. One might bite if it was grabbed, but otherwise they were pretty passive. Research has shown that adult male macaques are the ones most likely to bite, and adult male humans are the ones most likely to be bitten.

Not that the macaques at the Apes' Den relied exclusively on Ernest for their daily bread. Between 1918 and 1992, the responsibility for provisioning the macaques fell to the British Army. In 1992, they became the responsibility of the Gibraltar government through the Gibraltar Tourism Agency; then, in 1999, their feeding was assigned by contract to the GONHS, who provision them daily with water and fresh fruit and vegetables. In an average year, the apes of Gibraltar might be expected to eat their way through four tonnes of potatoes, seven tonnes of carrots, five tonnes of cabbage, four tonnes of tomatoes, two tonnes of pears . . . for a grand banquet in excess of forty tonnes. The Gibraltar Veterinary Clinic joins in with regular vaccinations, treatment for internal parasites, and testing for a wide range of diseases.

Ernest explained that his wife didn't want him to spend his days on the hillside attending to the apes, particularly after his recent heart surgery. But he wasn't keen on sitting at home watching television, preferring to be out in the fresh air, meeting new people, and sharing his day with the apes. And after all, he had given up smoking six months before, so where was the harm? He liked to talk to visitors and sold ape trinkets.

Suddenly the monkeys and Ernest roared into action as the first tour buses of the day arrived. One bus after another pulled up and disgorged its passengers until the contents of nine buses were making a fuss over the macaques. Cameras popped everywhere, and monkeys sitting on the shoulders of tourists provided the best photo opportunities. This seemed to me to be a very clear violation of the International No-Touch-Monkey Rule. Signs everywhere warned of the potential dangers, both to monkeys and humans. Other signs warned about a £500 fine for feeding the apes, and the drivers of one bus company seemed pretty good about trying to maintain decorum. However, drivers of another bus group had monkey treats in their pockets and used them to lure monkeys onto the shoulders of tourists, and then to lure them back off again. One of the drivers was eating the treats himself, whatever they were.

A young woman with long blond hair sported a monkey whose chief ambition seemed to be avoiding falling off. This was chiefly accomplished by grabbing her hair in big handfuls. I suspect that the woman was de-matting days later. I didn't tell her that 50 percent of Gibraltar macaques have lice.

I had to wonder if all of this contact was necessarily a healthy thing. The more closely related two species are, the higher the risk of them swapping diseases. Since macaques are reasonably close relatives of humans, it isn't out of the question that they might trade illnesses with us. Among the nasty diseases that have been found globally among macaque species are simian foamy virus, tuberculosis, and the monkey equivalent of HIV. Herpesvirus simiae is not a concern for infected macaques, but it kills 70 percent of humans who acquire it. Are Barbary macaques a risk to Gibraltar residents or tourists? In recent years, the macaques have been screened for a range of diseases and found to be nearly disease-free. The only one of significance is hepatitis A. Of course it is not impossible that the macaques in Gibraltar became infected by contact with people.

Each bus driver allowed his charges to play with the monkeys for fifteen minutes before herding the passengers back onto the coach. Several monkeys took departing buses as an opportunity for a ride downhill. Each gave a look to their colleagues that said, "So long, suckers!" I resumed my descent. Every couple of minutes I was passed by an embarrassed-looking monkey walking back up.

The early evening provided me with a not-to-be-missed opportunity. Some of the subtleties of the Ceremony of the Keys were lost on me, but I think I got the gist of it. A portion of the central parade of Casemates Square was roped off, and police chased everyone out of the partitioned area. Along with the other general riffraff, I seated myself in the bleachers on the Casemates' west side; others stood outside the rope. Gradually, Gibraltar's elite arrived in suits and fancy dresses and sat in chairs on the Casemates' east side. Gibraltar's super-elite followed, chauffeured in Ford Fiestas to be seated in the choicest spots on the east side. These were followed by a military marching band, dressed all in red, accompanied by an armed guard. Together they marched up and down the square. The governor arrived in his chauffeur-driven Nissan Micra. He held the keys to the gates of Gibraltar. After inspecting the guard, he turned over the keys so that the gates could be locked, after which he got the keys back. Flags were lowered. The band played "God Save the Queen." Everyone felt happy and patriotic. We all left.

ON MY LAST EVENING, I found a courtyard on Cornwall's Parade in which the after-work crowd was winding down. I ordered a glass of red wine, but should have ordered a *vino rojo*. Walking Gibraltar's streets over the past few days, I had found Spanish to be used at least as commonly as English. As I drank my wine, a stout white gentleman in a regimental blazer walked by with his Yorkshire terrier, but everyone else—absolutely everyone else—in the area was either of Mediterranean or African descent.

Gibraltar had been ruled by Phoenicians and Greeks, through Moors, then Spaniards, back to the Moors, back to the Spanish, and eventually on to the British. A referendum in 1967 had asked the residents of Gibraltar if they wanted more Spanish involvement or to remain under the umbrella of Britain. By an overwhelming majority of 12,138 votes to 44, they had voted for the latter. How British is Gibraltar? On my ride from the airport, the taxi driver had been listening to a British radio station describing traffic snarls on the M25. Sitting in a restaurant, I found myself watching the BBC. The breaking news at 4:00 p.m. was of a young boy who had gone missing in Lancashire. When, at 4:10, the station announced that the boy had been found, a waitress called out, "Sally, they've found that little boy. Yeah, they've found him!" with obvious relief, even though the event was happening 2,000 kilometres away.

There was a time when Gibraltar was more English than England, but it seemed to me that the region was slowly being taken over by everyone else. The official currency in Gibraltar is pounds sterling, but every shop accepts euros. At the Ceremony of the Keys, the gentleman beside me had enthusiastically sung along to "God Save the Queen" but had done so in a thick Spanish accent. I had to wonder how long Gibraltar would remain a Crown colony of Great Britain, whether the apes remained or not.

On this uncertain rock lives a primate species whose own future is less than perfectly certain. Given its small and declining global population, and the anticipation of future declines, the Barbary macaque is considered endangered. In Gibraltar, officials are faced with the conflicting tasks of nurturing these threatened creatures, while killing some to keep their numbers in check.

The next morning, I refilled my backpack and walked north along Main Street, through the gates at Casemates Square, marched across the airport runway, and crossed the border into southern Spain in search of sexy ducks.

CHAPTER TEN

Duck Hunt at the OK Corral

REASON NUMBER TEN FOR INTRODUCING A FOREIGN SPECIES: BECAUSE THEY ARE SO GOSH-DARNED CUTE.

ON A SMALL LAKE, not so many kilometres from my former home in Canada, breed small ducks whose mating displays are so devilishly cute that they cause me to laugh. Although female Ruddy Ducks are not particularly resplendent, males have baby-blue bills and stiff tails that they point skyward while courting. This explains two of the rather less imaginative nicknames that hunters have for this species—stifftails and bluebills. When amorous, a drake Ruddy Duck bobs up and down in the water furiously, calling *pita-pita-pita-pita-pita-peuuuuuu*. Some trick of his breast feathers means that, while bobbing, the water around him erupts into a bubbly froth. This is apparently irresistible to females.

Ruddy Ducks have a wide breeding distribution in Canada and the United States, which is all well and good. The problem began about a half century ago when someone in England decided to import Ruddy Ducks. Nothing ever stays in captivity for long, and these ducks soon managed to establish a modest breeding population on the wrong side of the Atlantic. By itself, this wasn't an issue. Ruddy Ducks in Britain didn't compete with local waterfowl, didn't eat anything endangered, and didn't transmit nasty diseases. And, best of all, they are terribly, terribly cute.

If the Ruddy Duck had stayed put in England, there would have been no reason for concern, but in the 1960s a few Ruddy Ducks left the British Isles and flew to continental Europe. When they arrived in Spain, they caused a major problem for a closely related local bird. Numbers of the White-headed Duck, *Malvasía Cabeciblanca,* were in decline all over Europe as a result of overhunting and wetlands degradation, and they had earned endangered status. Just when things looked bleakest for the White-headed Duck, things got worse. For reasons best known to themselves, when given a choice of mating partners, White-headed Ducks are rather keen to breed with Ruddy Ducks, *Malvasía Canela,* and it was feared that the former species, already in crisis, might be exterminated as a unique biological entity through hybridization.

In an attempt to save the White-headed Duck, the call went out to kill any Ruddy Duck that had the audacity to show up in Spain; this was not a universally popular decision. Even more controversial was the move to attempt to wipe them out in England, the source of the immigrants. This was clearly a complex case, and I was in Spain to find out more.

CROSSING THE BORDER from Gibraltar into Spain proved to be a remarkably straightforward affair, a pleasant relief considering earlier tensions between the two regions. In 1965, General Franco closed the border, which was only fully reopened after his death and the entry of Spain into the European Common Market. At the frontier, a uniformed woman asked to see my passport but declined the opportunity to stamp it. Moments later, another woman asked if I had anything to declare and seemed disappointed that I didn't. And that was pretty much that. I set down my pack, put on my hat to shade me from the blazing sun, and settled in to wait for Carmen Yuste, my Spanish guide and translator.

At the stroke of eleven, Carmen and her boyfriend, Cesar, pulled up in his grey Peugeot 205, but spotting me a moment too late, had to pull a U-turn and wait across the street for me. They were immediately pounced upon by the *policía* for stopping illegally, but they avoided a ticket by pointing out the hapless Canadian waving at them from across the boulevard. Because the Peugeot is a typical European car, there was no room in the trunk for my backpack, so it joined me in the back seat as we set off to pick up our rental car in Algeciras.

Like so many of his compatriots in southern Spain, Cesar spoke virtually no English, and as we drove, Carmen explained my adventures to him. He said something in Spanish, which Carmen translated as, "He says that you are like Indiana Jones." Well, I have always thought so, only cuter. After securing the rental, Cesar set off for his home in Huelva, while Carmen and I went in search of ducks.

Carmen was a recent biology graduate seeking full-time employment, and was charming and full of smiles. I was told that I could address her in a number of ways, including Carmen, Carmen Sol ("Carmen Sun," her family's preference), and Carmen Soledad ("Carmen Solitude," the preference of the priest who baptized her). As we drove, we discussed the difference between a nap and a siesta. It mainly came down to length: a siesta should be no longer than twenty minutes and is apparently far more rejuvenating than a nap. Carmen stopped just short of claiming that a nap was unhealthy.

We stopped for lunch in Nerja. This proved something of an issue, at least for the car's windshield-mounted navigation system, which shouted at us in a female voice. Carmen had programmed in the address of our hotel in Almería, and as soon as we left the main highway, the device told us in no uncertain terms that we were to turn around and get back on track. She really was a pushy little creature, and did everything but call me an *híbrido*.

I was keen to refine my use of Spanish, and Carmen was more than pleased to correct me, politely but firmly, when I made an error of usage or pronunciation. For instance, I needed to be reminded to drop the letter "H" from words, turning Carmen's home town of Huelva to "Well-va." Although spelled "Córdoba," a peculiar trick involving *b*s and *v*s meant that the city's name is pronounced "Cordova." Carmen said that I would not be incorrect in describing my beautiful wife with the expression *"Lisa es muy linda,"* but that it was really more of a Latin American expression. In Spain, I should say, *"Lisa es muy guapa."* I learned that *"guiri"* is a less than fully flattering expression for a sunburned tourist from abroad. Carmen's command of English was brilliant, but she did show some interesting peculiarities. Just as "Spain" was pronounced "Espain," "school" became "eschool."

We passed from the province of Cádiz to Málaga, through Granada, and on to the city of Almería and our hotel. After a two-hour nap for me and six 20-minute siestas for Carmen, we hit the streets, and Carmen explained the Spanish tradition of celebrating life late into the evening. In the following days, it became apparent that Carmen is one of the Mediterranean's greatest supporters of this tradition.

We walked the waterfront and many back streets. We came across a Horse and Wine Festival, which seemed an awkward combination. We also found that the region's wedding season was in full swing, and it can be no coincidence that Almería is pronounced almost exactly like "I'll marry ya." We spotted a bride being escorted to her reception, and a trio of women called out *"¡Que se besen!"* which I understand to mean "We want to see kissing!" Over dinner, we spotted a group of sixteen men sporting identical T-shirts. Each shirt had the caption *"Se nos casa Pepe,"* which to me suggested that Pepe had nowhere to live but according to Carmen meant "Pepe is getting married." When I commented on how well behaved the stag-night revelers were, Carmen explained that it was because the night was so young. And sure enough, the next morning as I stood on my hotel room balcony, I spotted the same group of sixteen men, now staggering and singing loudly: *"Alcohol, alcohol, alcohol, alcohol, hemos venido a emborracharnos, el resultado nos da igual."* According to Carmen, this means: "Alcohol . . . we've come to get drunk, the result is the same for us." A passing police car gave the group a wide berth.

FOR MY FIRST BIT of Ruddy Duck business, Carmen had arranged for us to meet Mariano Paracuellos at a small café in the vast and uncharted tracks of Almería province. Paracuellos works for a firm that monitors environmental issues in the region. He conducts research on wildlife, including a range of waterbirds, and collaborates with researchers at Universidad de Málaga. Finding him proved a bit tricky, because even though our navigation system accepted the café's address as legitimate, she wasn't quite sure how to get there. As long as we followed her directions she was happy, even when the directions were clearly wrong. If we went off in the more correct direction, she went into a sulk before giving us an alternative route in a rather intimidating voice. I told Carmen that I was coming to think of the navigation device as "Audrey." "After Audrey Hepburn? Oh, that's nice," she said. Actually, I was thinking of Audrey II in *Little Shop of Horrors*.

Paracuellos deserves double nice-guy points. He had a newborn daughter at home, but on the Sunday morning that we met, he was still pleased to give up several hours of his day off. When we arrived at the café, a bit late thanks to Audrey, we found that Paracuellos had been nursing a hot drink that looked like chocolate mousse. Carmen ordered tea and a toasted baguette, and I had a small pastry and a blow-the-top-off-your-head coffee in a demitasse cup.

I immediately liked Paracuellos. He sported long sideburns and bits and pieces of a goatee. He wore a pendant that looked like the tail of a whale but probably represented some sort of plant leaf. Each of my five-cent questions received a two-dollar response from Paracuellos. Carmen, working hard to keep up, was able to give me a thirty-cent translation. Paracuellos was particularly erudite when it came to White-headed Ducks, about which he seemed very passionate.

The three of us set off in our rental car, and I got my first impression of just how convoluted the situation was for the poor old White-headed Duck. We parked on a little hillside overlooking a number of small lakes where the ducks bred. When the area was colonized by Phoenicians, the region had been an estuary, but human activities closed the region off from the sea and the habitat became a series of small lakes. One of these lakes was known to pirates in the sixteenth century.

The view for me was very different from what would have greeted the pirates. Paracuellos described the lakes as "water islands in a sea of plastic." All around the lakes stretching as far as I could see were clear plastic greenhouse tents used to grow exotic fruits and vegetables. These *plasticos* even ranged up the hillsides where, I was told, they are illegal. They pushed right up to the margins of each lake, their distribution relieved only by access roads between them. Paracuellos explained that the *plasticos* of Almería can be seen by astronauts in orbit. *Plasticultura* interests in the area are keen to employ cheap African labour, but it is difficult for the companies to get contracts from the Spanish government to employ them legally, making the social situation all the more difficult for illegal immigrants. Racism haunts the region.

Along with the sea of plastic greenhouse tents come problems that are often associated with intensive agriculture, including the runoff of pesticides, herbicides, and fertilizer into the lakes used by White-headed Ducks and other wildlife. Rats are attracted by the agricultural produce, but also eat the eggs of birds. To further the ecological destruction of these lakes, mosquitofish, one of the most horribly invasive species in the world, had been introduced. They could be eliminated by poisoning the lakes, but that would wipe out everything else, including some endemic, globally threatened species.

Despite all of this degradation and destruction, these small lakes are among the most productive White-headed Duck habitat anywhere. A moderate excess of nutrients stimulates algal and plant growth, which increases the abundance of chironomid flies on which the ducks feed. The lakes are important, but they aren't big; I could probably kayak across each of them in about ten seconds.

Paracuellos described White-headed Ducks as "silly." In the presence of a male Ruddy Duck, White-headed drakes fly away, leaving all of the females for the invaders. Although it was just his impression, Paracuellos felt that the arrival of Ruddy Ducks in

Spain coincided with bad weather in other parts of Europe. A nasty storm in England could drive Ruddy Ducks to more clement Spain.

Paracuellos took the wheel to drive us to a number of nature reserves. He spoke to us about the environment with such passion that we cruised along at 80 kilometres per hour in a 120 zone, much to the displeasure of other motorists. At our first reserve, we looked down upon wetlands rich in Cattle Egrets and Greater Flamingos. The geography would have been familiar to the Romans, but human activity was profoundly altering operation of the local environment. At one time, the region would have been flooded only seasonally. Now, a lot of the water piped in for *plasticultura* finds its way into the wetlands, which are now deeper, less salty, and more polluted. This is bad for most wildlife but, paradoxically, suits the needs of White-headed Ducks.

At another nature reserve, we found brackish marshes separated from the Mediterranean by sand dunes. We spied stilts, avocets, egrets, flamingos, ibis, and the globally vulnerable Marbled Teal, which was breeding at the reserve. We also spotted feral dogs that are shot to protect the wildlife. We passed a spot where a female Ruddy Duck had been shot the week before. I was told that this isn't an easy thing to do. The vegetation is tall, and a duck can evade pursuers for a day or more. Ruddy Ducks can dive for a prolonged period and are safe from guns as long as they remain near White-headed Ducks.

We stopped at a marsh for my first close-up look at White-headed Ducks. An adult female was foraging near a car full of people who were tossing bits of bread out the windows; they probably didn't appreciate it when we leapt from our car and strolled up to the edge of the marsh. Two White-headed Duck drakes swam further out in the marsh, along with Mallards, Moorhen, Coots, and Crested Pochard.

White-headed Ducks expect three things from their habitat: they need water of just the right depth; they need brackish (slightly salty) water; and they need a belt of the right sort of vegetation, such as cattails. These conditions were apparently just right for a portion of the gay community as well; this bit of wetland was a well-known meeting place, and the general litter of candy bar wrappers and water bottles was supplemented by used condoms.

We finished our tour at a wetland that had sprung up by accident when sand excavation for agricultural use had created a pit that gradually filled with water from an underground aquifer, creating a reasonably large marshy lake. With no warning, Paracuellos stopped the car abruptly, but resisted the temptation to leap out and disturb the event in front of us. Six adult male White-headed Ducks were displaying vigorously to an equal number of females. It was a beautiful courtship. We slipped quietly out of the car, although we could probably have been accompanied by a Dixieland jazz band for all the attention we got from the ducks. Each displaying male sat low in the water and made a whirring noise. Facing the hen at an angle, the drake quickly twisted his body to face her from another angle. I was astonished to find that the display of a male White-headed Duck was completely unlike the displays of male Ruddy Ducks in Canada. I cannot imagine how they ever manage to attract each other.

Carmen and I set off for the seaside resort of Alicante on the Costa Blanca.

SPANISH GENEROSITY of time and spirit continued. At nine o'clock on Monday morning, we were met by José Luis Echevarrias. We followed him to a neighbourhood that is very popular for purchase by foreign visitors keen on warm winters and a less hectic pace of life. We breakfasted at a café as we began our discussion of ducks in the El Hondo wetlands.

El Hondo is the region that most Spaniards first think of when the topic of wetlands comes up. Echevarrias explained that until the 1990s, White-headed Ducks did not breed at El Hondo, but when they did arrive, Ruddy Ducks arrived as well. Years ago, the region's natural areas were not specifically protected, but the plight of White-headed Ducks made the region a conservation priority.

When the presence of Ruddy Ducks was brought to the attention of the local administration, the decision was made to kill them.

When White-headed Duck hunting was banned in Spain and efforts were made to protect their breeding habitat, their numbers started to increase. A survey in 2000 revealed 4,000 individuals. But there was some reason to doubt the resulting optimism. There was a drought at the time, but the El Hondo wetlands persisted because they did not rely entirely on rain; ducks may have moved to the region from drier areas, with no real overall increase in numbers.

Throughout Europe, wetlands are in danger, and one of the greatest threats is the encroachment of urban development and agriculture. In the El Hondo region, the government decided to take a greater responsibility for conservation, and a significant number of ecologically important areas were protected. Since then, EU regulations have resulted in the protection of even more spots.

The killing of Ruddy Ducks is an evolving process. In the early days, a handgun was used, but now a rifle is employed with much greater success. Luckily, said Echevarrias, Ruddy Ducks are "quite stupid," and a hunter can usually miss a few times without having the target fly away. A more sophisticated system was developed recently to kill Ruddy Ducks in El Hondo. A man in hip waders enters a blind made of vegetation, floats close to the unsuspecting Ruddy Duck, and then blasts it. Echevarrias explained that the blind is named "Dorothy."

"Why 'Dorothy'?" I asked. Echevarrias didn't know, so he put in a call to a colleague to find out. He discovered that in the film *Twister,* the hurricane-chasing group used a device named Dorothy to track hurricanes. I've not seen the film but suspect that this is a reference to the heroine in *The Wizard of Oz*. Perhaps those responsible for killing Ruddy Ducks think of them as blowing in like small, destructive hurricanes. Without Dorothy, the best system for killing Ruddy Ducks involves two boats. The first contains the shooter; the second is used to drive the Ruddy Duck toward a place where it can most easily be shot.

I asked Echevarrias how he would respond to the opposition of some animal rights activists to the cull of Ruddy Ducks in Britain. He thought very carefully before replying. First, he would invite those opposed to the cull to come to the region and try to identify the one duck in 10,000 that was a Ruddy Duck or a hybrid, and then try to kill it. It was much more practical to eliminate them at the source. Second, he went on to explain that there is currently very strong support in Spain for the conservation of White-headed Ducks, and funding is available to kill Ruddy Ducks as soon as they arrive. It may be difficult to maintain this support into the future, making it important to eliminate the Ruddy Duck threat now.

We then set off to see the projects designed to help conserve White-headed Ducks and other wildlife. The first was a nearby nature reserve, Aula de la Natura, del Clot de Galvany, where visitors, including schoolchildren, can get a first-hand nature experience. The wetlands in the reserve are maintained by treated waste water from surrounding communities. While watching White-headed Ducks from a blind, we were joined by a man who explained that he had moved to Spain from England. He said that England no longer seemed like home, claiming that it was too crowded and expensive. Echevarrias later said that this man was one of a number of "professional birdwatchers" who often come to the reserve. In a somewhat derisive way, he explained that after living in Spain for several years, the man still spoke no Spanish.

As we drove to the next site, I asked Echevarrias how those involved in the killing of Ruddy Ducks viewed their participation in the project. He said that they are not keen on the killing but realize the importance of their work. Echevarrias explained that those involved with the White-headed Duck project feel profoundly responsible for its outcome. When someone goes on holiday, they call home to see how the killing of a newly arrived Ruddy Duck is proceeding. I wondered if rat exterminators feel the same level of commitment to the cause.

We stopped at a habitat restoration area, part of the Parque Natural de las Salinas de Santa Pola. I asked Echevarrias if he felt pride in his work. He said that he did but was also "pissed off"

(Carmen's best attempt to find the right English words) about the length of time required to get a project approved and completed. He explained that the project in front of us had taken fifteen years to complete. Directorships are political appointments, so directors come and go, meaning that short-term and long-term objectives are difficult to establish, and small administrative problems can derail a project. Echevarrias explained that, in general, Spaniards are concerned about the environment. Interest in global warming, for instance, is very high, but engagement in species endangerment is much lower. Interest in the topic does not always translate into action.

We finished our five-hour tour with a visit to a very large and recently completed wetlands project, Parque Natural del Hondo, Generalitat Valencia, which had involved the creation of about 100 hectares of brackish marshes. Canals carried water to the wetlands from the mountains beyond and from agricultural land. Considerable structural complexity in the wetlands suits White-headed Ducks very well. Part of the motivation for the project had been habitat creation for Marbled Teal, a species that had not yet attracted as much public attention as the White-headed Duck. Echevarrias spoke with passion and conviction about this wetlands project. As a man of size and substance, he gave the sense that he could back it all up with a physical presence.

Listening intently can be tiring, but translating questions and answers at high speed must be really draining when done hour after hour. After we cleared Alicante and got on the road for the six-hour run to Córdoba, Carmen slipped into a deep siesta. Luckily I was driving at the time. We proceeded through dry low-lands and wetter highlands. We passed fields of olives, oranges, and cereal crops. For the most part, Audrey was good about the whole thing, but she sometimes became confused. When we got onto a newly constructed road that she didn't recognize, Audrey insisted that I drive cross-country by the shortest possible route to the roadway that she knew. At one point, I was convinced that she described me as an *idiota*.

After settling in at our hotel in Córdoba, we crossed the Río Gua-dalquivir to the centre of the old city in search of food. We watched as a police car stopped next to four young fellows who had been drinking and clearly thought that they were in for a bit of trouble. Instead, the officer rolled down his window, pointed to a well-dressed woman, then pointed to the litter she had just discarded, and insisted that she dispose of it properly. I love Spanish *policía*.

After dinner, while crossing a Roman-era bridge, Carmen received a telephone call. While she spoke, I wandered to a shrine on the bridge with candles to be lit for prayers. The shrine was propping up two men on bicycles who had been imbibing rather too well to prop up themselves. They babbled at me in slurred Span-ish. When I explained, in Spanish, that I didn't speak Spanish, one of them asked, "English?" When I answered in the affirmative, they started burbling at me in very poor French. They protested that the shrine wasn't just for lighting candles for fun; this was for prayers to the city's patron saint. I didn't have enough Spanish to explain that my mother-in-law was ill, and that the candle was meant to carry my prayer for her, so I just got on with it. I burned myself. Having finished her call, Carmen joined me, listened for a moment, and laughed at how the conversation had turned. The men claimed that I looked like Indiana Jones. Harrison Ford should be so lucky.

CARMEN HAD ARRANGED a 9 a.m. meeting with José Antonio Tor-res Esquivias, but until she told a colleague about the meeting, she hadn't realized just how important a man he really was. Esquivias was a high-ranking government official to start with, but when it came to White-headed Ducks in Spain, this guy was *it*. We took the elevator to the seventh floor of the building that was home to the Delegacion Prov. de Mesion Andalucia for Córdoba and were seated outside Esquivias' office by a secretary.

Esquivias was dressed in a navy blue sweater over his dress shirt and tie, and it was easier to imagine him safe in his office than in the field getting his feet wet. But first impressions are only that. In preparation for our visit, Esquivias had lined up a comprehensive set of supportive documents, including books and brochures about the difficulties facing White-headed Ducks. The package included newspaper stories, newsletters given to supporters, certificates given to donors, data printouts, scholarly articles, and even window stickers.

Carmen translated his story. Thirty years earlier, Esquivias had been working on a Ph.D. in Córdoba on habitat selection in songbirds. Whenever he went to a conference, everyone wanted to speak to him about White-headed Ducks because Córdoba was the only place with significant numbers of that species. Initially, he was dismayed that people didn't want to hear about his songbird work but then recognized a niche that he might occupy.

At that time, there were only twenty-two White-headed Ducks in the region, and hunting was still permitted. Esquivias would sometimes show up at a wetland to complete a duck census only to find people trying to shoot them. Many believed that it was impossible to save a species just by protecting its habitat. However, Esquivias and others insisted that the key to survival of the White-headed Duck was prevention of habitat destruction and elimination of hunting. In 1985, Esquivias and his group purchased the land around Zoñar Lake in order to protect it. It was the first purchase of this sort by a non-governmental organization in Spain. This caused the government to feel guilty that it had not done more to protect the White-headed Duck, and hunting was finally brought to an end in the region. As a result of their efforts, by 2000 the population had grown to about 4,500 individuals, and with the increase, the White-headed Duck expanded its range. With range expansion came further hunting bans.

In the early days, the public had no appreciation for the plight of White-headed Ducks. The association devoted to saving the species made its environmental campaign a very high priority, and at its peak had 2,000 members, including many from abroad. Responsibility for the White-headed Duck moved from the Ministry of the Environment to regional authorities, and association members became members of regional administrative efforts.

But just as the White-headed Duck started to make a recovery, Ruddy Ducks appeared, creating a new threat. Esquivias gave me a graph showing the climbing numbers of Ruddy Ducks and hybrids over time. At first, the decision to kill Ruddy Ducks and hybrids was a regional one, but as the problem increased, the need for a national response team was recognized. These efforts are aided by birdwatchers who notify the team about Ruddy Ducks. The team is a private company, paid for by the government, and Esquivias explained that it is an expensive proposition.

Esquivias said that if nothing were to be done about Ruddy Ducks outside of Spain he would be pessimistic about the future of White-headed Ducks. Most of the Ruddy Ducks are arriving from Britain, but now they are coming from Morocco too; one of these had recently shown up at Cadiz. If Ruddy Ducks and hybrids are not controlled in Morocco, he said, it is one more front of attack.

When I asked about British opposition to the Ruddy Duck cull, Esquivias said he believes that the problem is more a matter of appearance than of actually taking the extreme measures necessary to kill them all. One of the difficulties is that some people in the UK consider the Ruddy Duck to be a British species, introduced but naturalized, and legitimate in some way, so they are reluctant to take necessary extreme measures. Esquivias had visited Britain at the invitation of authorities to speak to activists and explain the problem for White-headed Ducks in Spain. He found it very difficult to exchange ideas with these people in a meaningful way.

Even in Spain, there are activists who are opposed to the shooting of Ruddy Ducks and feel that there should be some better way to control them, such as capture and release. Esquivias thinks that the issue must be dealt with from a scientific perspective. Not that an emotional response is irrelevant. He once went to the shooting of a Ruddy Duck and was so upset by the experience that he never went again. Even so, he understands the situation and fully supports the cull of Ruddy Ducks.

The Spanish population of White-headed Ducks is increasing, but the global population is still in decline. This shows the importance of

Spanish measures for the long-term survival of the species. Spain has been involved in programs of White-headed Duck reintroduction in France and Italy, but these have failed to produce results so far.

Without the elimination of Ruddy Ducks in Europe and Africa, the chance of long-term survival for the White-headed Duck is low, according to Esquivias. The Moroccan world is very different from life in Europe, he explained. Everything is hunted in Morocco, and the problem of Ruddy Ducks in that country should be eliminated by the local predisposition to blast away at everything that moves. However, significant wetlands are owned by the Crown, and hunting is not permitted. The Spanish royal family has good relations with the Moroccan royal family and have contacted them about the Ruddy Duck problem, without positive results to date.

When the population of White-headed Ducks fell to its lowest level, a captive group was established, partly in hopes of breeding individuals for release into the wild and partly as a repository of genetic variation. That captive group is still maintained. The difficulty with captive-bred White-headed Ducks is that they have not imprinted properly, and once they are released into the wild they fail to display the natural behavioural repertoire. They don't seem to distinguish between Ruddy and White-headed ducks, and so are particularly prone to hybridization.

Another difficulty for White-headed Ducks is that they are specialists and require conditions to be just right. Water must be the right depth. They need a supply of chironomid flies and pondweed seeds. In comparison, Ruddy Ducks are generalists and will usually win in a competitive situation.

I asked if the White-headed Duck was Esquivias' favourite bird species. His face developed a tender look, and he said that there is shared love with this bird. Others have photographs of family members in their office; Esquivias has photos of White-headed Ducks.

Esquivias had arranged an escorted trip to Laguna de Zoñar for Carmen and me with site manager Raphael Vega. Vega negotiated the company truck out of its parking stall and through the

Gordian knot of vehicles that represents a typical Spanish parking lot. En route, I began to feel a little carsick. Vega wasn't keen on posted speed limits, and as the truck surpassed 150 kilometres per hour, an interesting trick of harmonics meant that the vehicle started to vibrate. The front seat seemed stable enough, but riding in the back I got quite a massage, and every bit of my face jiggled. When Vega settled in at 160, the vibrations disappeared.

At Laguna de Zoñar, we were met by Manuel, a park warden. To me, he was a swarthy, dark-haired version of Homer Simpson. There was a vague threat of violence about him, but I assumed that it was a thin veneer over a softer interior.

Manuel is the man responsible for shooting Ruddy Ducks and hybrids in the area. He explained that the official policy is "If in doubt about whether an individual is a hybrid, kill it!" To date, genetic analysis of the corpses has shown that only one pure White-headed Duck has been killed.

Carmen, Vega, Manuel, and I went for a walk around the lake. It is a beautiful place where native vegetation has been planted and maintained to effect. Showing his softer side, Manuel pointed out patches of aromatic herbs. He showed us White-headed Ducks swimming in the distance, and explained that it is important to control voracious carp in the lake, since they are able to eat small ducklings.

Back in Córdoba, Vega suggested an out-of-the-way restaurant near his home. Parking spots proved to be a problem; there weren't any. I was told that in Córdoba, drivers double-park their cars but leave the handbrake off so that the car can be pushed out of the way if needed. This did not seem feasible in our situation, so Vega created a spot by driving up on the sidewalk and parking behind a dumpster. I thought it unlikely we would ever see the truck again.

The restaurant's owner was an ex-bullfighter, and every bit of wall space was dedicated to images of bullfighting. A television was broadcasting a bullfight. Despite my opposition to blood activities, I found the wine outstanding and the food hearty and traditional

for the region. The owner and I exchanged snippets of genial conversation in English and Spanish.

I was having difficulty believing how late in the evening Spanish people start the day's celebrations. At 8:30 p.m., Carmen and I
set off to meet Julio, a university friend. Carmen explained that she
could not imagine a trip to Córdoba without seeing him. Julio had
recently started a course of study toward a Ph.D. in molecular biology involving the study of diabetes. Although Julio's English was
rusty, we were able to swap expressions like "immunohistochemis-
try" and "polymerase chain reaction."

Julio had a general idea about the location of his chosen restaurant, but his navigation was pretty casual. We strolled through
a plaza that had once been used for bullfights. We passed through
a courtyard that had been, in some way, important to the story of
Don Quixote. When we got to the restaurant, we were joined by
Julio's impossibly beautiful Peruvian girlfriend, whose name flew
out of my head the moment it flew in. Over bread, cold tomato
soup, chickpeas, and aubergines, we laughed and teased and told
travel stories. Close to midnight, we tumbled back onto the street.
Walking through a plaza, we found a concert in full swing. Despite
the late hour on a weeknight, young children were playing in the
street. "Well, that's Espain," I was told. I had my first cheek-kissing
experience in Spain when I said goodnight to Julio's girlfriend; she
was not to be denied. When I told her that I hoped we would meet
again, she said, "Well, you never know. Life travels in circles."

SEVILLE IS A NOISY, BUSY CITY with a significant air pollution problem. It has myriad cars but very few parking spots. Audrey tried her
best, and Carmen helped by calling out, "No, not yet. No, not yet.
Yes, turn here. Now!" but it was still all I could do not to smack
the rental into other vehicles and run down a sizable portion of
Seville's pedestrian population.

After securing the city's last parking spot, we walked to the
Estación Biológica de Doñana Consejo Superior de Investigaciones
Científicas, a superior research centre. All major Spanish cities have

one or more of these. This one was particularly concerned with biological conservation. The building was alive with young people wandering the halls and exchanging ideas.

We met up with Andy Green, who suggested a nearby café for our discussion. Luckily, Carmen got a break from translating and could concentrate on getting her breakfast down. I asked how someone with the name "Andy Green" came to be working in Seville. He explained that while working at the Wildfowl and Wetlands Trust in Britain, he started considering the problems facing White-headed Ducks. He recognized a niche and slowly worked his way into a permanent position at the Estación in Seville, where he had been for the past fourteen years. He suggested that being bilingual helped him bridge the gap between England, the source of Ruddy Ducks, and Spain, their recipient. Whenever someone on either side needs information, they can come to him. Whenever a Ruddy Duck or a hybrid is shot in Spain, the corpse is delivered to him. This allows for all manner of coordinated research, including diet, genetics, and parasitism.

My understanding of the history of the plight of White-headed Ducks made a big leap forward when Green pointed out that the Wildfowl and Wetlands Trust was the group responsible for harbouring Ruddy Ducks in Britain in the first place. When I asked Green if the White-headed Duck was likely to survive without the elimination of Ruddy Ducks, he referred me to the similar problem created by Mallards in New Zealand. When I asked about British opposition to the Ruddy Duck cull, Green said that millions of Mallards are shot in Britain every year, "So what's the difference?" I asked about his work with Marbled Teal and was told that they were an "acquired taste."

Strangely, his answers were all a bit brief. Normally, when scientists are given an opportunity to talk about their work, it is hard to shut them up. In Green's case, I wondered if this was British reserve. Then he mentioned that he was leaving shortly for root canal surgery, which would make the most verbose person edgy.

Considering waterbird conservation, Green emphasized Spain's long history of hunting and the lack of good coordination between the hunting and conservation communities, which is odd given that they are often working toward the same end. Carmen interjected, explaining that there had been protests against new conservation initiatives in Spain. Green demonstrated the lack of conservation commitment by telling us that while more than one million Britons are members of the Royal Society for the Protection of Birds, the equivalent Spanish organization has only 9,000 members.

We were now in the part of Spain most familiar to Carmen, so we were able to put Audrey to bed for the drive from Seville to Parque Nacional Doñana. Adjacent to the national park is an equally large *parque natural,* which allows for a broader range of activities, including the cultivation of fruit. I read that the strawberry fields here were the inspiration for John Lennon's song of that name. I don't know what they looked like in Lennon's time, but they didn't inspire me. They certainly were nothing to get hung about. Over the years, these strawberry fields have been tended by women from Poland, then Romania, and now Morocco. Automobile collisions kill at least one of these women each year as they walk by the side of the highway. The highway also isn't much good for the Iberian lynx, *lince ibérico,* considered by the IUCN to be globally critically endangered.

We pulled into El Rocío, where Carmen had booked us into a hotel. A more peculiar community you are unlikely to enter. Cars slipped their way along wide sand streets that were better suited for horses. It seemed a ghost town, and I had the distinct feeling that El Rocío had been constructed by Hollywood set designers for a remake of *Gunfight at the OK Corral,* dominated as the place was by two-storey wooden buildings complete with hitching posts. As usual, I had the story completely backwards. In the early days of cattle ranching in North and South America, many cowboys had come from this part of Spain and had brought many of their traditions with them, including a sense of architecture. El Rocío did not look like the Wild West; the Wild West looked like El Rocío.

El Rocío supports only about 100 citizens on a day-to-day

basis, and most residences were locked up tight. The community featured many restaurants, but most of them were also closed. We had arrived two weeks before the start of the summer season, when the unoccupied residences fill with people fleeing the heat and congestion of Seville.

Another annual population surge had swept through El Rocío two weeks before we arrived. Each year at Pentecost, El Rocío receives one million devotees, *Rocieros,* on a religious pilgrimage, the Romería del Rocío. Part of their reverence is reserved for an image of the Virgin, La Reina de las Marismas, also known as La Virgen del Rocío, or La Paloma Blanca. Between pilgrimages, the image is housed at the beautiful white church, El Rocío's Ermita de Nuestra Señora.

Not everyone on pilgrimage is equally devoted. According to Carmen, who worked in the area, at least nine-tenths of those making the pilgrimage treat the trip as a fiesta. The highlight of these festivities is the parading of the Virgin through the town to the accompaniment of cheering, drinking, and fireworks. Many of the pilgrims and other partygoers make the trip by traditional routes, walking or on horseback, right through the heart of Doñana National Park. Two weeks after the big event, we found that streets, alleyways, and even the approach highway were still being cleared of rubbish.

Carmen rested while I strolled down to the wetlands, the Marismas de Doñana, which looked for all the world like a lake, but which Carmen later assured me is known as "The Mother of All Marshes." At a raised observation platform, I found two pairs of birdwatchers on vacation from England. The men were positioned behind their powerful spotting scopes, scanning the skies for rarities. The women were a little more casual, lounging with binoculars at their sides, soaking up the sun. I asked, as casually as I could, if they had seen any White-headed Ducks. "No, not here. Not yet." Still casually, I asked how they felt about the Ruddy Duck situation in England but couldn't get a definitive answer. "Yes, very contentious . . ." was all they would offer.

In the early afternoon, Carmen and I drove to the town of El Acebuche to join Carlos Gutierrez for lunch. Carmen explained that Gutierrez was someone we had to meet. He had a reputation as a great ornithologist, and although he was one of the more recent additions to the White-headed/Ruddy duck world, he was an important player.

I had reached an unusual and awkward position. Carmen had been so efficient lining up interviews with important people that I was starting to run out of relevant questions about ducks. I decided to space my material out a bit. Unfortunately, my first question seemed to turn Gutierrez against me.

"So, I understand that you are somewhat new to the world of Ruddy and White-headed ducks." He barked back that he had been working on the ducks since 2000, and then changed his answer to 2002. First he had worked with a private company, then with the Ministry of the Environment.

I tried another tack and asked a couple of questions about Doñana National Park. Gutierrez explained that the park had been established in 1969 and was about 50,000 hectares in size, but, he explained tersely, these were things I could look up on the park's website. It was becoming a pretty stilted conversation. One of the problems was that Gutierrez wanted to speak to me in English, rather than working through Carmen, and as I had discovered with some other Spaniards, it took a bit of practice before he remembered much English. I asked about the importance of Doñana to the White-headed Duck. Gutierrez said that the park had never been important to the duck, but that there had been a fish farm in the area, that a marsh had been destroyed, and something about 2,000 hectares of wetlands.

After a while, things settled down a bit, and I learned that although the wetlands in the area harbour a modest number of breeding White-headed Ducks, the region is important to the species as wintering habitat. In the autumn, Ruddy Ducks also arrive, and if they make it through the winter, they attempt to mate with White-headed Ducks in the spring. Up to fourteen Ruddy Ducks had been killed in a single year, a statistic made all the more incredible by Gutierrez's claim that no more than 400 Ruddy Ducks remained in all of Britain.

I was then told about another avian pest in the region. Just two days earlier, officials had begun to shoot Sacred Ibises. Native to sub-Saharan Africa, local populations had been founded from escapees from zoos in France, Belgium, and Spain. There were now hundreds of Sacred Ibises in the Mediterranean region, and as many as 5,000 in France. I asked why it was necessary to shoot them at all and was told that they prey on native birds and amphibians, some of which are threatened, and have shown their potential for very rapid population growth.

I then lost control over my destiny and was swept along by a wave of Spanish generosity and enthusiasm. I knew only that Gutierrez was going to give us a tour of Doñana National Park, a privilege normally reserved for those booking the services of a tour guide. We jumped into Gutierrez's white Land Rover, Carmen in front and me in back. We roared along the beach on the park's southwestern border. At low tide we might have driven sedately along the water's edge, but at high tide we had to blast through the adjacent dunes. Like Gutierrez and Carmen, I had to abandon my seatbelt to avoid being throttled. As the Rover bounced, I felt I might soon be able to prove my mortality.

We then bounded up into the dunes and the Monte de Doñana. Taking notes was impossible, and so I held on for dear life, leaning forward whenever Gutierrez had something to pass along. I heard about threatened endemic plants. I saw spots where moving sand dunes were about to swallow pine trees. From the tops of dunes I spied a sea of wetlands, somewhat shrunken by a dry winter. On we drove, north through the park. I heard about the plight of the Small Buttonquail, on which Gutierrez was working. The buttonquail was already very rare in Spain. Gutierrez felt that it was likely to become the first bird since the Great Auk to go extinct in Europe. Luckily it was doing a bit better in Asia and Africa.

One hour ticked into the next. I was shown woven-wood

enclosures, large and round, into which rabbits were thrown so that Imperial Eagles could hunt for them. I saw other, similar enclosures, not quite so high, that also received rabbits. They were high enough that rabbits couldn't hop out, but short enough that hungry Iberian lynx could hop in. I didn't want to seem ungrateful to Gutierrez for his incredible generosity, so I asked as many questions as I thought was reasonable.

"When the rabbits are added to the enclosures, how long does it take the lynx to find them? A day or two?"

"A minute or two" was the answer. "I think the lynx know the sound of the vehicle that delivers the rabbits." And on we bounced.

"This field over here? That used to be a wetland!"

"Oh dear."

"And this wetland over there? That used to be a field!"

"Really?"

"And this road? In heavy rain, it is completely underwater!"

"Uh-huh."

I was shown an area that had, in the past, been completely covered with introduced eucalyptus trees, but these had been cut down and the debris used to create rabbit warrens. I saw eucalyptus trees that had been allowed to remain standing because they contained eagle nests. We stopped at an interpretive centre to see the nests of Glossy Ibises, at which a team had been banding chicks all day.

Despite earlier tensions, Gutierrez was turning out to be a really great guy, and there was no way that I could ask if the tour was nearly over. When we pulled away from the interpretive centre, he asked if I was getting tired. I explained that it had been a long day, and that it had been a busy three weeks on the road, and that I was very tired indeed. Allowing myself to hope that this would signal an end to our expedition, I showed just how naive I could be. We bombed off toward our next destination, and I heard myself making whimpering noises. I wanted to ask if Gutierrez had a gun in the truck, allowing me to give myself a non-life-threatening injury so that I could go to a hospital for a little rest.

We saw an endless parade of spoonbills, ibises, herons, kites, and egrets, and even a few wild boar and a mongoose. We hadn't seen any White-headed Ducks, probably because the few that were around were busy breeding amongst the reeds. And then, as the evening skies darkened and our time in the field approached six hours, Gutierrez told me that he knew a place where we could be sure to see White-headed Ducks. I wanted to say that I wouldn't trade two rats' balls for the chance to see a duck, but instead I played along. He was teasing me slightly and took Carmen and me to a captive breeding facility for Iberian lynx that also held captive White-headed Ducks.

IN THE MORNING, we set off south along the highway to the offices of the Estación Biológica de Doñana to meet Hector Garrido Guil, known to his friends as "Chiqui." Chiqui had been involved with White-headed Duck conservation attempts and the fight against Ruddy Ducks for many years and had a reputation as a brilliant photographer. When we got to a gate that crossed the road guarded by an intercom, we were told that Chiqui had been called away to meetings in Seville but could slip in a quick discussion with us before he left. At a café. Back along the road we had come. About 200 metres from where we had started.

When Chiqui arrived, he launched into questions before I had a chance to. Heavens, I love that sort of inquisitiveness. He asked why I was so interested in the Ruddy Duck in Spain when there are so many other outrageous examples of introduced species. He cited examples of plants, turtles, crabs, and the Sacred Ibis. I told him about Ruddy Ducks breeding so close to my home in Canada. Chiqui told us that he would soon be travelling to Australia, where introduced Mediterranean rabbits are outrageously common but increasingly rare in Spain, where they are toward the bottom of the food chain and important food for species like the Iberian lynx.

When it came time for me to ask questions, Chiqui explained that he had been in on the ground floor, being on the scene when Ruddy Ducks first started appearing from Britain. Although he could not claim to have shot the first Ruddy Duck, he did kill the sixth. Shooting was not currently part of his job. Instead he worked with marksman Pepe, whom we were scheduled to meet later in the day. Chiqui was the eyes of the outfit, and Pepe was the gun. Chiqui said that their relationship was like that of two cartoon squirrels, which Carmen translated as "Chip and Chop." Cartoon squirrels? "Oh, do you mean Chip 'n' Dale?" Since Disney's squirrels are identical, I didn't ask Chiqui which one he was. Between Chiqui and Pepe, they could claim to have killed about 70 percent of the Ruddy Ducks in Spain. Although Chiqui now works on other projects and hasn't had the opportunity to work with Pepe for a year, he explained that they are still "a couple in love." That expression may have lost something in the translation.

I asked about the difficulties with Ruddy Ducks in Morocco. Chiqui responded with frustration about the failure of other countries to kill Ruddy Ducks within their borders. He explained that he had personally spoken to the Prince of Spain, asking him to ask the monarchy of Morocco to become more involved with the fight against Ruddy Ducks. However, he said, the government of Morocco is slow to respond to any challenge if it cannot see a short-term advantage. While at a conference in Morocco to present findings of a census of Slender-billed Curlews, Chiqui had taken the opportunity to discuss the Ruddy Duck problem with members of the Moroccan Ministry of the Environment. Everyone seemed to be onside, and two Ruddy Ducks were killed in the next two days. After that, the enthusiasm died away, and the remaining Ruddy Ducks were spared.

Chiqui said that it was important for persons resistant to the Ruddy Duck cull to remember that this was not a natural problem, but one caused by a person, the one who was responsible for the release of Ruddy Ducks from captivity. The cull is not an attack on nature but an attack on a human-created problem. Equally important is the realization that conservation is not an issue for a single person or even a single country. In one sense, White-headed Ducks in Spain belong to the world, and we all have a responsibility for their survival.

Was Chiqui optimistic about the future of the White-headed Duck? There was a time when he was very pessimistic. He and others blasted away at every Ruddy Duck that arrived in Spain and yet the birds continued to arrive, and in increasing numbers. The time came when Chiqui made a conscious decision to stay the course for two additional years and wait for England to come onside before giving up. Experts met, and the British government made a commitment to cull Ruddy Ducks.

I FELT THAT I HAD HEARD just about every technical aspect of the White-headed/Ruddy duck situation, and it seemed to be time to hear more about the emotional side. Carmen had arranged for us to meet Pepe, the man behind the gun, after work. We arrived at the agreed-upon bar in El Rocío at 8 p.m.

We were met by a curious group composed of eight young men and women and one older man with long dishevelled hair and a ZZ Top beard. This latter fellow seemed to be playing the jester, gesturing wildly and violating the personal space of others. They were kicking back after spending the day banding 500 Glossy Ibis chicks in Doñana National Park under the direction of the older fellow, Luis. Members of the group were at least mildly interested in my quest but were a lot more amused by the gentle teasing that I started getting from Luis. He started by ribbing me about speaking so little Spanish; I tried to hold my end up by using Spanish to say "Hello. My name is Glen. I speak no Spanish. Please bring me two beers." It got a good laugh.

Luis countered that "Glen" was not a real name and that I needed a proper one. By this he meant a Spanish name, and suggested "Guillermo," which translates somehow as William. I tried to get Luis off my back by giving him a little ribbing in return. I pointed out that he was the only person at the table, and virtually the only person I had seen in Spain, with blue eyes. I tried to say it in a way that suggested that his parentage might be open to discussion.

The group began dispersing into the night in ones and twos just as Pepe showed up. I asked him if he had been banding Glossy

Ibis with the others, and he explained that he had real work to do. Hmmm. Despite the diminished group, it was impossible for me to keep up with a minimum of three people speaking at a time. Carmen was able to translate only three or four words before someone else demanded that she tell me something. It was usually Luis. Frequently, Carmen said that his comments couldn't be translated into English, but said it in a way that suggested that what he was saying couldn't be translated without using words that her priest would have objected to.

Pepe caught my eye and discreetly gestured at his watch, indicating that if I had questions for him I should try to get on with it by gently ignoring Luis. Pepe seemed like someone's kindly grandfather with his pockets full of candies. He certainly did not come across as a heartless killer. He explained that at first there were many people opposed to the Ruddy Duck cull in Spain, including some biologists. He described fears in the early years of shooting hybrids in case they were, instead, pure White-headed Ducks. But Pepe and Chiqui had never got it wrong. Given this confidence, they now went with the familiar motto of "If in doubt, kill it!" Pepe told me about a trip to northern Spain where he had killed eleven Ruddy Ducks on a single pond. This was Basque country, and travelling around with a car full of guns was a dangerous proposition.

Carmen was called on to translate increasingly subtle concepts. Pepe explained that he had always been a hunter and had killed just about everything, but had long since traded in his gun for a camera, except when called upon by his position. Since he had shot more Ruddy Ducks than anyone else, I asked if he felt proud about his involvement, as I had been told others did. He said it was more a matter of completing a task; it was part of his job. Shooting a duck sitting on the water is difficult, and luck is often involved. For him it was a matter of mathematics, taking into account the wind, waves, and distance as the duck moved in three dimensions. Sometimes he killed the duck with his first shot and sometimes with the fifteenth. I asked if he, the expert, would go to England to kill Ruddy Ducks if asked. He said that he would go if told to by his boss.

Pepe told me that the man responsible for the release of Ruddy Ducks in Britain was Peter Scott. I finally had a name to go with the act, and when I started looking into Scott, was surprised that I hadn't stumbled across him before. Scott had won an Olympic medal in yachting, and was a British gliding champion. Serving as a lieutenant commander in WWII, Scott had come away with an M.B.E. and a D.S.C. An early conservationist, he had founded the Wildfowl Trust and was chairman and one of the founders of the World Wildlife Fund. Scott was knighted in 1973 for his service to the environment.

It wasn't all sunshine and light though. Somewhere around 1948, Scott imported three pair of Ruddy Ducks from North America to a reserve on the Severn estuary in England, where they commenced breeding. The plan was to trim the wing feathers of all the ducks to keep them from escaping. Could anyone possibly fail to see what would happen next? Because Ruddy Ducks are so good at avoiding capture, not all the young ducks had their wings clipped, and by 1952 or 1953 some had escaped. You know the rest.

Luis was clearly disappointed that he had lost his audience. He poked at me until I turned to face him and then asked if I spoke French. I said that I spoke *un peu*. He then demanded that I do so, so I launched into a sentence about my desire for an additional glass of white wine. He cut me off, insisted that I was doing it wrong, and used his own ten words of the language to attempt to construct a sentence. Very badly. He then went off on a tangent about all women being the same after the lights had gone off. I felt sorry for Carmen, as he insisted that she translate his vulgar opinions. I put away my notebook hoping that he would shut up if he saw that I was no longer writing.

It didn't work. Luis claimed that he was insulted because he had not been contacted for an interview about Ruddy and White-headed ducks. He was also "pissed off" (I suspect Carmen of cleaning up the language) in general about people who claimed to know about these ducks when they didn't go into the field to study them.

He was also "pissed off" because those I had spoken to were not, in his opinion, reliable sources of information. This all came as he blew cigarette smoke in my face. I was getting rather pissed off myself. As I sipped my wine, Luis jabbed his finger in front of my face, making point after point. I wanted to bite his finger, but feared nicotine poisoning. When Pepe got up to leave, Carmen and I took the opportunity to slip away.

After a late dinner, Carmen returned to her room, while I went for one more walk through the streets of El Rocío. I was trying to put in order all my thoughts of ducks and Spain. I was also trying to ward off homesickness. Then I stopped in front of the church of the Virgin of El Rocío. Despite the darkened skies above, House Martins were still foraging furiously for insects attracted to the cathedral's bright lights illuminating the plaza. I realized that my Ruddy Duck story wasn't quite complete.

THERE ARE TIMES when I don't want to know all sides of the story. Ignorance makes decisiveness so much easier. It was clear that I shouldn't leave the story of the White-headed Duck without hearing more about the opposition to the Ruddy Duck cull in England.

I arrived at Ebenezer Hall in Tonbridge, Kent, in time for the appointment I had made months before, but had trouble convincing myself that I was in the right place. The address I had been given was for the Old Chapel in Bradford Street, and this was the only old chapel in the neighbourhood, but I couldn't find a sign to confirm my destination. When I walked right up to the building, I found two windows that were discreetly etched with the words "Animal Aid," but they weren't visible unless I stood in exactly the right place. A much more obvious sign announced "Notice: Employees Only." I tried the door and found it locked. I pushed a button and introduced myself to the ethereal voice at the other end. The voice buzzed me in.

Andrew Tyler was the director of Animal Aid, an agency dedicated to an end to animal abuse and the promotion of a cruelty-free lifestyle. Tyler wore a polo shirt over a T-shirt, and sported a small earring. He greeted me into his office by saying he hadn't been sure whether I would be coming. I checked my watch. "We said eleven o'clock on the 28th, right?" I asked. Perhaps he wasn't sure whether I was serious about the whole thing. Tyler's was a wonderful office, as cluttered as mine, and with the perfect admixture of professional paperwork and personal items.

As our discussion began, Tyler seemed on edge. The better part of his edginess might have been the result of his anxiety about a dog that was at the veterinarian for an eye operation; Tyler was waiting for the call about the outcome. Beyond this, I wasn't sure—perhaps he was accustomed to being treated as something of a nutter, the director of an organization that some would say was full of nutters. I asked a couple of general questions to get us started. Tyler explained that fourteen people worked in the offices, but he didn't introduce me to any of them. It may be the sort of place where names are not disclosed without a good reason.

I explained that I was interested in the nature of the opposition to the Ruddy Duck cull in Britain, having spoken to so many people in Spain who were heartily supportive. I leaned back in my chair, notepad and pencil ready, and let Tyler speak.

He told me about Tom Gullick, a leading English ornithologist living in Spain, who had first alerted the Spanish government to the plight of the White-headed Duck after doing surveys in about 1973. Initially Gullick was not opposed to the Ruddy Duck cull, but later came to think of it as a scandalous use of limited conservation funding and described it as a pointless and expensive massacre. I wasn't familiar with a leading English ornithologist named Tom Gullick. I was familiar only with a Tom Gullick widely regarded as the world's most eminent birdwatcher.

Tyler went on to express the opinion that too many people had now "stuck their necks too far above the parapet" to admit that they were wrong about the need to kill Ruddy Ducks to protect White-headed Ducks. He claimed that the White-headed Duck had become fetishized; the cull was no longer about saving the species but designed only to save reputations. Tyler suggested that conservation issues like the White-headed Duck situation can lead to a feeling of impotence that can be circumvented, in part, by killing Ruddy Ducks. "It's politics. It's religion. It's potency." What we lacked, according to Tyler, was people with sufficient competence and wit to actually fix the problem. We constantly co-opt and reconstitute nature and wildlife with a desire to see the animals of our youth, even though we have so radically transformed the landscape that everything is out of balance.

Tyler claimed that the media in Britain had two types of stories when it came to Ruddy Ducks. The first was about the great cost involved in culling Ruddy Ducks. The second was about randy Ruddy Ducks seducing White-headed Ducks in Spain.

I was following the thread, but then Tyler seemed to fall off the tracks a bit. He claimed that at the heart of the Ruddy Duck cull was a desire to help a cherished species because it was threatened by a foreign species. We simply weren't able to tolerate two species. "If they are close enough to hybridize, it doesn't matter. It's killing in the name of blood purity." He used the word "fascistic" to describe the situation, and then told me to cross it out of my notes, which I did. But then he went on to use the word four times more, and I felt justified including it.

Tyler then spoke in general terms about the opposition of members of Animal Aid to actions of this sort. He said that those with even a basic understanding of the issues see an administration that supports and facilitates the killing of wildlife for profit. He cited the example of pheasants and partridge, which are produced in the tens of millions in the UK so that they can be shot. Native stoats, ferrets, foxes, and hedgehogs are considered "vermin" because they interfere with the production of game birds.

"So people in this country see a regime that supports agriculture over nature, and then they hear that we kill Ruddy Ducks on the nest because of a duck that they have never seen, whose numbers are reduced by hunting and habitat destruction." I was starting to understand his visceral opposition to the cull.

"I find the whole business of genetic purity . . ." He let the sentence trail off, and I think he felt he was getting too close to making an inflammatory parallel. Instead he took a different tack and made a particularly salient point. He explained that the British population of Ruddy Ducks had grown from a very small founding population. Unless all the Ruddy Ducks are eradicated in all European and African countries where they are currently found, then the eradication endeavour was pointless.

"Logistically it can't be done," said Tyler. "Morally it is vile, politically it is cynical, and the whole proposition is . . ."—Tyler paused to let me catch up and to collect his thoughts—". . . an absurd and gross objective through killing. Eradicating the impure," he said, "is foul, absurd, and doomed to failure." I think that Tyler, and perhaps other members of Animal Aid, see animal rights activism as an extension of a grander social conscience. He spoke of how a culture can be completely intolerant of behaviours like kicking a dog, but comfortable with a state that subsidizes and supports vivisection and the mass production of farm animals.

I then asked Tyler an impossible question, and apologized for asking it. "If a button could be pressed, eliminating all Ruddy Ducks in Europe and Africa without causing any suffering, could you and other members of Animal Aid support the action?" Tyler stared at me, and I couldn't tell if he was formulating an answer, or irritated at being asked a question without an answer. He prefaced his response by saying that it was something of a cop-out. He said that suffering *is* involved in the Ruddy Duck cull. Some people, himself included, feel that suffering is the bottom line. However, people need to face up to the consequences of greedy and stupid use of the world. On the other hand, one needs to be practical and pragmatic when dealing with animal issues. For Tyler, the bottom line is that the cull shouldn't proceed; the cull is scapegoating. "If we want the benefits, let's do it without the killing. We can still obsess about the White-headed Duck."

I HAD SET OUT TO HAVE A BIT OF FUN with ducks. Instead I was left trying to juggle pieces of a subtle issue complicated by endless technical aspects and charged with emotion. Was it even possible to summarize the story?

From 100,000 individuals a century ago, the White-headed Duck was on its way out, the result of galloping habitat destruction and unsustainable hunting. Although the species is by no means out of trouble yet, with continued declines in the global population and an "endangered" designation granted by the IUCN, significant progress has been made, particularly in Spain, where its numbers are increasing. It was absolutely wrong to bring Ruddy Ducks from North America to Britain, but the act was completed without malice and in a different age with different perspectives, and no one could have foreseen hybridization with White-headed Ducks in Spain. Ruddy Ducks came along at exactly the wrong time for the White-headed Duck. To anyone with a background in the biological sciences, there can be no doubt that the White-headed Duck is a distinct biological entity and worthy of preservation. Although the position is not incontestable, it seems that the genetic integrity of the White-headed Duck is threatened by Ruddy Ducks, although the ultimate extent of the threat is not currently knowable. The heart of White-headed Duck recovery efforts is currently in Spain, but the long-term future of the species also depends on efforts in other jurisdictions.

This is a human-created problem, and nature is not responsible; it is irrelevant that ducks frequently hybridize when placed in unnatural circumstances. Is the problem insurmountable? I have no idea, but I do recognize that White-headed Ducks are now important beyond themselves, as a flagship species for conservation efforts. I also saw the interactions between Ruddy and White-headed ducks as a near-perfect example of the unforeseen and perhaps unforeseeable consequences of introduced species.

THERE ARE TIMES WHEN I THINK that God is giving Himself a good laugh by making me run around in circles. His latest circle was going to take me to the vanishingly small village of Peakirk, north of Peterborough in central England. Five months after I left Britain, I found out that Sir Peter Scott had, half a century earlier, set up a waterfowl centre in Peakirk, and had managed to convince a publican to change the name of his pub from The Black Bull to The Ruddy Duck. I had done everything else I could possibly think of associated with the Ruddy Duck; surely I had to drink a pint at the pub that bore its name.

Regrettably, my next opportunity came more than a year later, a week before Christmas, and a day after what locals described as the worst winter storm to hit the British Isles since the invention of weather. Three centimetres of snow, a bit of slush, fog, and temperatures about ten degrees below normal . . . the kind of thing that brings Europeans to their knees. Lisa and I were travelling together and managed to convince John and Joyce Chaperon to join us. John and Joyce are my only remaining relatives in the UK, although I am not exactly sure what our relationship is. We are second cousins or something like that.

Despite the predictions of frustration, calamity, and imminent demise by the BBC's morning news, Lisa and I caught the train north to Peterborough from Kings Cross, and John and Joyce came across from Leicester. From the train station we caught a cab to Peakirk and plonked ourselves down for lunch at The Ruddy Duck Free House & Dining Rooms.

I am not the sort to arrive unannounced, elbow my way up to the bar, and ask a bunch of foolish questions. What would my mother say? I had, instead, written to the owners of The Ruddy Duck two months in advance telling them about my quest and proposing a date on which they might take a minute or two to speak to me. They had ignored me. Or perhaps my letter had become lost in the post. They had probably just ignored me.

When John and I found our way to the bar to order lunch, Sue Ruddy did not immediately make me love her.

"Are you a senior citizen?" she asked. "We have a seniors' menu."

I wanted to say, "No, I'm bloody well not. Sod off!" but felt this might be an unwise opening salvo. Instead I said, "No, I'm

Canadian. We all look like this." After a thoroughly enjoyable lunch of roast lamb, mixed grill, lasagna, trifle, crème brûlée, roast apples, and cheesecake, washed down with wine and beer, Sue spoke with me about her establishment.

Andy and Sue Ruddy had moved to Peakirk to manage The Ruddy Duck in June of 2003, and when the owners were ready to sell up a year later they gave them first refusal. Given their surname, it seemed as though fate was involved. Sue explained that the pub side of the establishment had formerly been a row of four two-storey seventeenth-century cottages, but these had been knocked together at some point in the past. Despite being a listed building, recognized for its special historical significance, it wasn't clear exactly when the cottages had become a pub. The restaurant side of the establishment had been added later.

"Have you ever seen a live Ruddy Duck?" I asked.

"No, I don't think I have."

I explained that they were beautiful birds in the flesh, and that the antics of a male in search of a mate were quite charming. I then asked if she knew about the controversy surrounding the Ruddy Duck in Britain. She said that she had heard that they were "naughty ducks, and not well-liked." I expanded on the story, telling her about the difficulties with White-headed Ducks in Spain.

She pulled a framed document down from the wall. It was a typed sheet of paper that had been created "On the Occasion of the Opening of the 'Ruddy Duck' on 30 October 1964." It consisted of a long list of alternative names for the Ruddy Duck, taken from a book about waterfowl by F. H. Kortright, and may have been presented to the pub by Sir Peter himself. Among the names listed were Buck-Ruddy, Chuck Duck, Greaser, Shot Pouch, Biddy, Hard Head, Spike-tail, Stub-and-Twist, Wiretail, Creek Coot, Dip-tail Diver, and Bumblebee Buzzer. Given the amorous successes of the Ruddy Duck in Spain, my favourite name on the list was Stiffy.

Sue explained that Peakirk's waterfowl centre had closed down eight or nine years earlier and had since become overgrown. While we waited for a taxi to take us back to Peterborough, Lisa, Joyce,

John, and I strolled toward the site. A couple of Mallards flew over-head. Ruddy Ducks were nowhere to be seen. I suspect that soon there won't be Ruddy Ducks anywhere in Europe.

CHAPTER ELEVEN

If You Have Snails, Blame the Romans

REASON NUMBER ELEVEN FOR INTRODUCING A FOREIGN SPECIES: BECAUSE THEY TASTED SO GOOD BACK HOME.

IT WAS AUGUST OF 55 BCE, and Julius Caesar found himself a long way from home. Three years earlier he had been appointed governor and military commander of the province of Gaul, and had spent the time enlarging the Roman empire to include major chunks of western Europe. And so, instead of soaking up the Mediterranean sun with his wife at his side and a glass of fine wine in his hand, he found himself on the dreary eastern side of the English Channel, staring across at the White Cliffs of Dover. Great Britain sat there, just waiting to be conquered.

Caesar could think of at least three good reasons to run roughshod over the island. He knew of Britain's substantial mining operations, particularly rich in tin and copper. Then there was talk of abundant corn crops, which would help to feed his hungry troops. Finally, Caesar was getting damned ticked off at Britain as a source of fierce Celtic warriors who sailed across to the mainland to help in ongoing resistance to the Roman occupation. And so, with about 10,000 soldiers, Caesar sailed northwest with mischief in his heart.

The operation immediately started to go wrong. When Caesar's ships sailed up to the cliffs at Dover, they found them lined with angry British warriors spoiling for a fight. When Caesar sailed the few kilómetres north to the pebbled beaches near Deal, his troops encountered a large British force equipped with horse-drawn war chariots, something that Caesar's army was notably lacking. But the Romans persisted and managed a foothold. When Caesar's cavalry tried to cross the channel to reinforce the foot troops a few days later, they were driven back to Gaul by bad weather. That same storm damaged many of Caesar's ships on the British beach, and so the whole crew beat a sane and strategic retreat.

Caesar was back in July of the following year with even more men, more horses, and a full picnic lunch. Their landing was unopposed; seeing the size of the invading army, the British retreated inland with Caesar hot on their heels. Mighty battles raged while another summer storm bashed the Roman ships. The British tribes proved unexpectedly resilient and news came to Caesar of troubles needing his attention back in Gaul. And so in September, with Britain thoroughly unconquered, Caesar and his legions turned around and buggered off back to the mainland. He would have to wait ten years, six months before being named Dictator Perpetuus of the Roman empire, and ten years, seven months before being stabbed to death by sixty of his closest friends.

The world continued to spin around the sun. But the Romans hadn't entirely forgotten about Britain. Details are a little sketchy, but it seems that, as Emperor of Rome, Gaius Caligula marched his troops to the English Channel in 39 CE and had them attack the seas and collect seashells as evidence of his victory over the god Neptune. Some see this as evidence of Caligula's madness. Others claim that the seashells story is a result of a mistranslation, and that Caligula either had his troops collect small boats or dismissed his men to indulge in the offerings of local brothels. Ancient languages are a devil to translate properly. Unlike Caesar, after his aborted attempt to subdue the British, Caligula had to wait only two years before being stabbed to death by his chums.

But in 43 CE, at the order of Emperor Claudius and under the command of General Aulus Platius, Roman troops came storming back, crossed the English Channel, set up shop at Richborough, and settled in for a good long stay. When the Romans left Britain for good, nearly four centuries later, they left behind a peculiar little life form they had introduced from Gaul.

IN THE LATE 1990s, plans for a housing estate a few kilometres from Ashford in Kent required a survey to make certain that the bulldozers weren't going to rip up anything important. A group of archaeologists found the remains of a previously undocumented Roman town. Probably not the ritziest of villages in the Roman empire, it was still a substantial settlement, covering roughly the same area as six Olympic-sized swimming pools. By the time news of the rediscovered Roman town hit the press, archaeologists had recovered 3,000 artifacts. Most of these were the typical roof-tiles-and-cooking-pots sort of thing, but among the artifacts was a living, breathing population of edible snails. They are common in France and known variously in Britain as Roman snails, Burgundy snails, and apple snails. Not considered the very best of candidates to beat the record for swimming across the English Channel, it seems a lot more likely that the snails were brought to Britain by the occupying Romans. The Romans had long since left, but 1,600 years later the snails remained. Unlike the Romans, the snails hadn't any notion of expanding their empire, and so they persist in just a few locations on the chalk-rich soils of southeast England, and if you know where to look you can see them to this day. I knew where to look and was off to find them.

While conducting earlier research on Labrador Ducks, I had become friends with a British vandal named Errol Fuller. To my delight, Errol had agreed to join me for the first wave of my Roman adventure. Living in Tunbridge Wells, not so far from the chalky downs of Kent, he told me that if I could get from Gatwick Airport to his local train station, he would pick me up, catch me up, and join me in my snail quest the next morning. The trouble was that

Errol never quite got the hang of doing nothing, or even doing one thing at a time, and so he had double-booked himself. As well as being due to pick me up at the train station, Errol was due to make a presentation on Dodos to a natural history society in Cambridge. In his place, Errol had arranged for his lovely girlfriend, Cath Wallis, to pick me up and entertain me until he got back.

Cath and I set off for a country pub, The Spotted Dog, which had apparently been a rather rough place in its day. The rough edges had long since been polished, and we found the car park occupied by only the most genteel automobiles. Most of the patrons sported dinner jackets and posh jumpers. A roast dinner for two was on offer for £43, but that didn't seem to include drinks, so Cath and I settled for white wine and bitter ale instead. We sat at a table overlooking a small, quiet, wooded valley and talked about life.

INTEREST IN ROMAN SNAILS does not end at the tables of snooty restaurants. Research papers on the species appear in scholarly journals at a rate of about fifty per year. Most of these fall into one of two categories. Neurologists are interested in the properties of nerves of Roman snails, and biochemists are keen on the chemicals that these molluscs produce; some may have commercial or medical applications. Most of these publications are pretty opaque, but the Roman snail paper with the most tortured title must be "Solid-phase synthesis of a pentavalent GaINAc-containing glyocopeptide (Tn antigen) representing the nephropathy-associated IgA hinge region."

As a bird biologist by training, I had absolutely no idea how tricky it might be to find snails, or to distinguish one type of snail from another. I had purchased a guide to snails of the British Isles, which described Roman snails, *Helix pomatia,* as "creamy-white, very opaque, usually with a few faint, broad, pale brown spiral bands," which seemed to me to describe 85 percent of the British public. The guide went on to describe the shell as having "coarse growth lines, but no wrinkles. Adult shells usually more than 35 millimetres wide." I was after the biggest snail species in the British Isles.

The guide explained that although it is an introduced species, the Roman snail is both rare and protected because it is collected for food; they apparently have a subtle, slightly grassy taste. The guide also explained that my snail was confined to just a few calcareous districts in the south of England. Luckily, Jan Light, president of the Conchological Society of Great Britain and Ireland, had given me precise map coordinates of Roman snail sightings.

Even though Errol had arrived home from Cambridge very late the previous evening, he was willing to make an early start of it. And so, equipped with maps provided by the good people at the British Ordnance Survey, the three of us piled into Errol's Nissan Tino and set off. The car was well adorned with items whose immediate function was not apparent. Put more simply, the vehicle was full of rubbish. I shovelled myself a spot to sit in.

Out of Tunbridge Wells, we took the A21 north and the M25 west toward London. At the A226b turnoff we headed north through the villages of Cheatingham and Wrecksley. A left and two rights brought us to an unsigned car park. We had arrived at Broadshield Downs, one of the best spots in Britain to look for Roman snails.

We set off along a trail between oak woodlands and cultivated fields, poking and peeking into the trail-side shrubbery every few steps, each keen to be the first to see a really big snail. It was cool and breezy as the morning tried to decide between low cloud and high fog. This seemed like perfect weather for snails, if not for Romans. As we wandered, Errol claimed that, as a child, he and his father had come across gigantic snails at Marley Hill, Knebworth. Looking them up later in a book, Errol's father had concluded that they must have been Roman snails.

And then, between the nettles, I spotted what must surely be the creature we were after. Creamy-white, opaque, no wrinkles . . . Was it really a Roman snail, or could it be Britain's second-largest snail, *Helix aspersa?* In order to be certain, I pulled calipers out of my pocket to measure the shell's width. Forty-two millimetres across—there was no doubt about it. I had found a Roman snail. I wanted a photograph to commemorate the occasion, and so Errol and Cath kindly nudged the nettles out of the way with their shoes. I used a pencil to carefully move aside the last stalk, but nettles are inherently evil creatures and I got stung pretty badly.

We wandered on and Errol found himself a snail. He rubbed in his success by saying, "Only one member of our merry little band hasn't found one yet!" Cath soon got her own back by finding a field full of them. Or at least we assumed that the field was full of them; their empty shells were scattered everywhere, but given the abundance of nettles, we weren't willing to risk our hides on a very careful investigation for their live counterparts. Errol expressed disappointment at the size of the snails, claiming that they had been much larger when he had seen them as a ten-year-old. He speculated that we might have stumbled across a population of hybrids instead of pure Roman snails. Errol speculates about a lot of things.

It was a pity that snails have such rudimentary eyes, because the landscape was truly lovely. Oaks dominate, but the coniferous yew trees made a pretty good show. The ground was rich in great nodules of flint that reminded me of knucklebones. And, sure enough, chalk outcrops broke through the soil in places. I speculated that constructing so large a calcareous shell would require snails to feast on a calcium-rich diet. But even the beautiful view couldn't keep my mind off the burning of my hand from the nettle stings. Cath gathered up and crushed some dock leaves. I suppose that every child in Britain knows that dock grows close to nettles, and that the juice from the crushed leaves of the former relieves the sting from the latter. It was news to me, but it certainly seemed to work.

Errol is, in some ways, magical. For instance, he seems to get by on very little food, with long, long periods between meals. Even though he had a refrigerator the size of a walk-in closet, there never seemed to be much in it. At Errol's house, breakfast never appeared to be on offer.

It was rapidly approaching noon, and Cath and I convinced the magician to stop for lunch at a pub in Wrecksley. Then, having seen the snails and consumed some beer, I was keen to learn more about the Romans who brought the snails to Britain. We set off for Lullingstone near the town of Eynsford, site of what may be the best-preserved Roman villa in Britain.

It seems that this particular villa was constructed shortly after the 43 CE invasion and was in continuous use for the better part of 350 years before being gutted by fire in the fifth century. Excavation had provided evidence of both cult worship and early Christian prayer, with shrines converted to Christian chapels. The villa had a verandah, a three-room bathing complex, underfloor heating, and magnificent mosaics on the floors of the reception room and dining hall. Today, the excavated remains of the villa are all under a protective cover that reminded me of a giant garden shed.

Looking at a painted reconstruction of what the villa might have looked like, Errol said, "I bet it didn't look anything like that. It looks like a modern housing development." In a sense, it did. Perhaps the Romans were particularly forward-looking in terms of housing.

We viewed a lead coffin decorated with scallop shell symbols that housed the remains of a twenty-five-year-old man who had stood roughly five foot ten inches. We also saw a fourth-century goose, buried for good luck. The burial of an Alsatian-sized dog had probably not been ceremonial. Although this had been the residence of a well-to-do family, they had not been invulnerable to heartache; we saw a display of the skeletons of three newborn infants.

The walls of the villa had been constructed of flint boulders. Signs indicated that this section had been a verandah, this bit had been a living room, with bedrooms over there. After nearly two millennia of neglect, you had to use your imagination. There was an interesting sequence of rooms labelled as the bath block. Bathing was apparently a big deal to the Romans; it was a shame they hadn't got the hang of soap the way the Brits had. From what I read, I gathered that occupying the dining room involved a lot of reclining on cushions. Eating preceded orgiastic behaviour by about five minutes.

Peering down a well, I found it contained a wide assortment of coins dating to the rule of Emperor QEII. I spotted a bench plaque dedicated to Josephine Birchenough (1920–1994), widow of Edwyn, co-discoverer of the site. I suspect that the Romans had discovered the site long before Edwyn, and the paleolithic people of Britain may have had something to say about the Roman "discovery."

The best part of the villa was the beautiful and elaborate mosaic floor. Designs would have been chosen from a pattern book. Among these designs, often repeated in the mosaic tiles, were swastikas, which held no special negative association before being adopted by Nazis. Errol noted that the gift shop's postcards of the mosaic floors had been very carefully doctored to remove or de-emphasize the swastikas.

As we prepared to leave, Cath explained that she always found sites like this a bit of an anticlimax. She fully appreciated the significance of such spots, but when only the foundations remain, she is left with a lust for more. She was cheered a bit as we drove down Lullingstone Lane and back to Eynsford; the bells of St. Martin were pealing, celebrating a wedding.

That evening, Errol and I descended on The Weavers for a pint and the opportunity to sort out the world. The pub was surprisingly crowded with rather intoxicated gentlemen dealing with the outcome of both the FA Cup, won by Liverpool, and the Scottish Cup, won by Hearts of Midlothian. The local chaps had bet on the wrong team in both matches. Even though they were on the punch-up side of the fine line between sober and sloshed, I knew I had nothing to fear. Errol is just the sort of companion you want on your side if things get rough.

ACCORDING TO MY EDITION of *The Joy of Cooking*, ancient Romans were addicted to snails, which they raised on ranches. At this point I conjure images of snailboys and snailgirls eating beans around a campfire after a day or lassoing and branding . . . but perhaps that is just me. Admittedly these are big snails, but the effort required to prepare them for consumption barely seems worth the trouble. First they are starved for a couple of days to allow them to poop out whatever noxious material they have been eating. Then they are fed nothing but fresh lettuce leaves for two weeks. When the time is right for a feast, you scrub and scrub them until no more slime is apparent. A Roman snail would, presumably, make a lot of slime. There is no talk of a merciful death. Rather, the snail's operculum, which it uses to lock itself in the shell, is sliced off. They are then placed into several rinses of water and vinegar. Apparently, if this isn't enough to make the snail poke its head out of its shell, you chuck it away. They get boiled for five minutes, ripped out of their shells, cooked until tender, seasoned, and then put back in their shells for presentation. And just before you eat one, remember that a snail is just a slug with a house.

Every time I arrive in Canterbury, my first stop is the gates of Canterbury Cathedral, at the heart of the old city. I took advantage of a bench near the cathedral to catch up on my notes. An elderly lady, laden with shopping bags, took the spot next to mine. As I scribbled, she pulled a few slices of bread from her bag to feed to pigeons. We were both immediately overwhelmed by the flurry of dozens of wings. She apologized by saying, "There were just three of them. They must tell each other." I reassured her that pigeons do not faze me at all, and speculated that the flock may have spied her loaf of bread and followed her, waiting for a generous feeling to settle on her.

"Oh," she said, hearing my accent. "You must be American." When I corrected her, she went on to explain that Canadians had been a big presence in Canterbury during WWII. A group of them had been billeted next door to her, "And they were always so nice!" I laughed and suggested that this was exactly the image Canadians go for. We love everyone and want to be loved by everyone.

In Canterbury, you can't dig a hole without hitting something left behind by the Romans. Even Canterbury Cathedral was built on the remains of a Roman temple. And not far from the cathedral walls lay one of the best examples of pre-Christian Canterbury— the Roman Museum. Down the stairs to a level below the streets of the pilgrim city, I entered a time long before Chaucer's pilgrims arrived.

The setting was vaguely eerie. Not because of dim lighting and creaking floorboards, but because I was the only patron. It was just me, the displays, and the soft hum of air conditioning. On display were harness fittings and buckles and amulets and coins with the image of Emperor Caligula. Carefully arranged behind glass were an oak and iron Roman spade, clothing fasteners, bone hairpins, and pottery weights. It was all starting to look like every other museum of archaeological artifacts that I had ever seen. Building tiles and plaster and beakers and bottles and a lead drainpipe. Not that every bit of it was dusty and dry; the museum had a large, cool green bottle holding the cremated remains of a twenty-year-old woman from the second century. Of course it made me wonder how they determined the era, age, and sex of the deceased from ashes. *CSI Canterbury.*

On display were bits and bobs from a household shrine, contributed in memory of the late Dr. Frank Jenkins. Among these items was a small, headless, footless statuette of a naked woman. Someone had chosen to display the figurine back-to-front, so that the naughty bits could be seen only by craning my neck. I suppose the best bit of the museum was the tiled floor of a Roman house. It really was a nice bit of tile work. Sixteen hundred years of shifting ground had turned an originally flat floor into a rigid bouncy castle. The sign indicated that the house had been occupied from 70 CE to 380.

So here is what I gathered about the city of Canterbury from the museum's plaques and displays. Before Caesar's arrival, there had been no Canterbury. At the time, Britons lived in small homesteads, not cities. There was a hill fort at Bigbury with ditches and ramparts for defence. In 54 BCE, Caesar and his bullies stopped briefly at what was to become Canterbury, and were impressed by the locals. According to Caesar, they fought naked and painted themselves blue.

When the next Roman crew arrived in 43 CE, they found

Durovernum, the settlement of a local leader. Recognizing the strategic importance of controlling the crossing of the River Stour, they threw together a fort and named it Durovernum Cantiacorum, which translates as the marshy, alder tree grove of Cantii. Within a century, the Romans had erected a honking great settlement, with a town hall, marketplace, temple, theatre, public baths, another temple (now buried under Canterbury Cathedral), and several cemeteries. The city was home to soldiers, merchants, visiting traders, labourers, slaves, and the whole sort of general mishmash. By 300 CE, the layout of Canterbury had been established by a girdling wall, and that layout persists today.

But nothing lasts forever, including the Roman occupation of Britain. On display in the Roman museum was a lovely set of silverware that had been buried by someone waiting for safer days to return to the region. Instead, the treasure lay buried for 1,550 years until it was exposed by road works. If the world were a kind and gentle place, Roman Canterbury would have slowly evolved into the modern Christian Canterbury. Instead, when the Romans pulled out in 410 CE, disorder ruled, and the town disappeared. Buildings decayed and streets became overgrown. The defensive walls and massive theatre remained, but everything else got covered over by time. A century later, a new town sprang up and was named Cantwaraburg. The Pope's missionaries arrived in 597 to meet with the local honcho, King Ethelbert. The king's wife was Christian, and so he allowed Christianity to establish a foothold in Britain.

When it comes to aimless wandering, Canterbury is one of my favourite targets. It is certainly not the only city in Europe whose streets change names every few steps, but it is one of the best. I offer as evidence the section of pavement named, from northwest to southeast, Whitstable Road, St. Dunstan's Street, St. Peter's Street, High Street, The Parade, St. George's Street, and St. George's Place before finally settling on New Dover Road. My favourite example involves a short street with a single name change; just east of the city walls, Love Lane turns seamlessly into Monastery Street. I can easily spend a day walking in lazy circles, peering into shop windows. The window display of *Dickies Suit Hire for Men and Boys* featured a lovely assortment of lavender and lime-coloured formal gowns. When Canterbury shops close for the evening, I can always head for a Canterbury pub. And usually do.

The Three Tuns is situated almost exactly at the centre of the old walled Roman city of Canterbury. The pub is at the intersection of Castle Street, St. Margaret's, Beer Cart Lane, and Watling Street. I would soon be looking for the other end of Watling Street at Richborough. Painted on the pub's outside wall were the words:

The Three Tuns Hotel. 15th Century Inn. This Inn lies on the site of Canterbury's Roman Theatre which was built around AD 80 (About the same time as the Coliseum in Rome) it was rebuilt in about AD 210 as one of the largest Theatres in Britain. The walls were mainly robbed out by the 11th and 12th centuries but much still survives below ground today.

I had walked past The Three Tuns many times since my first visit to Canterbury as a child, but I had never been in. It was time for a drink.

Under the low, low ceiling, I found two punters with pints on one side of the bar and a barman propping up the other. I ordered a pint of Spitfire and waited for an opening in the conversation. I jumped in when the talk turned to diamonds. Jim, a forty-six-year-old decorator and painter, claimed that the price of diamonds was so high because all of the diamonds in the world were controlled by De Beers. I stepped in and explained that large diamond mines had recently opened in northern Canada, and that to the best of my knowledge, they were not owned by De Beers.

From there, the conversation swerved wildly from employment to football to women to ancestry. Joe, unmarried and somewhere in his mid-twenties, was of uncertain profession, but after finding out that I had spent considerable time in Glasgow, told me that he was a big supporter of the Celtic football squad. Although he wasn't absolutely clear on the matter, Joe implied that he was of Romany descent. Jim the painter explained that he was currently working on a retirement complex. He had a thirteen-year-old daughter who wanted to be a dentist, and an eight-year-old daughter who had properly put off major career decisions until after she had all her permanent teeth.

We were soon joined by another local, Brian, who, despite making a late entry, seemed entirely more inebriated than anyone else. He steered the conversation toward the relative merits of various Kent communities. He described Faversham, west of Canterbury, as "Chaversham," which I gather is some sort of insult. Brian went on to explain that the worst place in all of Kent was the Isle of Sheppey, north of Faversham. In a just world, explained Brian, the British government would blow up the bridge to the Isle of Sheppey. Then it would blow up Sheppey. He also wasn't very nice to the Isle of Thanet, source of many of my genes, but I let this slide.

When Jim was ready for another pint of Guinness, he also got in a pint of Fosters for Joe and a pint of Spitfire for me. He wisely avoided getting Brian anything further to drink. Jim asked, "So you said that you were a biologist?" I confirmed that I was. He went on to explain that his elderly father was suffering from pernicious anemia, and asked if I knew what that was. I explained that his father's guts were not absorbing sufficient vitamin B_{12}, so he was having difficulty creating red blood cells. As is so typical, physicians and nurses had told Jim about his father's treatment, injections of B_{12}, but had not told him what was actually wrong or why treatment was necessary.

"Michael" the barman was not officially working at The Three Tuns, but helping out a friend and taking his pay under the table. Michael claimed that he hadn't done well at his first go at college; I suggested that he have another go at it when he felt the time was right. When he heard that I was interested in Roman Britain, he gestured in the air, indicating that the stage of the Roman theatre had been about here, and that the audience would have been seated over there. Despite my entirely unsubtle hints, Michael did not invite me to go down to the cellar to see the foundations of the amphitheatre. Even after I bought him a drink.

It was just a bit early to return to my hotel room, so I walked down Castle Street to Canterbury Cathedral. It was closed for the night, but the few attendants didn't seem to mind as I walked through the gates and stood looking up at the cathedral's west end. I stood staring until my feet hurt.

IF YOU THOUGHT that the ancient Romans got up to a lot of mischief after dark, they were nothing compared to molluscs. Members of some species are both male and female at the same time, which must make them doubly disappointed when they spend Saturday night alone. Many start life as males, but go through a transformation as they age, changing into females or back into males. Some spend years in therapy.

When it comes to sexual shenanigans, creatures like the Roman snail really know how to make things complicated. Even though individuals are hermaphrodites, when it comes to copulation, one acts as a male and the other as a female. This is usually based on which one likes chocolate more. The pair then dance in a circle, kissing and touching tentacles, before intertwining their bodies. In the vagina is a sac that makes a bony harpoon. The individual acting as the male pierces the body wall of its partner with the spicule to stimulate her/him/it. Ensuing copulation involves a lot of mucous.

I was working my way from west to east, following the River Stour downstream, and back in time to the earliest days of the Roman presence in Britain. In essence, I was looking for the origin of my snails. I might have started at Deal, where Caesar had first landed, but that effort had been an aborted attempt. I might have gone to France to meet the snails on their home turf, but I took it as given that edible snails existed there. Instead, I hopped on the 112 coach that took me out of Canterbury and east along the A257, following the track of the Romans to the origin of Watling Street.

During their time in Great Britain, the Romans had constructed 13,000 kilometres of roads. The very first, Watling Street, started at their coastal base at Richborough, proceeded west through Canterbury and past The Three Tuns, on to London, and then ran northwest to Wroxeter. I wanted to see the oldest end of that street.

The double-decker coach took me through Littlebourne, Wigham, Shatterling, Brambling, and Ash backward in time to 43 CE. Much as it had been two millennia earlier, this was agricultural land, rich in hay and grain, stubble and rapeseed, potatoes, and ornamental nurseries. Each town had a church, a chiropodist, a butcher, two florists, three pubs, four cottages with thatched roofs, a chemist, an Indian takeaway, a Chinese takeaway, 712 sheep, and a brick coach shelter. I got off the coach in the historical town of Sandwich, one of the few communities in Great Britain without a sandwich shop. Closing in on my target of Richborough, I walked down a pleasant lane lined by modest homes all down one side. The lane became a little less pleasant when the sidewalk ran out. The few passing lorries had me scrambling up into the verge.

My trek was about three kilometres, but the walk made me feel a little more authentic. To the best of my knowledge, the Romans never travelled by coach. My attention was diverted by a squawky chirp, and I looked up to see a Ring-necked Parakeet. Native to India, this species has been a popular cage bird since Victorian times. Escapees have been breeding in England's southeast since the late 1960s and now number over 5,000. I continued past high bordering hedges, under the Sandwich bypass, and over the railway line between Sandwich and Broadstairs.

Just before getting to Richborough, I pulled out the hand-drawn map I had been given by an employee of British Heritage. It instructed me to turn at the remains of a stone railway pillar and tramp through a grazed field. I pushed on through a small woodlot, past a palisade of nettles, and into a field of thistles and horsetails. I was looking for the remains of Richborough's Roman amphitheatre. Some sort of semi-circular depression in the ground, I guessed. Waiting for a "Eureka!" moment, I wandered around and around. I could see some semi-circular depressions, but honestly, I have seen more convincing alien crop circles. Perhaps the whole thing looks great from the air, or after several pints. I retraced my steps back to the road to Richborough.

As part of Britain's millennium project, 1,000 milepost signs had been erected across the nation. One outside the site at Richborough cleverly indicated:

DVROVERNVM 15½ M
LONDINIVM 105 M
DVBRIS 17½ M
ROMA 1176 M

There were only three vehicles in the parking lot at Richborough, including an electrical repairs minivan. "You have the site to yourself at the moment," said the fellow who sold me a ticket.

Richborough, or Rvtvpiae, as it was known at the time, was the site where as many as 40,000 troops set down in 43 CE. The soldiers immediately dug steep-walled ditches and erected defensive wooden ramparts, allowing the site to serve as the harbour and base camp for the Roman invasion of Britain. The region was occupied for the entire period of Roman Britain. After two decades as the gateway to Britannia, a twenty-five-metre-tall triumphal arch was erected, built in flint and chalk, clad in fine Italian marble and decorated with statues in bronze. The arch was later pulled down, but its base remains. The rich civilian community of Richborough grew up around the fort. Two centuries later, the threat of invasion required great stone walls to be added to the fortification. So well constructed were these walls that major portions still dominate the landscape more than 1,700 years later. Watling Road exits the fort at its west gate. Or rather, a narrow dirt and gravel road exits at the west gate. Humble today, it was the spot where the great Roman invasion of Britain began.

By the time I got to the "Supply Base" part of the tour, a group of seven developmentally delayed adults arrived with their three minders. As they passed me, each of the minders apologized, presumably for disturbing my peace. Each time, I said that no apology was necessary. I hoped that everyone was enjoying their day as much as I was. And after all, we eleven visitors were not the most intrusive invaders that Richborough had ever seen.

Low clouds obscured the towers of the electrical power-generating plant in the distance. The breeze blowing from the east was just cold enough to make my back ache a bit. I sat on a section of ruined wall and contemplated the end of my journey. The Romans had left behind snails. They had left behind a significant cultural influence that, according to Monty Python's *Life of Brian*, included sanitation, medicine, education, wine, public order, irrigation, roads, a freshwater system, and public health.

And after more than three centuries of occupation, it seemed a fair bet that the Romans had left behind a substantial quantity of genetic material in Britain. No one can keep their genes in their jeans for that long. A good chunk of my heritage comes from that part of England, and of my 40,000 genes, I suspect that a portion of them could be traced back to Rome. Perhaps my ancestors ate snails.

CHAPTER TWELVE

"How Are You?
RAHHUUURGGGH!"

**REASON NUMBER TWELVE FOR INTRODUCING A FOREIGN SPECIES:
BECAUSE I HAVE RUN OUT OF FIREWOOD.**

"DO YOU FEEL EIGHT YEARS YOUNGER?" Having been awake for thirty hours, I felt dizzy and slightly nauseous, but in the nicest possible way. I was in a cool, dimly lit cinder-block room at the offices of Galaxy Express in Addis Ababa in central Ethiopia, trying to avoid nodding off. The question about my age had come from one of the firm's junior employees who was keeping Lindsay Eller and me company while our guide, Legese, and our driver, Hassen, completed paperwork and packed a white Toyota Land Cruiser for our trip. Lindsay and I had boarded the airplane at Heathrow in June but had stepped off at Bole International Airport in May, eight years earlier. It had been more than 400 years since the rest of the world had adopted the Gregorian calendar, but Ethiopia had refused to give up the Julian one—hence the eight-year jump.

While we waited, Lindsay and I were served mind-blowing coffee, easily the best of my life, but this brought on the need to pee, which came with its own difficulties. Ethiopia was in the midst of a drought. Because the country is almost totally reliant on hydroelectric power, each community had to deal with a series of rotating blackouts. Three to four days a week were spent without electrical power, and it was the capital city's turn. It made for a very curious trip down an unlit hallway to a bathroom with no windows.

I had met Lindsay at a biology conference two years before, and soon after hired her to teach biology laboratories part-time while she pursued graduate studies in kinesiology. Lindsay had done a lot of travelling, was slight but hale, and appeared to be a genuinely happy person, and so seemed the ideal companion on my latest quest. Perhaps most importantly, she didn't object to sharing a series of hotel rooms with me.

Neither of us had ever engaged a professional to get us around a foreign country, at least not for more than a couple of days, but Ethiopia was a different matter. I could muddle by in Russian or German when called on, but printed Amharic looked like so many squiggles to me. Guidebooks made travelling through Ethiopia unescorted sound like a challenge. It seemed that if Lindsay and I were to make the best use of our time, a search for introduced eucalyptus trees, we were going to need help. I chose Galaxy Express because it seemed the most uptempo of the firms working out of Addis Ababa and they answered their email messages most promptly.

It is not possible to understand our Ethiopian quest for eucalyptus, or indeed understand modern Ethiopia at all, without knowing a bit about the life and times of Emperor Menelik II. He was born Sahle Miriam in 1844 in Ankober, in the Showa region of what is now Ethiopia. His father, Haile Malakot, was king of Showa and married Menelik's mother, a court servant, shortly after Menelik's birth. If the family is to be believed, Menelik's heritage can be traced all the way back to King Solomon and Queen Sheba, who had a son named Menelik I. Not at the time, of course; they probably just called him Menelik. And, according to historians, he probably never existed.

Menelik II took over the reins as king of Showa at the age of twenty-one but had to wait an additional twenty-four years for the deaths of Tewodros II, Tekle Giorgis, and Yohannes IV to become

Emperor of Ethiopia. Menelik was reportedly an imposing figure, with a dark complexion and good teeth, but his face had been pitted by smallpox. From 1889 to his death in 1913, Menelik worked to amalgamate a series of smaller states into a single Ethiopian empire, expanding the country to nearly its present limits. He captured the attention of the world by turning back an Italian invasion in 1896. Menelik went on to institute a system of ministries, modernize the education system, install telephone and telegraph systems, and bring the railway to Addis Ababa, Ethiopia's new capital city.

Menelik's modernization of Ethiopia was all very well and good but resulted in a rapidly growing human population and far greater urbanization, particularly in and around the country's new capital. Native forests were cleared in the pursuit of fuel and building materials. Menelik attempted to deal with the tree shortage by forbidding the cutting and burning of trees without permission, but his edict was largely ignored. Being a clever fellow, he asked for the help of the international community to find a replacement. He needed a tree that would thrive in a hot, dry environment. It had to grow fast for a quick harvest, and burn with a hot flame.

This resulted in the introduction of eucalyptus plants from Australia starting in 1895. Seeds and young trees were distributed at little or no cost, and land planted with eucalyptus was exempt from taxes. They were planted in such great numbers that travellers in Ethiopia could tell when they were approaching a settlement by the abundance of trees. Eucalypts grew so quickly and regenerated so readily after harvest that some authorities claim that they have been among the most important factors in creating a modern Ethiopia. Indeed, Addis Ababa means "new flower," the name chosen by Menelik II for the newly planted eucalypts. Addis Ababa has been described as a "city in a forest"—but the same can be said of Puerto Princesa in the Philippines, Knysna in South Africa, Dalat in Vietnam, Olsztyn in Poland, and Atlanta in the United States.

The debut of eucalypts in Ethiopia was one of the rare examples of a species that had been successfully introduced with tremendous benefit and no immediately obvious negative consequences. I had been told that large chunks of Ethiopia are now covered with several species of eucalyptus, and Lindsay and I were off on a two-week circuit to see them.

On other adventures, I always felt a modicum of anxiety that I might not be able to find my chosen introduced species. Not a problem in this case; Lindsay and I saw eucalyptus trees and their impacts even before we left Addis Ababa. Legese explained that they grow furiously but aren't allowed to attain great height before being harvested. Even so, they were generally the tallest trees we saw. Eucalyptus is used as a building material; in rural settings, traditional round dwellings are constructed on a framework of eucalyptus branches, completed using mud, straw, and cow dung. Twigs and leaves fuel cooking fires. However, its role as scaffolding material in the cities was easily the most dramatic. Sections of eucalyptus trunk were tied together with cord; we spied this rickety-looking scaffolding everywhere in the capital city. Almost every building was under construction or rejuvenation, and all of them had eucalyptus scaffolding. Two storeys up, three storeys up . . . I saw workers scrambling over eucalyptus scaffolding nine storeys above the unforgiving pavement. I wouldn't have been willing to join them.

It took us quite some time to clear Addis Ababa. With 3.6 million residents already, it is growing at the astonishing rate of 8 percent per year. Housing fully 19 percent of the population of Ethiopia, Addis Ababa is the world's largest city in a landlocked country. Even so, at the city's largest intersection, traffic came to a halt to allow a herd of goats to pass. Traffic moved, but slowly and erratically, with frequent, rapid, and unsignalled lane changes. As a driver, I wouldn't have lasted five minutes. Driving with a broken horn would be neither practical nor safe. Many vehicles spewed masses of black smoke, which left Lindsay and me with sore throats even before we left the capital heading south.

The rotating power outages had come to Sodo, our stop for the night. It was late, and we had had a very long day. However, we felt there was nothing to be learned of life from sitting on the porch of our modest hotel room, so Lindsay and I set out for a walk along Sodo's main street.

Most of the 55,000 residents of Sodo were walking the packed-earth street that evening. We were an oddity, and virtually everyone stared long and deeply. Most tourists drive through Sodo without stopping, and so a couple of *faranji* (Amharic for "foreigner") walking the darkening streets was probably an uncommon sight. "Hello, hello!" was a common greeting. "You, you, you!" was another. We heard shouts of *"Faranji, faranji!"* which is not always used in a derogatory sense, so I was fine with it. A few people shouted "American!" after we had passed them, and it was said in a way that didn't sound entirely welcoming.

Approaching the edge of town, we had gathered an impressive collection of children, who turned back toward the hotel when we did.

"Hello, hello," they sang.

"Hello," we replied.

"How are you?"

"I am fine. How are you?"

"I am fine."

"Good. My name is Glen." That last one required a bit of gesturing to get the point across.

"I want money."

"I am sure you do."

"I want money!"

"And I want a pony, but I'm pretty sure I'm not going to get one."

"What?"

Lindsay was keen to buy fruit from roadside vendors, whose wares were spread out on blankets in front of them. She tried to get a shy young girl to tell her the price of a banana. Nervous chuckles were all the girl could manage. I suggested that Lindsay try to negotiate a price with the vendors herself. Sitting on their heels in front of their offerings, they were all staring at us and smiling, and there was no way under Heaven's skies that any of them were going to try to cheat her.

Lindsay squatted down in front of one woman, probably five years her junior but who looked twenty years older. The dozen or so youngsters who had been following us squatted around her. Lindsay negotiated for two bananas and a mango (1 birr, about 10 cents, each) and a pineapple (2 birr). The children were having a great time watching Lindsay as though the circus had just come to town. Lindsay didn't mind being a source of entertainment. But among the growing crowd, there was a vague sense of hostile anxiety. Unbeknownst to Lindsay, six men had gathered behind her. They did not have the smiling faces of the youngsters, and I thought that we might be in for a bit of trouble. If someone made a grab for Lindsay's wallet, the skirmish was going to be lopsided. I probably looked like a fossil with grey hair, thirty-two years older than the median age of Ethiopians and five years beyond the country's life expectancy. With an air of confidence that I didn't really feel, I stepped between Lindsay and the six men. As soon as she had collected her fruit, in the evening's rapidly vanishing light, I told her that it was time to get back to our hotel. We walked briskly, and the words directed at us became a bit louder and a bit more hostile. Just before we got to the hotel compound, someone threw a wrench and it caught me in the calf. If I remember my Sunday school lessons properly, Sodo is where Noah's wife was turned into a pillar of salt.

I HAVE BEEN TO MANY of the great art museums of Europe. I have seen many, many depictions of Eden rendered by the world's greatest oil painters. These all seem to feature landscapes that look surprisingly like Cornwall. Each of these painters might have had a much better go at depicting Eden if they had visited Ethiopia. After all, as far as we know, this region is the birthplace of humankind. Many important fossils of our pre-human ancestors were found in Ethiopia, including "Lucy," a 3-million-year-old, one-metre-tall *Australopithecus afarensis*, discovered in 1974. Vegetation in the southwest of Ethiopia featured shades of green that had never before struck my eyes; not blue-green, yellow-green, or Danube Canal–green, just really, really green. Eden-green, I suppose.

In places, eucalyptus trees added greatly to the greenness. There are over 900 species of plant in the genus *Eucalyptus,* and almost all are native to Australia, where they dominate many landscapes. In fact, the only places where eucalypts are not found in Australia are the interior shrublands and the highest sites in the southern alpine zone. Variation within the group is substantial, with some maturing as low shrubs and others as giant trees. The leaves of many eucalypts have oil glands, making them aromatic. The flowers of most species are white or creamy, but some have red, pink, or purple flowers. Eucalypts really are a clever group of plants. If a stem dies as a result of grazing, fire, or being cut down, then buds develop from woody growths at the plant's base. These are known as lignotubers and grow into new stems, allowing the individual to soldier on.

Horticulturalists are an ambitious lot, and almost 200 species of eucalypt have been tried as exotic imports somewhere or another. Not surprisingly, most of these have failed, but about two dozen have been spectacular successes. By far the most widely planted eucalyptus has been the Tasmanian blue gum. Of the twenty or so eucalypt species in Ethiopia, this is easily the most common. Growing to a height of fifty-five metres, it is characterized by a straight trunk and a large crown of foliage. It performs well because the leaves are unpalatable to cows and sheep. It is joined in Ethiopia by the red river gum, the sugar gum, the Sydney blue gum, the flooded gum, and the yellow box.

The rainy season was overdue, making everyone nervous about the possibility of food shortages, but as we rose to start the day, the skies opened. Our breakfast at a covered café consisted of coffee, banana juice, toast, and scrambled eggs. We watched the locals watching us and peering out at the cool, life-giving rain.

Driving carefully on the rain-slicked roads, Hassen piloted us out of Sodo. Unfortunately for the anxious farmers of Ethiopia, the rains didn't last long, and the thirsty soil looked parched again almost immediately. It was the last heavy rain we were to see.

Because we were driving along a goat track, our progress was gla-cial, and we often had to slow down even more for creek crossings or sharp turns. At every spot where we had to slow down, one or more children had set up shop. Most of them would simply scream, "You, you, you!" and stick out their hands for money or candy. Those who had wandered away from the road for a moment came streaking across the fields when they heard our vehicle approach.

Great mountains one moment and deep valleys the next, this was a big and glorious land. The ground was parched and dazzling because of it. As we moved further south, eucalyptus trees were replaced by acacias and scrub. Here and there rose great termitaria, like giant, proud, sandy penises.

I HAD SET MY ALARM for 6:00 the next morning so that I could work on my notes, but I found the skies completely dark and the power out. I tried again at 6:30, and then at 7:00, and finally gave up. After a very, very cold shower, I went for a walk along the main road of Jinka, giving Lindsay a chance to ready herself for the day.

Jinka is a small community that serves as the administrative centre for the South Omo region, and at that hour the road was mainly occupied by uniformed students walking to school. I joined the procession. I received a lot of greetings, but no one engaged me in serious conversation until Phillip got off his bicycle and fell in with me.

"Hello," he began.

"Hello. How are you?"

"I am fine. I am going to school." Phillip's vocabulary was better than most.

"That is very good. I think that your school uniform is handsome."

"Thank you. Where are you from?"

"I am from Canada."

"Is that in Europe? No, it is in North America, correct?"

"That is correct. My name is Glen."

"My name is Phillip. When I finish school, I will go to univer-sity. I will probably go to Oxford in England."

"That is good, Phillip. I am a university professor."

"Really?"

"Yes."

"You?"

"Yes."

"Really?"

All right, Phillip; I get the idea. "Yes, me. I teach biology."

"I love biology."

"Well, I am going to turn around here, so goodbye."

"Maybe I will see you tomorrow," said Phillip, and I got the impression that I would be seeing him tomorrow no matter where or at what time I went for a walk.

After a hearty breakfast of tea, banana juice, and French toast, we were on our way. Unlike the previous day's roads, which were all under construction, the roads Hassen drove us over now were as complete as they ever would be but terribly rough, rolling, and weather-worn. As we climbed, Legese pointed out that while northern Ethiopia had long been strongly influenced by the Arabian Peninsula, the south had always had closer links with the rest of Africa. I think I saw what he meant; as we approached the mountain peaks and looked down on the savanna, the view looked, somehow, quintessentially African, as though a deeply buried part of my mind was speaking to me of humankind's origins. The region was dominated by acacia with a sprinkling of juniper, eucalyptus, and other broad-leaved shrubs and trees.

When we got to the limits of Mago National Park, a sign written in English gave us a list of dos and don'ts. Among the prohibited activities were the use of machine guns and the disruption of park staff. Beautiful beyond words, Mago was completely uncontaminated by tourists, save for us. At a river crossing deep, deep in the park, we came to a rope across the road, which separated us from what lay beyond. After paying a fee, the rope was dropped, and Legese jumped into the back with Lindsay and me to make room for our park-mandated guide. I had to wonder what officials at the Chelsea Football Club would think if they knew that one of their scarves was being used as a sling for our guide's rifle. The guide's position was probably a make-work project, but the rifle's official function was to protect us from lions and other dangerous wildlife.

We arrived at the village of the pastoralist Mursi people, probably best known for their beehive-shaped huts and the large clay disks that women wear in their lower lips. At the age of about twenty, a cut is made in the woman's lower lip to insert a small disk. Larger and larger disks are inserted over time to stretch the lip more and more. Apparently the ideal situation is to have a woman's lip so distended that she can pull it over her head. Lindsay asked Legese why these women subjected themselves to the mutilation required to fit disks in their lips. He said that the original function was lost to the mists of time but may be related to disfigurement that made one less desirable as a potential slave. The tradition continues as a thing of beauty and desire.

Twenty-two men, women, and children rushed the vehicle on our approach. I would have dearly loved a long chat with some of them, utilizing a two-stage translation through Legese and our park guide. But this was not the way things worked here. We were led from the vehicle to one part of the beehive village and invited to take photographs. Bare-breasted, droop-lipped, and willing to stand wherever we wanted them to. Lindsay wanted pictures but didn't want to be behind the camera, so she handed it over to me. If I said, "All right, how about you and you and you over there?" the park guide would cut those people from the pack and line them up. The visitor then snaps a photograph and pays each person in the photo 2 birr, about 20 cents. Others would try to sneak into the picture so that they could claim their 2 birr, but the guide would promptly cut them back out.

"Okay, perhaps you and you and you," I said to three women. I snapped a photo and then walked forward and said, "Thank you very much," while handing each a couple of dirty, brown 1-birr notes. The last woman was upset at me; she wanted an additional payment for the baby she was holding. I hadn't spotted the baby, so I handed her 2 birr more, which started a massive fight between the mother, who wanted to keep both bills, and our park guide, who insisted that she get only one so as to not ruin the payment scheme for following tourists.

I wanted to talk to someone about their huts and how long it took to build one and whether they were sufficiently breezy on a hot day. I wanted to ask how far it was to the nearest medical facility and how frequently the people had to shoot wildlife to protect their livestock. I wanted to ask what lion tasted like. I also wanted to know their position on clitorectomy and other forms of genital mutilation reportedly practised in the region. However, there was a bit of a to-do brewing between those whose pictures had been taken and those who had missed the opportunity to earn some cash. We beetled back to the vehicle. Along the way I purchased a clay lip disk ("Only one . . . thank you, I really only need one . . . see, I already have one!") for 10 birr. Back in the truck, hands reached through the windows and loud voices asked, *"Luckity, luckity, luckity?"*

"What is *luckity*? I don't understand."

"It means 'plastic.' They want plastic water bottles." We found three and handed them over.

We dropped our guide at his original post and continued on. We spotted an astounding range of wildlife, including bushbuck, Yellow-mantled Widowbirds, Abyssinian Rollers, White Wagtails, Northern Carmine Bee-eaters, and Hammerkop, heron-like birds whose heads are shaped rather like a claw hammer.

We came across a group of six men on foot, all in military-like fatigues and sporting high-powered rifles. Being so close to the Kenyan border, I began to wonder whether I would ever get to see my retirement and regretted not registering with the Canadian Consulate before leaving Addis Ababa. It turned out that these men were park wardens on the lookout for poachers. Men in the local tribes feel it is important to show their bravery by killing large animals. Why can't they just pee their name in the snow like men elsewhere?

SCIENCE FIRST STUMBLED across eucalyptus plants in 1777. On James Cook's third voyage, crew member David Nelson collected a tree on Bruny Island off the coast of southern Tasmania. Back at London's British Museum, French botanist L'Héritier described the plant and named it *Eucalyptus obliqua*. He coined the genus name on the basis of the Greek words *eu* and *calyptos*, implying that the flower bud's operculum was "well covered." The species name comes from the Latin word *obliquus*, on the basis of an asymmetric leaf whose two sides do not meet the stem at the same place. The general name *eucalyptus* stuck.

In preparation for our trip to Ethiopia, Lindsay and I had visited a travel clinic in Canada, and between us had been given more than $1,200 worth of inoculations and pills. We were topped up for diphtheria, meningitis, malaria, yellow fever, typhoid fever, tetanus, polio, and hepatitis A through Z. If I was going to get sick, God was going to have to invent new diseases. Our arms had become so sore from the injections that we had trouble raising them for a couple of days. We also got prescriptions for oral inoculations against most forms of traveller's diarrhea. At the appropriate times, I had mixed up and drunk the horrible concoction that was supposed to keep my intestines moving at the proper rate. Lindsay had forgotten to take hers.

Lindsay had been feeling a bit unwell the previous day, and at midnight she erupted. The walls and doors of our hotel room may have been adequate for keeping out wildlife, but they were useless at blocking sound, and so every echo of explosive diarrhea was a shared experience. To save her the potential embarrassment of being sick, I pretended to sleep through it. Lindsay wasn't back in bed for too many minutes before she made a return engagement to vomit her lungs out and plead for mercy.

Mark Twain wrote that the "one thing in the world that will make a man peculiarly and insufferably self-conceited" is to have a settled stomach while those around him are vomiting. I was doing my very best not to feel self-conceited that I had remembered to drink my anti-diarrheal potion.

On my pre-breakfast walk through Jinka the next morning, I chose a small side road lined with family dwellings and an elementary school. My wanderings attracted the usual smiles and surprised looks, and also attracted Phillip. He was delighted when I greeted him by name. He must have been searching very hard to find me on a back street, and I felt rather complimented. We talked about Canada and Ethiopia, giving him a chance to practise his English and me a chance to practise talking to young people.

Our group drove east toward Key Afar. En route, I noticed that a lot of men were sporting rifles. Surely this had nothing to do with protecting livestock from wildlife, particularly since the main industry seemed to be road construction. Legese explained that different tribal groups maintained antagonistic relationships. Violent conflicts broke out over stolen cattle or goats, and over disputed territory. Lindsay asked where the guns might be acquired. "We are close to the border with Kenya," said Legese. "Getting guns is easy."

Key Afar is a sleepy little spot for most of the week, but on Thursday, market day, it comes alive. We walked along the main street, passing many people bringing goats, chickens, and produce to market. We took a quick look around the market plaza to see what was on offer. We found spices, ochre used in personal decoration, and sandals made of old automobile tires nailed roughly into the shape of a foot. At that point a young man made a very amateur attempt to steal my wallet. He bumped into my shoulder and then made a grab for the wallet in my front pocket. Unfortunately for him, the pocket was buttoned, and he slunk away with a disappointed look on his face.

Whatever had made Lindsay so ill overnight struck me, and I retired to a small café. Bilious waves of nausea hit me, and I was self-conceited no longer. Hoping to settle my stomach, I ordered a Fanta but received a Sprite. Feeling worse by the minute, I nursed my drink in the shade.

A lovely calm settled over me. After all, if I was going to be nauseous, where better than the shade of the verandah of a café in a small village in a remote corner of Ethiopia? I felt a prod at my leg and opened my eyes just enough to see a young man with his hand out. Behind him were three more waiting to have their turn at me. I said, "No," shook my head, closed my eyes, and refused to open them. For one older fellow, this was not sufficient hinting. Over the drone of market day, I could hear him talking to me in one of the ten dialects of the south Omotic language, but I refused to look. Then he started tapping my leg. When that didn't work, he shook my leg. A lot. I opened my eyes, said "No!" as emphatically as I could without being too rude. Then I mimed vomiting, but it didn't work, so I just went back to ignoring him.

Whatever trite little self-pitying thoughts I managed to accumulate were not allowed to last long. After an hour on a dusty, rutted track, we pulled into a small village near a dry riverbed. The road ahead was choked with a throng of about 200 people, all walking the same direction we were driving. My first impression was that we had found a funeral procession. Fortunately, I am often wrong. Unfortunately, this time I wasn't. Hassen and Legese unrolled their windows to see what they could glean from the bits of language they shared with these people. They rolled the windows back up.

"Do we know what's going on?" I asked.

"Death," replied Legese. As we inched through the crowd, trying to make progress without being too disrespectful, I tried to learn a little more.

"Do we know anything about the person?"

"A woman," said Legese.

At the head of the procession was a white pickup truck laden with crying mourners and, presumably, the deceased. The truck was surrounded by a church choir in robes. My stomach problems seemed pretty small.

A few hours on, we arrived at a beautiful shady campground bordering the Kaske River, a couple of kilometres from Turmi, the traditional home of the Hamer people. The river was bone dry, awaiting the start of the rainy season. Because the rains were due to begin at any moment, smarter tourists had all gone home and we had the campground to ourselves.

My intestinal tract finally showed its full ferocity, and I dashed off to the distant toilet. "Toilet" in this case is such a generous word, since the structure consisted of a hut around a hole in the ground. Correctly anticipating an eruption, I doffed my trousers and underpants and hung them over the wall of the hut. I was surprised by how long I could squat.

Knowing that it was only a matter of time before the peace at the other end of me was shattered, I sought out a quiet corner of the compound and wandered back and forth, sipping water and spitting, waiting for the inevitable. As I waited, the rainbow I had created with crayons as a child formed across the failing African sky.

And just as I started to vomit, I found that my secluded niche was actually on the path leading from a Hamer village to the river. A man walked by. "Hello!" he called out.

"Hellouuurrggggh," I replied.

"How are you?"

"I am blluuurgggggh fine," I said. "How are you? RAH-HUUURGGGH!"

"I am fine, thank you."

"That is good. Harruuggggh!"

I spent the rest of the day and most of the night alternating between the pit and my vomiting area, dodging baboons and civet cats. The Hamer man was probably still telling the story of the crazy *faranji* a month later.

THE RAINS WERE OVERDUE everywhere in Ethiopia. Trees and shrubs were doing their best to hold on to a bit of colour, but the groundcover had faded to grey. I could spot no eucalyptus. The cows and goats looked to be in for a pretty rough ride; so, too, would the pastoralists who depend absolutely on their stock. In the case of a famine, those people living closest to the road would likely get some relief from aid agencies, but those whose traditional lands were much further from roads would probably miss the aid, and many were likely to die. "Very sad," said Legese.

We pulled into a village of the Elbore people. At first, it didn't seem like much more than a couple of stick-and-grass huts and some goats under a shade tree. We rudely displaced the goats so that we could park our truck in their shade. Word spread quickly, and we were soon surrounded by fifty friendly villagers. Legese could speak the local language and so got a lot of attention, particularly since he had a pocketful of small bills. I had some money, but only in ridiculously large denominations that I had got at the airport. And that was fine, because I wanted to talk to the children, and they quickly accepted that I had neither cash nor candy for them. Girma, perhaps nine years old, wanted to trade watches with me. Mine read 9:07. His flashed 88:88. I think that mine was closer. His friend, Ali, perhaps six, wore a pendant made from a broken metal wristwatch strap.

I pulled out my notebook, which inexplicably caused half of the children to run away and the rest to retreat to a safe distance. I can't imagine what they thought I was going to do. So I sat on a tree stump, ripped out a few pages, and started folding origami cranes, which has never once failed to get me the attention of young children. The cranes were well received, but it seemed that they would have been much happier if I had been handing out pens, although I cannot imagine why if paper frightens them.

Many hours later, we arrived at a Konso village above the town of Karat-Konso. A remarkably robust stone-and-wooden fence circled the compound. Inside, almost touching one another, were twelve circular huts with walls of sticks and mud a little over a metre high below soaring conical straw roofs. The compound immediately gave the impression of great age. We were given a tour by the hereditary chief, who had adopted the post when his father died at age 60. He in turn had adopted the post when his father had died at 100. I asked the chief to what his grandfather attributed his tremendous longevity. In impeccable English, the chief's response was "Probably lineage. Other than my father, all of the men in my family lived very long lives. And probably to a life dedicated to prayer and contemplation rather than hard work."

The Konso certainly knew how to work hard, scratching a living out of the terraced hillside, growing sorghum, beans, corn, and coffee. The chief showed us huts for communal cooking and for eating meals celebrating Christian religious festivals. One hut was set aside for resolving conflicts, and another for the detention of transgressors. A particularly chilling hut was the dwelling place of the grieving widow of a chief. She is meant to reside there for nine years and nine months after the chief's death. I love my wife, but if she predeceases me, I plan to get on with my life.

THE FOLLOWING DAY was about wildlife in overwhelming quantity and novelty. We had a very early breakfast to give us the best possible start on Nechisar National Park. If roads in Ethiopia are less about engineering and more about faith, then roads in Nechisar are more a state of paranoia and misguided optimism—narrow tracks on a steep and rocky path, with no guardrail to separate us from eternity. If it had rained any time recently, the roads would have been impassable.

The road, such as it was, rose through a forest as imagined by a child raised in inner-city Detroit. Lots of overstorey trees, not so tall as to be boastful, and not so dense as to choke out all the light for understorey vegetation. Warthogs peeked from between trees. Olive baboons dashed across the road, always trying to present their backsides to us, while duikers and velvet monkeys were pleased to stop and have a little look as we passed. Even at slow speed I couldn't identify most of the birds that flitted past. Up and up we drove, and Hassen got big credit for not tipping us over one cliff or another.

As we descended to the Nechisar Plain, I was vigilant for the Nechisar Nightjar, an enigmatic bird known only from a single wing salvaged from the corpse of an individual found at the side of the track in 1990. We didn't spot one. Even so, there was no shortage of other great birds, including Abyssinian Rollers, giant African Fish-eagles, Secretarybirds, Kori Bustards, Kurrichane Buttonquail, Helmeted Guineafowl, and Yellow-necked Spurfowl.

Most wildlife lovers probably come to the Nechisar Plain for the mammals. We saw Swayne's hartebeest, Grant's gazelles, and dozens of Burchell's zebras, which, as long as we were on foot, allowed us to approach amazingly close. I realize that travellers to Africa are supposed to describe zebras in their millions, but as someone who had never previously seen one in the wild, "dozens" seemed pretty good.

At lunch I probably managed to re-inoculate myself with whatever bug had been making me ill for the past few days. I ordered assorted vegetables, assuming that they would arrive steaming hot. Most of them had been cooked, but not well and not recently. Lindsay joined Legese and Hassen in two rounds of *injera*, a sour, nutritious, pancake-shaped flatbread served with *wat* stew. She wanted to know what each of the bits was.

"What's that?"

"Meat."

"And what's that?"

"Meat."

"What kind of meat?"

"We don't know. Maybe chicken." Sometimes it is better not to ask.

ASSIGNING A EUCALYPT to a particular species requires a lot more botanical knowledge than I have. I might have some luck in deciding if a tree's bark is smooth, scribbly, powdery, pepperminty, ironbarky, or tessellated, and I could probably distinguish between seeds that are red, brown, grey, and black. However, in distinguishing between leaves that are orbicular, lanceolate, falcate, peltate, amplexicaul, concolorous, or emarginate, or fruit that might be sessile, ribbed, urceolate, truncate-globose, obconical, or cupular, I would be at a loss.

If someone sent you to Australia to find a suggan buggan mallee tree, you might be facing a significant quest. You would know it to be a small, slender-stemmed tree found amongst the rocky hills and gorges of far-eastern Victoria around the Stradbroke Chasm. That is the easy part. Upon arrival, you would have to search for a plant with a strongly beaked operculum with scars, campanulate fruit with a flared rim, flattened-ellipsoidal lacunose seeds, unbranched inflorescences, smooth sessile buds appearing in threes, glaucous juvenile leaves, and a crown consisting of lanceolate or falcate leaves with large island oil glands.

If I couldn't figure out exactly which eucalyptus tree I was seeing in Ethiopia, I wasn't going to be too fussed. Back on the main road, eucalyptus trees started to regain their abundance as we travelled north. In contrast to my loathing of rhododendrons, I was becoming very fond of eucalypts, with their long, dagger-shaped leaves and tall, straight trunks.

As eucalypts flashed by, I told Lindsay about some of the demographics I had looked up before coming to Ethiopia. I had learned that the country's per capita gross domestic product was just $780 per annum, which didn't compare favourably with that of, say, Iceland, at $29,750. Indeed, Ethiopia is credited with being one of the poorest nations in the world. While everyone in Iceland has access to safe drinking water, the same can be said of just 23 percent of Ethiopians. For every 100 girls of secondary school age in Iceland, 113 actually go to school. I'm not sure how that works, but it sounds pretty good. In Ethiopia, the number is just 22 per 100 girls. Infant mortality is nineteen times higher in Ethiopia than in Iceland. A woman in Iceland has a 90.7 percent chance of living to reach sixty-five years of age; only one-third of women do so in Ethiopia. All in all, the numbers suggest that Ethiopia can be a pretty rough place to live.

And to prove it, just south of Sodo we came upon another funeral procession. This one had only twelve mourners and no choir. For the sake of the family, I hoped that the gathering would pick up steam as it moved along. North of Sodo, we came across another. This time, hundreds of people were in attendance, and the closer we got to the truck with the deceased, the more grief-stricken the mourners looked. I probably wouldn't cross paths with three funerals in three years at home.

In the fading light of late afternoon, we pulled into Wondo

Genet, whose wooded hills are among the last of the original Ethiopian forests, dominated by podocarp trees. Perhaps this was why there was a forestry college and a centre for biodiversity nearby. We checked into a government-operated hotel, part of which dates to the rule of Emperor Haile Selassie. My guidebook described the hotel in less than glowing terms, claiming that it makes "an elegant case for the introduction of architectural crimes against humanity as a hanging offence." Well, rubbish. The dated architecture might inspire a sound thrashing at best. The hotel had cockroaches but no bedbugs, at least not in our room, and I'll take cockroaches over bedbugs any day.

When Lindsay heard that the town had a hot-springs pool, she immediately decided to have a go. I was torn between a hot soak in a hot country and sitting quietly in the shade to catch up on my notes. While Lindsay shaved her legs in the windowless bathroom by the light of her Petzl headlamp, I lay on the bed to decide what to do. Then I spied her small floral bikini.

At the pool, the pre-soak shower issued from pipes coming out of a rock face, and pummeled my body with glorious scalding water. In contrast, the water in the pool was tepid, and the pool walls were algae-covered, but I hadn't brought my swimming gear all the way to Ethiopia to let it sit in my backpack. And there was, of course, the bikini, which was considerably less modest than the bathing costumes of the several other women in the pool, all locals. The men wore bathing suits straight out of 1983, in contrast to my knee-length trunks. My body was the oldest one in the pool by nineteen years. Lindsay's was second oldest.

On our way out of Wondo Genet, we came across yet another road-blocking congregation. Surely not another funeral . . . As we approached the gathering, it seemed even more ominous, and police lights flashed on a pickup truck approaching from our right. When Hassen tooted the horn to get by, as he had with previous funeral processions, we got some very hostile looks, and I feared that we might be immersing ourselves in one of the things I dread most in a foreign country—an illegal political protest.

Reality was far worse. From what we could gather from the throng, a child had been stoned to death by another child, and at that moment I simply could not imagine anything more dreadful. One young life was gone and another lay in tatters. Far more than just a funeral procession, we were watching the outpouring of a community in deep, deep grief and anguish.

As on previous days, we started climbing and climbing, and it occurred to me that I was having trouble remembering many descents to match the ascents. Perhaps we would eventually find ourselves at the top of the world. East out of Wondo Genet along Highway 40 until it turned into Highway 8; it should have been a piece of cake. Our planned route was only the length of my index finger on my highway map. Poor Hassen—every bit of the road was under construction.

As Hassen struggled, the rest of us watched the scenery, which included some patches of big and stately podocarp trees. I spied tremendous eucalyptus trees, monsters every one. In places, they made the landscape appear as something out of a Turner oil painting. The higher we got, the more the terrain looked like the Russian steppe, or what I suspect the Russian steppe looks like. Horses became more and more common, and the riders sat comfortably in the saddle. Legese explained that the Bale region was among the wealthiest in Ethiopia. Wheat farming is really big here, and Legese said that farmers can afford to use tractors and combine harvesters to farm the vast fields. This may be, but all of the plowing I saw was being done with single-blade plows pulled by pairs of oxen.

At the road's peak, after Hassen had battled construction trucks and endless buses hour upon hour, we pulled over for a quiet lunch. It was only quiet for a few minutes until word got out to the children of the dispersed community that *faranji* and their minders had arrived. They appeared out of nowhere. I really wanted to munch on my boiled potato and egg in a bit of windy peace while trying to identify a few birds, but it wasn't to be. "Hello-how-are-you-I-am-fine" was getting a bit tiresome, but the twelve-year-old who shadowed me had picked up a little more English.

"That is a house!" he said.

"Yes, I know it is a house."

"That is a rock!"

"Yes, it is most certainly a rock."

"That is a rock!"

"You are correct. That, too, is a rock."

"That is a donkey!"

I was growing a little tired of the dialogue and decided to try some gentle teasing. "No, it's a mongoose," I claimed.

"What?"

"It is not a donkey. It is a mongoose."

"It is a donkey!"

"No, it's a mongoose."

"Now you give me 120 birr."

"I'll buy that mongoose for 120 birr."

"What?"

"If you bring me that mongoose, I will give you 120 birr for it."

"You want that donkey?"

"No, I want that mongoose. The one right over there."

"Okay. Too much. Now you give me 100 birr." And so it went.

On the downhill slide from the peak, we spotted an assortment of cool mammals, including warthogs, mountain nyalas, and a rarely spotted serval cat. At the Bale Mountains National Park headquarters, we spied grey duikers and Menelik's bushbuck. A sign at the entrance to the park's headquarters indicated that nine rivers and streams between Adaba and Goba contain rainbow and brown trout. Both species were introduced to Ethiopia in 1967 via Kenya and quickly spread, as introduced species so often do. These trout are now fair game for anglers.

It was bamboo market day in Goba. As we drove through town, we were held up by legions of horses and donkeys dragging their loads of bamboo to market from wherever uphill it had been harvested. At a crossroad, the beasts were relieved of their burden and moved off to the side. Cash earned from the sale of bamboo would be spent on essentials and a few luxuries at the weekly market, due to start in a few hours.

The road passed substantial eucalyptus forests on one side of the road, and juniper and *Hagenia* forests on the other. For the first time, I saw eucalyptus trees in flower, little starbursts, and it looked as though these trees would erupt in the following few weeks. For now it was just the odd little bright and creamy puff here and there. These eucalypts seemed pretty happy with life, growing straight and strong, and with a sense of smug superiority. This wasn't so unusual; eucalypts introduced to foreign lands often do much better than they do in Australia, having left behind their natural predators, parasites, and diseases. The soil into which they are introduced is sometimes much more nourishing than the nutrient-poor soil of Australia.

As the road climbed to the 4,000-metre-high Sanetti Plateau, constituting the northeast portion of Bale Mountains National Park, the landscape lost its thick vegetation and turned to low scrubby brush and bare ground, punctuated by the occasional giant lobelia tree rising a couple of metres. A few lobelia had generated huge phallic structures at their tops, each containing several thousand flowers, with each flower producing several thousand seeds. Pity the poor lobelia; after the plant reproduces, it dies. Lindsay pointed out that you have to admire the strength of anything that manages to survive in the alpine.

Wherever a depression in the ground had allowed a little water to accumulate, we saw more wildlife, including Blue-winged Geese, an endemic to Abyssinia, and Yellow-billed Ducks. Hassen spotted a giant mole rat, found in the Bale Mountains and nowhere else. The oversized creature lumbered across the landscape, giving us plenty of time to stop the car, get out, wander over, take some pictures . . . um . . . poke it with a stick . . . Giant mole rats do not move quickly. A few minutes later we spotted a fox. The fox did not spot the mole rat. We spied Thekla Larks,

Wattled Cranes—a vulnerable species—and Bale Parisoma, found nowhere but the Bale Mountains.

We continued on to Tullo Deemtu, which at 4,377 metres is the highest peak in the Urgoma Mountains, the second highest in Ethiopia, and among the highest peaks in all of Africa. Any more than a few minutes and the cold wind would have been too much, but it was one of those magical moments when everything else in sight is down. It did seem a bit of a cheat though, driving to the top of a mountain, but there was an automated communications tower at the top, and I suppose it requires periodic servicing.

Scooting downhill, it wasn't long before we came to a Jawa at the side of the road. Or at least it looked like a Jawa. It unfolded itself to reveal a small child, perhaps six or seven years old, bundled up against the cold wind. Legese passed the child a few biscuits and a banana, while I contemplated where in the world the child's parents might be. Ethiopian wolves and African hunting dogs are rare in the Bale Mountains, but it still seemed pretty chancy to me. Legese pointed out a herd of goats and cows crossing the plateau below us about a kilometre away and speculated that the child's parents must be herding them. Sparsely populated, the Sanetti Plateau has long attracted herders, and the tradition continues despite the region's designation as a national park.

THE FOLLOWING DAY was one that I had not been looking forward to since booking the trip. Legese had not built it up as anything more than it was—a very long drive from Goba back to Addis Ababa for a flight north the next day. Over the horrid road we had travelled just two days before, Hassen set some sort of record by getting us from Goba to Sheshemene in just six hours. Highway 6 north is as significant as any road gets in Ethiopia, serving as the major route between the Kenyan border and Addis Ababa. It is nicely paved except where it isn't. Imagine the 401 through Toronto redesigned as a carnival ride. Users of the highway include cattle, goats, horses, donkeys, horse-drawn carts, donkey-drawn carts, tractors, and a few motorized vehicles. Competing hitchhikers wouldn't stand a chance if they stood politely at the side of the road, and so they positioned themselves in the middle of the lane they hoped to travel in. Not content with the universal extended thumb, they used semaphore, without the flags, until the moment before death by collision became inevitable. As we sailed by, we got a lot of looks of resignation but also a lot of gestures that I can only assume were rude.

Lindsay toured the grounds of our Addis Ababa hotel. I sipped a gin and tonic in the hotel bar while writing up my notes. The bar was pretty full since the hotel was hosting a conference of ministers. After ninety minutes, I tried without success to catch the eye of my server to get another drink. Then, sitting at a table by herself, a young woman started to wave coquettishly, smile, and wink at me. Well, obviously not at me, but at someone who must have been standing behind me. I casually looked over my shoulder and found that I was alone. I looked back at the woman, who continued to gesture and nod in a way that suggested "Yes, you!" Why me? I knew only a handful of people in Africa, and I was pretty sure that she wasn't one of them. She most definitely seemed to be gesturing at me.

And then I had a dreadful thought. Could it be that this woman was a prostitute? Was I being propositioned? Was I being utterly stupid? I looked around the bar and saw only one other woman sitting by herself. She was trying to catch my eye too, but a little less obviously. I had my guidebook with me, and I checked the index under "prostitution" and then tried "sex trade," but found nothing.

Then a man with a convention badge, presumably a minister, sat down at the table with the first woman. Ah, see—she isn't a prostitute, just someone at the conference trying to get the attention of her colleague, and shame on me for thinking that the situation was anything more sordid than that. Even so, I was left with the impression that the couple at the table were negotiating, and after a few minutes, having failed to come to a resolution, he got up and walked away. She resumed winking at me. I gave up on trying to find my server, walked to the bar, paid for my drink, gave the seated woman a polite smile, and received a very nice offer for sinsof-the-flesh at a very modest price. I high-tailed it back to the room. Alone.

WE WERE DROPPED AT THE AIRPORT ninety minutes before our flight. This might be cutting it close at O'Hare or Frankfurt, but in Ethiopia it was about eight-eight minutes early. We were eventually waved over to the check-in desk and issued boarding cards that were entirely blank; no names, no flight number, no destination, nothing. "They are blank," we were told by the check-in clerk when he saw us staring at them. "Don't worry."

An old and crowded Fokker delivered us to Axum, home to 70,000 people. The fields around the town were rocky but carefully plowed, waiting for the rains that were now two weeks overdue. Our guide, Testeye, told us that the land was very fertile, and anything would grow in it. I sincerely hoped that it would, and soon. I looked for eucalyptus trees. They had been rather rare in Ethiopia's far south, and I hoped to find them in greater abundance in the country's far north. Nothing . . . nothing . . . Ah, there's one. And there's two, and a bunch more. By the time we got to Axum, finding a eucalyptus was as challenging as finding my elbows in a brightly lit room, and to my great joy, they were in full flower. No one will ever suggest that eucalyptus flowers become the next big thing on Valentine's Day, but the little starbursts were a treat to me.

After a quick lunch, we were picked up by Testeye and our driver for the three-hour tour of the sights and sounds of Axum. To understand Axum, it is necessary to know four things about it. First, the community was hopping and bopping at least 300 years before Christ and became the capital of the mighty Axumite empire. Second, Axum is the pillar of Orthodox Christianity in Ethiopia and home to the largest and oldest Christian sanctuary in the country. Third, while the city was a big deal then, and is a big deal today, it has had the living daylights beaten out of it several times over the millennia. Finally, Axum is really, really close to the border with Eritrea, the width of my thumbnail on the map, and despite earlier close relations, tensions run high, particularly after a major and bloody border conflict just a decade before. Our families would have been anxious if they had known exactly where we were. It was a good thing we hadn't told them; we wouldn't have wanted them to worry.

We started our tour with the stelae field for which Axum is most famous. I gather that Axumite rulers had carved-stone monoliths erected to signify their power or majesty, or perhaps their manliness. The largest of the lot is attributed to King Remhai, who ruled the region in the third century. It lies on its side, in pieces. Having dragged the ten-metre-long, 500-tonne monstrosity four kilometres from the quarry, it fell and broke while workers struggled to put it up. The chief engineer's next words were probably his last. The highlight of the collection was probably the stela that had recently been repatriated from Rome following its theft by Mussolini's troops. Besides returning it, the Italians were paying for it to be put back up, piece by piece. While most buildings in Ethiopia are erected using rickety scaffolding made of eucalyptus poles, this monolith was being re-erected using a frame that wouldn't have looked out of place on the International Space Station.

We drove to the bathing pool of Queen Sheba, mother of Menelik I. Testeye was very frank in pointing out that there was no good reason to believe that the site had anything to do with Queen Sheba, or that Queen Sheba had even existed. Naughty young boys dove and swam naked in the reservoir, and women gathered drinking water from stone steps. Given how vile the water looked, it may have been safer to drink pee.

We continued to the hilltop tombs of Kaleb and Gebre Meskel. The crypts had fluorescent lighting but no power, so we used thin candles to light our way. The traditional interpretation is that palaces of the sixth-century father-and-son emperors once stood on the site, but only the tombs remain. This interpretation isn't helped by counterclaims that Kaleb is buried at a monastery five kilometres out of town, and that Gebre Meskel is buried eighty kilometres away in Debre Damo Debir.

Lindsay and I looked north. Testeye told us that great historical and religious sites lay between Axum and Eritrea. Largely unknown to the Western world, they will probably soon be major tourist destinations. Testeye also explained that part of the reason for the demise of the Axumite empire was the demolition of the region's great forests to meet demand for timber in Egypt and China. These tall trees had moderated the climate, and their destruction had made the region much hotter and drier. Some of the surrounding hillsides were now covered with eucalyptus forests, and for the first time, I heard something negative said about them. Testeye claimed that they drew a lot of water from the soil, making it less suitable for crops. Great for building and burning, they were not so great for the landscape.

But is the claim that eucalypts are harmful to soil legitimate? Australian soils are among the oldest in the world, and have lost many of their inorganic nutrients, particularly phosphorus, essential for plant growth. Having evolved under these circumstances, eucalypts are well suited to deal with that problem. Much of Australia is dry, and although eucalypts are not impervious to drought, many are at least tolerant of periods of water shortage. It is strange, then, that when planted in foreign lands, they might be accused of taking too many soil nutrients and utilizing too much water.

The care and cultivation of eucalyptus forests is a field of considerable interest. Experts try to determine which species should be used in establishing plantations in foreign lands. After finding species that are well suited to local conditions, it is important to choose types that grow as quickly as possible. Silviculturalists attempt to establish whether eucalypt forests are particularly flammable, study ways to harvest eucalypts forests in an environmentally sustainable way, and determine whether or not eucalypt plantations deplete soil nutrients or use excessive water.

The problem seems to be one of expectation. Eucalypts are planted because they grow quickly, but growing trees use a lot of water and nutrients; eucalypts are probably no worse than any other group of trees. Eucalypts are popular, in part, because they can be harvested not so many years after planting, given the right conditions. However, it is in the first decade or so that these trees extract the most water and nutrients from the soil. If harvesters were a bit more patient, felling the trees at a greater age, soil depletion would be less severe. Also, in many countries, the leaf "litter" that accumulates under the trees is taken away. In doing so, many of the nutrients that would eventually be returned to the soil by decomposition are lost. The bottom line is that you don't get anything for nothing.

We drove back downhill to the compound of the Cathedral of Tsion Maryam, or St. Mary of Zion. Testeye pointed out the building where the Ark of the Covenant is said to reside, guarded year in and year out by a priest. Fans of *Indiana Jones* will remember that the Ark is the chest that the Hebrews used to hold the tablets bearing the Ten Commandments. I asked Testeye if he believed that the Ark really was inside. After a pause, he said that he really did believe for three reasons. First, if it weren't there, why would so many thousands of people make a pilgrimage to the site every year? Second, why use the word "Zion" if the contents of the building did not have some formal link to Israel? Finally, why would a priest dedicate his entire life to the protection of the Ark if it didn't really exist?

We then descended to a museum that housed some really fabulous historical artifacts. Among these were the robes and crowns of all the Ethiopian emperors dating back as far as these things go. I crossed my fingers and asked if the robe of Emperor Menelik II, the man who had brought eucalypts to Ethiopia, was there. "Absolutely," I was told. I was delighted to find that Menelik's robe was deep red and lavishly decorated in gold. Unless Menelik had dragged his robes across the dusty ground, then he must have been a really tall chap. I pushed my luck and asked about Menelik's crown. "Why certainly, right over here," I was told. It was solid gold and monstrously large. Menelik must have had a great chiropractor. No one could explain to me why the crown has earflaps. Despite their immense value, the artifacts were protected by nothing more than the cheapest of sliding glass doors and locks. While the Axum airport is guarded by military personnel with machine guns, these treasures are guarded by a young woman and an old man, both with archaic metal-detecting wands. A gang of thieves wouldn't have to be particularly well organized to stroll off with whatever they wanted.

As I FLEW NORTH over the Sahara Desert, I reflected on my time with Lindsay. The bad things in Ethiopia are twice as bad as I have summarized, but the good things are five times better than I could possibly describe. Ethiopia is not a travel destination for the faint of heart. Outside the compounds of the few hotels with many stars, Ethiopia is a gritty place. Lindsay seemed surprised when I said that I didn't think Lisa was tough enough for an adventure like ours. Indeed, I am not sure how many other friends I would have wanted beside me on this trip.

CHAPTER THIRTEEN

Geothermal Heating and Diabolical Clichés

REASON NUMBER THIRTEEN FOR INTRODUCING A FOREIGN SPECIES: BECAUSE ALL OF MY SOIL IS BLOWING AWAY.

ROBIN JONES DIDN'T MAKE me love him at the Icelandair check-in desk. The snotty woman behind the counter said that she wasn't going to let him board the flight. Apparently, the name on his passport didn't match the name on his ticket. When he asked me to book our trip, Robin had failed to inform me that his real name was Leslie. Robin pulled at his eyebrows as he always does when he is at all nervous. This tugging can go on for ten minutes without a break. Surprisingly, he still has intact woolly eyebrows. After some sweet talk that stuck in my throat, Robin was finally permitted to board.

Robin latched onto my guidebook to Iceland like one of those fish that glom onto passing sharks. I had been assigned a window seat, but somehow I wound up in the middle seat so that Robin, a committed photographer, could snap away during takeoff and landing.

Robin and I were off to Iceland in search of lupines. Not just any lupine—we wanted to see the Nootka lupine. Big, beautiful lupines with masses of purple flowers and an optimistic outlook. Who doesn't like lupines? Well, it seems that Icelanders don't, and they are regretting their decision to introduce them. They are now thinking of clever ways to get rid of them.

I was a little concerned that I might not find any lupines in Iceland. If I didn't, it was going to be a very expensive vacation; Iceland is a costly place. I need not have worried. I had spotted eucalyptus trees within an hour of landing in Ethiopia, but I beat that record in Iceland. Just before touchdown at Keflavík, I could see their happy purple spikes smiling up at me from adjacent fields. First a small patch, then a big patch, then a field full of lupines.

Too wired to sleep on the hour-long bus ride from Keflavík to Reykjavík, I peered out the window and studied the sleeping faces around me. As my wristwatch ticked over midnight, the sun had still not touched the horizon. It did so about fifteen minutes later, but it didn't stay hidden for long. Visiting in late June, Robin and I were going to see a lot of sunshine.

WHEN ICELAND WAS FIRST SETTLED by Vikings about 1,100 years ago, the island had forests. Not mighty, great green coniferous forests, but miserly, scrubby birch forests. Still, wood is wood, and the new settlers promptly got on with cutting it all down. The situation wasn't helped when sheep were introduced to Iceland, as they chewed up every brave little birch seedling. And so, with nothing to hold it in place, the island's soil started to blow away. This is never a good thing.

A number of solutions were considered, including the introduction of lupines. One of the nicest things about lupines is that their roots house special bacteria that can extract otherwise useless nitrogen from the atmosphere for incorporation into the plant's tissues. When the plant dies and rots, the soil is enriched with nitrogen, and following generations of plants have a better chance of surviving. Lupines were expected to have a further benefit in Iceland—they could be used to feed livestock.

On paper, it looked like a good plan, and the plant was sown

as early as 1885. However, the wrong species was chosen for introduction. Some lupines are perfectly palatable, but other species
are toxic, containing noxious chemicals. These plants even have
a special poison named after them: lupinine. Symptoms of lupine
poisoning, also known as lupinosis, include numbness of the feet
and hands, nausea, drowsiness, headaches, and dehydration from
diarrhea, leading to shock. Individuals have been known to experience hallucinations and convulsions after eating lupines, followed
shortly after by death. Before you start feeding lupines to your pet
rabbit, check with an authority—you may have purchased one of
the nasty ones. Iceland made that mistake.

Nootka lupines, native to Alaska and coastal western British
Columbia, are among the poisonous ones, making them pretty rot-
ten fodder. Furthermore, the diversity of native Icelandic plants
drops significantly where lupines grow densely. Although lupines
have some value in controlling erosion in badly degraded habitats
in Iceland, the country was increasingly under siege from a purple-
flowered invader that many did not want.

When I woke the next day, I found that our hotel room was
furnished in pieces from next year's Ikea catalogue. Smartly kit-
ted out, it was a stark contrast to the earthiness of hotel rooms in
Ethiopia. The room was so clean that it squeaked even if I didn't
touch anything. The lights worked and the drinking water was safe
but smelled of sulphur. I tried to wake up slowly, but when Robin
noticed a sliver of eyeball between my eyelids, he started reading passages to me from my guidebook which had, for all intents,
become his. As I lay in bed, I composed a little poem about Iceland:

> Roses are red,
> Midnight's bright blue,
> Lupines are purple,
> A soft mauvey hue.

Suggestions for a much better poem for the book's next edition should be sent to:

> Dr. Glen Chilton,
> School of Marine and Tropical Biology,
> James Cook University,
> Townsville, Queensland, 4811, Australia

Reykjavík, Iceland's capital, is home to about 115,000 people. Suburbs like Garðabær, Bessastaðir, and Hafnarfjörður swell the city's population to 200,000, or two-thirds of the country's total population. After breakfast, Robin and I strolled east along the waterfront, and I tried to form some first impressions of Reykjavík in full-blown daylight. Let's see. . . . Well, it smelled a bit of fish. Not so unusual for a country almost entirely dependent on the sea's bounty. Other than the fishy smell, the city was fantastically tidy and unpolluted. There were a lot of buildings, and so there must be a lot of people, but they had either already arrived at work or were still asleep after enjoying the nightlife that, famously, does not begin until people in every other part of the world have gone to bed. In either case, Robin and I had the waterfront walk pretty much to ourselves. Even though Reykjavík isn't a skyscrapery sort of place, it certainly had lots of construction cranes on the go. What I could see of the city seemed either newly constructed or newly scrubbed. Well into the second half of June, there was a distinct chill on the breeze, and I was pleased that I had brought a fleece jacket.

I had met Robin a few years earlier while living in Scotland, but until now it hadn't occurred to me that he was a habitual talker. As we walked, the chatter flowed—it was really quite amazing. I don't know many people who are unable to tolerate silence, and I wasn't entirely sure of my role. Even when his dialogues had run their course, Robin continued to talk, only more quietly and in sentence fragments.

This was a photographer's holiday for Robin. It became quickly apparent that he liked to take his time setting up each photograph.

He even held up his thumbs and forefingers and peeped through the resulting rectangle like a 1940s film director. When he settled in to take some snaps, I found a place to sit. I discovered that there are few things in life more boring than watching someone else take a photograph. Watching someone listen to an audiobook might qualify. Having not yet succumbed to the allure of digital photography, Robin had soon finished his first roll of thirty-six shots.

"How many rolls did you bring?"

"About twenty," he replied.

We walked to a city park around Tjörnin Lake, home to the world's most optimistic ducks. I found Reykjavík so polished and pretty that I started to wonder what they did with residents who had had a run of bad luck. What happened if you ran short on cash and didn't manage to maintain your home and yard to the highest of standards? Did they knock down your house, clear away the rubble, and put you on a flight to somewhere less pretty?

It would be unfair of me to say that all Icelandic men and women are beautiful. After all, I haven't seen them all yet. Even so, I started to wonder what happened to those who exited adolescence a little less beautiful than the remainder of their cohort. Did they knock down your house, clear away the rubble, and put you on a flight to somewhere less discriminating?

It was a bright day, and the breeze was tasty. There was an abundance of park benches, and none of them had those depressing plaques that read: "In memory of Erik Johansson, whose miserable, lingering death put an end to his miserable, lingering life." I sat on a bench while Robin took photographs of brightly painted corrugated metal roofs. I watched an older park worker scrape weeds from between paving stones with pride and enthusiasm, while his younger partner watered pansies to perfection while dancing to the music from his headphones.

We ascended a hill for a view of the city. We passed through fields of cheerful lupines to get to the top. As ornamental flowering plants go, lupines are rather attractive creatures. In describing their leaves and stems, experts use expressions like "petiolated," "densely pubescent," "oblong-obovate," and "glabrous." It all sounded vaguely naughty. The flowers were even worse: "more or less cleft" with "broad calyx lobes."

Robin took photographs while I leaned back on a rock and told him what I had read about the word "lupine." That spelling is a little more common in North America, while "lupin" is more frequently used in Europe. The *Oxford English Dictionary* even credits the spelling "lupyne." According to an assortment of dictionaries, the word can be pronounced "lü/pīn," "lü/pən," "lü/pin" or "l(j)u:pin." Those same dictionaries gave me endless hypotheses about linguistic origins. There is no doubt that the word is derived from the Latin words *lupinus* and *lupinum,* meaning wolf-like, but the connection isn't clear. Some said that ancients considered lupine seeds suitable only for consumption by wolves. Others claimed that lupines were considered to rampage over the landscape like a pack of ravenous wolves. Perhaps there was a feeling that lupines steal nutrients from the soil like a pack of ravenous wolves, even though we now know that lupines contribute to soil fertility. Take your pick, or make up something else.

That evening, Robin and I set off to find a moderately priced restaurant. Failing that, we found a nice-looking curry restaurant, and I tried to ignore the prices. I quickly settled on soup and a main course, but Robin repeatedly sent the server away because he was deep into a story about Canterbury and too busy to look at the menu. To be fair, I had asked him about his time in Canterbury, but by the time the story was finished, it was nowhere near where it had started. Robin changed his mind back and forth about what to eat and finally settled on fish soup and Arctic char. Our server gave me a conspiratorial shoulder shrug. The bill was $150 and should have come with the sort of offer I had been given at the hotel in Addis Ababa.

IN SCHOLARLY CIRCLES, lupines are a hot deal. Of the roughly 200 research papers that are published on lupines each year, most deal with their biochemistry. What sort of nasty chemicals do they produce? What sort of useful chemicals do they produce? Can I make money from either? My database search for scientific publications on the Nootka lupine in particular returned an awful lot of articles about Iceland. These papers addressed three major questions. Is it possible to use lupines to help reclaim badly degraded habitat in Iceland? Can lupines help in re-establishing Iceland's forests? Could Iceland grow lupines, chop them down, and then bury them as a way of sequestering carbon dioxide from the atmosphere? Each of the papers I consulted carried the warning that lupines are invasive and unlikely to stay where they are put. It seemed like a good time for me to look for more lupines.

June twenty-first marked my fiftieth summer solstice. And since I was closer to the North Pole than I had ever been, it was to be the longest day of my life. It seemed like the sort of day that needed to be celebrated in a special way. Robin found a description of a hiking trail that fit the bill. The wildflowers and scenery sounded just right for Robin, and the rocky scramble from sea level to 780 metres seemed the right challenge for me.

Reykjavík sits on the south side of Faxaflói Bay; the Mount Esja ridge runs across the north side. We walked to Reykjavík's bus terminal and caught the Number 15, driven by a man who detested piloting a bus that early on a Saturday morning. He blasted us with a radio station playing all of the worst music from the '60s and '70s. "I'm a Believer" was rattling through my head for the rest of the day, and I hadn't liked The Monkees even when I was ten.

Leaving the Number 15 at Mosfellsbær, we got on the Number 27, driven by the only person in Iceland over the age of six months who didn't speak fluent English.

"Does this bus go to Mount Esja?"

"Já."

"Is the ticket we bought in Reykjavík good for this part of the ride, or do we need to buy another ticket?"

"Já."

"Could you tell us where to get off for Mount Esja?"

"Já."

"Is there a troll in your trousers?"

"*Já.*"

Luckily, there was a young woman from China who was studying at the university in Reykjavík (which sounds like the start of a limerick) who spoke perfect English and was able to show us where to get off. We never got to see the troll.

And then I ran into a little problem. Just one minute down the trail, Robin stopped for several minutes to take a photograph of a creek. After another thirty seconds of hiking, he stopped to take a photograph of the same creek from a different angle.

"Did you bring enough film today, Robin?"

"Six rolls of this, two rolls of that, and two rolls of the other; I should be fine."

"Well, Robin, I don't want to rush you, so how would it be if I go on ahead? I'll push on for the top and pick you up on the way down. All right?"

Stunted pine trees and birch bushes decorated the lowest portions of the trail. These quickly tapered off, and I was surrounded by fields of cow parsley, which were equally quickly replaced by dense stands of lupines. The shiest lupines came to my hip, and the bolder ones reached my ribs. About half the plants were in flower, and it was clear that we had timed our trip perfectly to see them. A week earlier and the flowers wouldn't have yet unfolded. A week later and the flowers toward the bottom of the spike would have been dropping off.

I plucked a spike to examine the flowers in more detail. Each spike had eight or ten nodes, each with a whorl of eight flowers. Flowers evidently matured at the bottom first, and later near the top. The lower petals of each flower were indigo, and the upper ones were whitish. When I stood back to look at thousands and thousands of flowers swaying slightly in the breeze, I found that some trick of perception meant that I couldn't focus on any of them. It was like watching a documentary about bumblebees with the projector slightly out of focus, or an amateur stage production of *The Sound of Music.*

As I climbed, even the lupines couldn't hold on, and the vegetation turned to ground-hugging tufts of green fuzz dotted with the tiniest flowers in yellow, white, and blue. The soil got thinner and the boulders became more abundant, and I tripped several times. The trail officially ended after a particularly steep bit, and most people had signed their name in a guest book before heading back down. Not being "most people," I continued on over loose rock and rubble, pushing for the very top. I tried to walk but felt the need to tackle the last bit on all fours.

If the summit of Mount Esja is 780 metres high, then I got to 765. Beyond this point, progress was less a matter of hiking and more a matter of climbing and possibly plunging. Instead I found a nook between two rocks, plonked my bum down, and admired the stunning view below me while enjoying a good long think. And the thoughts came easily. Among them: (1) What a lucky sod I am; and (2) For the cost of last night's meal, I probably wouldn't have too much trouble getting someone murdered. On the descent I found Robin and heard all about his photographic adventures.

Over a pizza dinner, the cheapest restaurant option in Reykjavík, I asked Robin what he wanted to do with the following day. He had found a brochure describing a guided excursion to some of southern Iceland's greatest geological attractions. It included a series of geysers and a visit to a giant rip in the earth. Robin was particularly keen to see the spot, having watched a television show about it a couple of months earlier. He passed me the brochure.

"I see it's 8,500 krona," I said. "And that's about . . . well, it's a lot of money."

"Yes," Robin replied. "But it's a once-in-a-lifetime opportunity."

A VAN FROM REYKJAVÍK EXCURSIONS picked us up outside our hotel and dropped us at its bus terminal. Making the fundamental error of being prompt, polite, and organized, the firm was now suffering from its own success, with ever so many clients, drooling in anticipation of seeing geysers and other holes in the ground. The first bus with an English-speaking guide filled up, followed by a bus with a guide who could give commentary in both French and English, leaving us to board a bus with Péter, a guide who didn't exactly speak English or French, but didn't quite speak Icelandic either. Fifty-seven clients times three buses times 8,500 krona . . . I suspected the company could easily afford the outrageous cost of gas in Iceland.

We were off on the Golden Tour, which sounded vaguely dirty. Péter provided anecdotes about Reykjavík's largest shopping mall, salmon fishing in the city's streams, and locals going to Austria to ski, and then told a little joke about what we should do in case of an accident in which he was rendered unconscious. Whenever Péter got stuck for an expression in English, he gently slipped into Icelandic. Even in English, his accent was a bit thick, and it took me several guesses about "lovers' tourists" to realize he was saying "lavatories"—not a mistake that anyone wants to make.

As we passed swaying purple fields, Péter trotted out his stories about lupines. He mistakenly told us that the plants had not been introduced to Iceland until the 1950s. They had rapidly become a pest, and in an attempt to combat them they were being harvested for use in the production of fertilizer. I think that Icelanders are a little embarrassed about the way their ancestors cut down all the forests, leaving just a few scrubby little trees. Péter told us that the birch and willow shrubs around us were native, but that everything else had been introduced from other nations with similar climates. The habitat struck me as stark, although Robin suggested the altogether better expressions "sweeping" and "rugged." It was a lot of bare ground and sparse cover, and it left me wondering how much of it had been forested before the first human occupation.

We stopped for fifteen minutes at a volcanic explosion, Crater Keri, one of a chain of craters and the easiest to get to by bus. This crater was surrounded by the contents of eight tour buses. Keri had exploded some 6,500 years earlier and was half-filled with beautiful blue water. Having taken an antihistamine to counter the pollen-rich air of southern Iceland, I was feeling pretty mellow about the explosions, landslides, and frequent earthquakes Péter told us were shaping the local topography.

We arrived at Gullfoss, which I gather means "golden waterfall." In the distance, we spied a substantial icefield, and to the right was the eponymous waterfall, which isn't the sort of thing you would go over twice. Broad and arcing with a two-step drop, it was all about noise and visitors. Water from the River Hvíta fell into a narrow gorge, which meant plenty of mist, plenty of happy moss, and a nice rainbow.

From there we moved on to a geyser field. The biggest of the lot, named Geysir, was old and tired. Although it was a real whopper when it went off, it did so with diminished frequency, saving itself for the aftermath of earthquakes. Despite its geriatric predisposition, every geyser in the world is named after it. Its smaller brother, Strokkur, erupts on the scale of Old Faithful in Yosemite Park at twenty-five to thirty-five metres, which it does every two to ten minutes. I sat on a bench and watched it erupt several times. Robin took lots and lots of photographs.

Just beyond Þingvallavatn, Iceland's largest inland sea, we found ourselves at Þingvellir National Park, which is particularly significant to geologists. According to a plaque, "The junction of the tectonic plates is more clearly visible here than anywhere else in the world." I was expecting some sort of fire-and-brimstone setting, the kind of place where you might throw an enemy to send them to hell. Not that I was disappointed exactly, but this meeting of tectonic plates was a groove in the Earth, five or ten metres across and about the same depth, half-filled with cheerful blue water. Bouldery to be sure, but not hellish. We were told that the American and European plates move apart by two centimetres a year, meaning that GPS calculations have to be updated once per decade. Robin's reaction to the whole thing was "That's brilliant, that is!"

WHEN ROBIN HAD ASKED ME to set the itinerary for our trip, he explained that whatever looked good to me would be fine with him. And so I checked to see where we could get to on Air Iceland from Reykjavík. I read the description of each of the communities in a guidebook and chose two that were most likely to support lupines.

Most airlines have a great screaming infantile fit if even one passenger isn't strapped into their seat forty minutes before the scheduled departure time. This does not apply to Air Iceland. Arriving at the regional airport in Reykjavík two hours before our flight, we were turned away from the check-in desk and asked to report back in ninety minutes. Five minutes before takeoff, we were summoned to the airplane. No metal detectors to walk through, no X-ray machines for the carry-on luggage, and the woman who checked our boarding passes saw no reason to ask for identification.

By coincidence, the Fokker 50 that had taken Lindsay and me around northern Ethiopia was the same model that took Robin and me to Heimaey on the Westman Islands off Iceland's south coast. Same model but built in a very different era. Unlike the filled-to-the-brim planes in Ethiopia, there were only nine other passengers on the fifty-two-seater here. Robin had no trouble getting a window seat.

Heimaey is one of Iceland's largest communities, even though it is home to only 5,000 people. Its airport is, in a word, cute. For the impatient traveller like me, it is possible to grab one's luggage as it is lifted down from the hold. For those with more patience, a trolley with the luggage is driven straight into the departure lounge. Outside the terminal, the taxi rank sat empty, and no one stopped to give us a lift into town. It was time for a tramp.

Unfortunately, Robin was still wearing his camera around his neck, and as soon as he saw some interesting rocks, he stopped to compose a photograph. Twenty seconds later, he spied a rock with an interesting flower and stopped to compose a photograph. Fifteen seconds later, he spotted a mound he could stand on to compose a better photograph of the rock with the flower.

"Look, Robin, rather than standing around strapped to this very heavy backpack while you snap photos, shall we walk into town first?"

"Oops. Sorry. Yes . . . I, um, forgot about the backpack," and although he didn't put the camera away, he and his little suitcase on wheels did struggle to keep up.

We found our guesthouse and dropped our bags before setting off in search of adventure and food. I was distressed to find that Robin still had his camera around his neck and a pack full of camera accessories on his back. He went almost two minutes before pulling off the lens cap, but in the next ten minutes we didn't move twenty-five metres. Or rather, I didn't move twenty-five metres; Robin was fifty metres up a hillside.

Watching someone else take photographs is like watching them trim their fingernails while muttering about F-stops, shutter speeds, and depth of field.

"Robin, you need to get off the road."

"What?"

"You are standing in the middle of the road, and you are about to get run down." I snapped. "Robin, I'm going to leave you to it. How would it be if we met up in a couple of hours, say four o'clock? You have the key to the room."

And then I marched off in a straight line to get some food.

I was well into an internal dialogue that featured Robin as a really poor choice of travelling companion. The dialogue changed to a consideration of Iceland as a poor choice of destinations. If this was, indeed, Iceland's second biggest community, I had seen a good chunk of it in less than an hour, and there wasn't a bloody lupine in sight. And when I found the so-called grocery store, it was about as well stocked as the top drawer of a nun's bedside table and didn't have a single carton of milk on the shelves. But after I stuffed back a banana, some yoghurt, and a bag of salty peanuts, the world started to seem a cheerier place. Robin wasn't a buffoon; he was Robin, and it was as much his photo holiday as it was my lupine adventure. I felt like a jerk.

And Iceland started to look pretty good again. I spotted hillsides with patches of lupines and took the time to look at the soaring, volcano-created peaks around me. I watched children who had just started their summer holidays. Some were kicking footballs, some practising their hopeless golf swings, some splashing in the pool, and some roped up on a cliff face. I started to examine closely the whimsical houses that made up Heimaey. One looked like a cross between a Scottish petrol station and a Nevada brothel. Another was based on a Swiss chalet designed by a blind Cuban architect who didn't know where Switzerland was.

I walked by the town's facility for generating heat for its homes. A plaque out front explained that heating oil had fallen out of favour after a series of nasty fires. After a volcanic eruption in 1973, someone got the idea of using the lava's heat to warm homes and started a pilot project on five houses and the hospital in 1978. Ten years later, the lava cooled down. Now the island is heated by electricity from the mainland, supplemented by heat from the community's garbage incinerator.

I walked to the edge of the town's lava flow, the result of the volcanic eruption. I watched the ferry as it docked. I strolled along the harbourfront and watched a cliff of nesting kittiwakes. When I met Robin, I offered up a bottle of red wine and a package of cookies, and asked him all about his photographic ramblings.

AFTER A BREAKFAST gleaned from a slightly better-stocked grocery store, we trundled off along the island's west shore, heading south. We followed a line of lava cliffs—not the sort that anyone would make a grand suicide attempt from, but death would almost certainly result from a misstep. Rough and jagged black lava stripped the tread from my hiking boots.

In terms of birdlife and plant life, an important ecological principle was demonstrated here. Close to the equator, you find lots of diversity but low abundance. Here, closer to the pole, lives a lesser diversity of form but in tremendous abundance. White Wagtails skittered everywhere, and oystercatchers and redshanks scolded us unremittingly. Robin took lots of photos of the lava and offshore sea stacks, and spent not an insubstantial portion of my day trying to get just the right shot of fulmars soaring by the cliff edge. I lay on the grass while all this was going on, thinking pleasant thoughts.

We walked toward a series of tall wooden racks. They were obviously designed to dry something, but from a distance, we couldn't imagine what. As we got closer we found, hanging from blue nylon ropes, many thousands of fish heads. Why in the world would anyone want to dry a fish head, let alone thousands of them? They certainly weren't going to get any drier, so why hadn't they been collected? Perhaps they make really good soup. The racks were close enough to town to be convenient, but far enough to keep down complaints about the smell. Resources from the sea. The coinage of Iceland tells me that islanders recognize and appreciate their tie to marine food. A cod is found on the 1-krona coin. The 5-krona coin features a dolphin, with a capelin on the 10 krona, a shore crab on the 50 krona, and a lumpfish on the 100 krona.

At the south end of the island, like a big blob of quickly drying paint, is a piece of land hanging on by a narrow isthmus, no doubt the result of some long-extinct volcano. Robin followed the roadway to the peak, but I circled from the periphery. This grassy peak, named Stórhöfði, hosted a lot of sheep. With sheep comes sheep poop, and with that come flies. They didn't bite, but had no end of fun getting up my nose. I was puzzled by the wealth of small burrows in the hillside. I saw no evidence of rabbits. Then it occurred to me that the holes were puffin nesting burrows. The ground beneath my feet must have been full of growing puffin chicks, and I kept to the trails to minimize the risk of collapsing a burrow.

Back in town, Robin and I walked to the lava field. The ground underfoot was tortured and twisted, but also remarkably fragile. Somehow I expected cooled lava to be as hard as steel, but it broke and crumbled rather easily. Wherever a little ash had settled to make the beginnings of soil, lupines had established themselves. And I suppose that this was the point, really. They had been introduced to Iceland to stabilize the soil where nothing else would grow.

We took the most gradual route I could find to Eldfell's 200-

metre peak. Beyond lupines, what vegetation did manage to get a foothold was very tiny. The stones underfoot were thumbnail-sized, and this made for a lot of backslip. It was a tough climb, but our efforts were rewarded with a stunning view. I have been up a lot of mountains, and the view from this one ranked highly. Grassy green hills and plains lay to the east and south. Lava fields to the northeast were sage-coloured from lichen and moss that bravely clung to the land. The town lay to the northwest. To the north across the channel were the peaks and glaciers of mainland Iceland, and all around was a whole lot of ocean stretching to infinity. The breeze blew from the east, and as it climbed the dark lava rubble, it warmed. Having been to the Westman Islands, I now have no need to travel to the Galapagos.

While we had been hiking, Heimaey had been invaded by a battalion of ten-year-old boys. It was something like *Lord of the Flies,* but on a much larger scale and with fewer spears. In a café, Robin and I were told that a three-day soccer tournament was about to begin, and that the island's population had just swollen by 1,000 boys and their guardians. The café was filled with little people kicking toilet doors, trying to get their teammates to hurry up. Our server explained that the chef had "gone away to sea," and that the items on offer were rather meager. Most of the beverages were gone too. The chef had probably run away at just the right time. We high-tailed it back to Reykjavík.

I WAS IN GREAT ANTICIPATION of the forty-minute flight from Reykjavík to Ísafjöður. It seemed a delightful opportunity to see the country from above, particularly since the skies were completely clear. Well, I can report that most of the interior of Iceland looks remarkably like the back of Robin's head.

I tried to imagine the meeting between the Ísafjöður town council and Iceland's Federal Aviation Authority when the application for an airport came up for discussion. "Now, let's see if we understand you. You want to build the airport on the far side of the fiord from the town? Well, that's up to you. Now, to get to the runway, planes will have to fly down a particularly narrow valley with their wings practically touching the cliff faces on both sides, right? And to lose altitude, in a couple of places the planes will come within six metres of the ground before diving over the next cliff, is that right? And then, at the very last minute, the plane will have to bank hard to starboard to have any chance of snagging the runway? And you think that passengers are going to go for this? You do realize that planes will be able to land only during daylight? So in the middle of winter, that will be about ten minutes each day. Well, good luck!"

And goodness knows there are a lot of valleys and fiords in this region. Boasting 35 percent of Iceland's coastline but only 8 percent of its land mass, the northern fiordlands looked like the head of a dragon to early cartographers. To me, a map of the region looked like the head of a dragon puking up islands.

As we prepared to explore Ísafjöður, I prayed silently. "Please don't let Robin bring his camera. Please don't let Robin bring his camera." There is no God.

Ísafjöður is beautiful in every meaningful way. Situated on a spit of land, it is surrounded by cliffs and water. The architecture is the perfect juxtaposition of warehouses and fish plants against brightly coloured single and multi-family dwellings. Not every building was slapdash, but there was an organic realness to the place.

The town's tourist information office was situated beside a café. Robin got the first round of drinks in while I inquired about hikes. Then I noticed a poster for the Óshaíðarhlaupið. If I could trust my grasp of Icelandic—which I couldn't—it seemed to imply that the town was going to host a half-marathon race two days hence. Checking with the endlessly friendly information staff confirmed my suspicions. A fellow showed me the point-to-point route on a map and offered to help me register for the race online. I asked his name. When his response finished rattling around in my brain, it came out sounding like a dirty word, so I thought of him as "Lars," which probably isn't even an Icelandic name. "You will be our only foreign runner. Prepare to be famous!" said Lars.

"Um, twenty-one kilometres is a long way. . . . I haven't been doing a lot of training over the past few months. . . ." A half-marathon was bound to leave me feeling pretty stiff. There were two other distances, but surely the four kilometres was for children and the ten kilometres was for sissies. If I ran twenty-one kilometres, it would give me the chance to see more of the coastline—roughly twenty-one kilometres more, I should think. Oh, what the heck?

While getting in a second round of drinks, I spoke to the barmaid, who didn't seem the typical blond-eyed, blue-haired Icelandic type. She explained that she was from the Philippines and had been a professional singer. While on tour in China she had met an Icelandic gentleman and had moved to be with him. That was eight years earlier, and she had to admit that she was still struggling with the language.

ROBIN AND I SET OFF for a hike. We passed through Ísafjöður, aiming for the closed end of the fiord. Several well-tended gardens sported lupines; they weren't the nasty purple variety that infested large chunks of Iceland, but pink, red, cream, and white forms. Just beyond town, on avalanche-prone hillsides, grew wild invasive lupines with their toxic purple horridness.

We arrived at a very tall waterfall in the Tunguskógur region. A very pretty cascade indeed, the water took its time passing down various ledges, but did so in a nearly straight line, making it easy for Robin to get it all in one photograph. On some slopes, coniferous trees had been planted. In most spots, they were doing rather poorly. The ravages of winter, or perhaps an insect pest, had turned most of their needles brown. By the waterfall, the trees were a little more proud of themselves, many having reached the lofty height of four or five metres. However, it was clear that the optimist who had ordered the planting of these trees wasn't fully committed to native species. *Picea sitchensis*, Sitka spruce to me and Sitkagreni to an Icelander, had been introduced from Alaska in 1951. Russia had contributed *Larix sibirica* in 1951, Alaska had provided *Pinus contorta* in 1958, and *Picea abies* had made the leap from Norway in 1961. We took a gentle hike through a very short forest.

Back in town, I picked up my race package for the following day. To that point, Robin and I had been blessed with continuous good weather, but the moment I was handed the package the whole scene changed. Dark clouds blew in, the temperature fell, and it started to rain. It was as though the Nordic weather gods were going to punish me for having the impudence to register for a half-marathon without sufficient training.

At 12:45 p.m. the next day, a bus took a few dozen half-marathon runners up the fiord to the small fishing community of Bolungarvík. As we piled on, only one runner wasn't equipped with clothing appropriate for the weather, and he was clearly a lot more frightened than the rest. As we drove, a race organizer stood up every few minutes to give instructions about the course. In Icelandic. I was sitting at the front of the bus, and he couldn't see the terror in my eyes. "I am going to get lost and die of hypothermia," I thought.

We tromped off the bus in Bolungarvík, voted Iceland's most depressing community four times in the last six years. The digital readout on the postal building claimed that the temperature was 5°C. I didn't need the postal service to tell me that the wind was howling, rain was falling, and I was bloody cold. I was instructed to drop my jacket in a van that would be waiting for us at the finish line, for those of us who lived that long.

"Are you from Canada?"

"What? Oh, right. Um, yes I am." My country of origin was printed in large friendly letters on my shorts.

"Did you come here just for the race?"

"Honestly, until two days ago, I didn't know that there *was* a race. I just saw a poster," and part of me wished that I hadn't. The clock thermometer indicated that the temperature had fallen to 4°C.

We were called to the starting line. A man on a phone was in contact with the official timekeeper at the finish line.

"*Prír fundargerð!*" he called out. The rain was turning to sleet.

"*Tveir fundargerð!*" Does that mean we are almost ready to go?

"*Einn fundargerð!*" Just don't get blown into the fiord.

"Þrír, tveir, einn, fara! Góða ferð!" This is it. I am definitely going to die.

We were off. Eight seconds passed, and a delightful thing happened—I became strangely and completely calm. Having run somewhere between 250 and 300 races, my brain and body had long since learned exactly what to do when the starter's pistol went off. I relaxed.

Five young men shot to the front of the pack, and I knew that I would next see them at the finish line. After a couple of minutes, as the first spike of adrenalin disappeared, runners ahead of me started to slow down, and suddenly I wasn't at the back of the pack. By the one-kilometre marker, I was trotting along at a comfortable pace, completely within myself and doing quite well, all things considered. At the two-kilometre marker, I passed an Arctic Tern colony, and a few of them decided to have a go at me. I was later told by a runner behind me that I was the only runner who got dive-bombed.

The great fiord to my left was decorated with whitecaps. The cliffs to my right were decorated with nesting kittiwakes. Not expecting pedestrian traffic, the highway had no shoulder, and we were running on the right with the traffic at our backs—not exactly what I had been taught about road safety by Elmer the Safety Elephant. I passed a cross and memorial plaque, probably for one of last year's runners.

On I dashed, past hillsides covered with blooming lupines, feeling happy about life and hypothermia. Four kilometres, five, six. Less than four months from my fiftieth birthday, and I was doing quite well in a long footrace in Iceland. Seven kilometres, eight, nine. At the halfway point of the race, I was sitting in about tenth place.

On and on. And then I saw Ísafjöður looming ahead. That can't be right. We still have six kilometres to go. Oh, now I remember. We have to run past the town, turn around at the end of the fiord, and then run back to Ísafjöður. This meant running the last couple of kilometres into an almighty headwind. I was forced to mix running with walking.

But none it of really mattered. Most of the people in the race were a lot younger than me. I was the only person in the race who hadn't had a home-cooked meal in two months. The vomiting and diarrhea in Ethiopia had probably slimmed me down a bit, but I couldn't claim to be at the peak of health. And who cared anyway? I was going to finish well, and felt pretty proud of it. Robin proved himself to be a star in the clutch. He had been standing at the finish line for twenty minutes and snapped my photograph as I crossed. He and I snacked on the banana, bagel, and chocolate bar in my finisher's goodie bag, and I swung the finisher's medal around my neck.

THE CLERK AT THE ÍSAFJÖÐUR AIRPORT check-in counter took our luggage and issued us boarding passes. Then he turned to me and said, "There is a man looking for you."

"Did he say anything about his wife?"

"What?"

"Nothing. Just a bad joke. Where is he?"

It was Lars from the tourism office. He had driven out to the airport because I had won a small trophy for placing well in the forty to forty-nine age class. I had also won two draw prizes—a training jersey and a cap.

Robin asked Lars why a truck with a flashing light was driving up and down the runway. Lars explained that the driver was trying to frighten Arctic Terns away from the runway so that they wouldn't smash into the plane's propellers. We watched the incoming plane swoop down into Ísafjöður and make a heroic turn the moment before touchdown. Robin and I both said "Shit!" when the left wing almost hit the tarmac.

But our plane got away safely, and fields of purple lupines fell behind. I drank a complimentary glass of water and sucked on an Air Iceland chocolate wafer. I have been told that the single worst cliché in the world of travel writing is "Iceland is a land of fire and ice." While watching the back of Robin's head, I struggled to come up with a replacement. I settled on "Iceland is a land of lava and lupines." The royalty cheques should start arriving from the Iceland Tourism Board any day now.

CHAPTER FOURTEEN

A Leap of Faith

REASON NUMBER FOURTEEN FOR INTRODUCING A FOREIGN SPECIES: SOMEONE MUST HAVE GOOFED.

WHEN I FIRST SAW ROXY, she was swimming lazy laps of her indoor swimming pool. She wasn't looking well, and the tumours all over her body didn't add to her appeal. It was time to drag her out of the pool for a closer look.

Roxy is a green turtle, one of seven species of sea turtle recognized. All of them are doing very badly. The IUCN considers loggerheads and green turtles to be endangered, implying that both species are doomed unless the causes for their decline are reversed. Three other sea turtles, the leatherback, the hawksbill, and Kemp's ridley, are critically endangered—doomed, only more so. The olive ridley turtle is doing slightly better, with the designation of vulnerable to extinction. This leaves the flatback turtle, about which we know so little that we can't even assess how doomed it really is.

For a year, Roxy had been in the care of Dr. Ellen Ariel. Ellen is Senior Lecturer of Virology at the School of Veterinary and Biomedical Sciences at James Cook University in Townsville, Australia. She had long been interested in diseases of wildlife, and her recent efforts had been directed at viruses of turtles. Roxy had been brought to Ellen because her condition was so dire. If she had been left in the wild, she would have met her end rather quickly. Other facilities in the region were already full of turtles in need of aid. During her spell in captivity, Roxy's condition had waxed and waned.

Most members of the scientific fraternity were working on the assumption that the tumours sometimes seen on sea turtles were the result of a virus known as fibropapilloma-associated turtle herpesvirus, mercifully abbreviated as FPTHV. The virus had been isolated from turtle tumours, but some researchers felt that the association between growths and the infectious agent was a just a coincidence and that some other causative agent was involved.

Some of Roxy's tumours were as small as marbles, but others were the size of billiard balls. Growths that I took to be the youngest had small, pink, finger-like projections, hence the name "papilloma," from the Latin word *papilla* for "nipple." Others were smoother, in various shades of cream through grey. Some of the tumours toward Roxy's backside looked as though they were necrotic, dying, and Ellen speculated that the tissue might have been attacked by a bacteria. Most of the tumours had a good grip, but others were attached by only a thin stalk, and I wondered if this separation might progress to the point where they might simply fall off. The tumours around her eyes were not the biggest, but they were among the most debilitating. Like blinkers on a racehorse, by creating a barrier they partially blinded her. After smelling food in the water and narrowing down the spot where she knew it must be, it took her several attempts to grab it.

Ellen said that she had named the turtle Roxy because she thought that it needed a strong name. She could only assume that Roxy was a female. Currently in middle age, with a carapace length of forty-eight centimetres, he/she/it will have to grow to eighty-six centimetres before it will be possible to determine its sex without an autopsy. At that point, Roxy will be nearly twice the size, so almost eight times the mass. If she lives long enough, she might grow to a length of 130 centimetres and could weigh between 140 and 160 kilograms. Green turtles have been known to grow to 230 kilograms.

Since she had been taken into captivity, Roxy had periodically been taken out of her tank so that blood samples could be drawn and photographs taken to chart the progress of her condition. On the day of my visit, Roxy was booked in with JCU's Veterinary Emergency Centre and Hospital so that she could be X-rayed. As bad as Roxy looked on the outside, her future would be far bleaker if the tumours were also internal. I had volunteered to assist with some of the dirty work.

Ellen and I donned dark blue, heavy-cotton lab aprons and surgical gloves. Ellen was tiny enough that she could loop her apron strings twice and tie them in front; I had to knot mine in back. We laid a third apron on the floor. I got my instructions. The trick was to get the turtle safely out of her swimming pool and on to her back on the apron without breaking any bones—hers or mine. I stood quietly beside the waist-height pool and waited for Roxy to swim past me. I then reached in, took hold of her front flippers gently but firmly next to her armpits (flipperpits, I suppose), and scooped her up. In doing so, I had a good grip on a couple of tumours; there was no way to avoid them. I laid her down on the apron, and we ever so slowly and gently reflected her front flippers to her sides. We then used the margins of the apron to secure her. We loaded Roxy onto a large top-loading scale, and Ellen was displeased to see that the turtle had lost mass since her last weighing. Well secured for the short walk to the veterinary clinic, Roxy lay in my arms completely docile. I took each step with no less caution than I would use for a small, sick child.

About halfway to the clinic, I came to an interesting realization. Sea turtles are heavy. Nowhere near full-grown, Roxy was still 12.5 kilograms, and she wasn't equipped with a handle. I stopped beside a parked truck, put my foot on its bumper, and rested Roxy on my leg to give my arms a break.

In the clinic's waiting room, I sat with the turtle on my lap while Ellen spoke with the receptionist. In a veterinary facility that is capable of treating both companion animals and large-bodied production animals, just about every sort of creature must come through the door sooner or later. Even so, the receptionist's eyes got wide when she looked at Roxy and me.

"I think there's something wrong with my rabbit," I said, trying to break the ice. The receptionist smiled in a way that said she didn't think I was funny.

We were met by Mike Jeffery, the clinic's veterinary radiographer, and led into the X-ray facility. Like all people involved in the care of animals, part of Mike's job was to deal with the anxiety of owners. Ellen looked comparatively calm, but she must have been worried about what news the examination might reveal. I certainly was. In just over an hour, I had become very attached to poor Roxy.

With the turtle on its back, securely wrapped and positioned carefully on the X-ray table, Mike, Ellen, and I retreated to the safety of the shielded portion of an adjoining room. When the first digital image came up, Mike let out an "Oh my!" I am not an expert in radiography, and all my previous experience involved examining X-rays of humans, but even I could see that the situation wasn't great. The tumours stood out from the rest of the image as bright white spheres. They were large and numerous. If Roxy had been a pet dog or cat, she would have been euthanized immediately.

Mike repositioned Roxy a couple of times and snapped additional images. He said that we might get additional worthwhile information by capturing X-ray images horizontally through Roxy's body. The difficulty was that the machine wasn't designed to do that sort of work. The device that emitted the radiation could be swivelled, but the imaging plate couldn't. "I need a volunteer," said Mike. I immediately agreed to hold the plate in place and walked toward a rack of lead-lined aprons that would, presumably, protect me. I had a choice: there were bright pink aprons and others decorated in camouflage colours. I picked one of the latter and felt that I was being embraced by a heavy soldier. I wrapped a lead-filled collar around my neck to protect my thyroid gland and snugged up all of the necessary straps.

As the device shot X-rays at Roxy and me, two things came to mind. First, why was I protecting virtually all bits of me except my head? After all, my brain is one of my favourite organs. Then I wondered just how much radiation Mike was using. Surely it takes a lot of zapping to get through the massive shell of a sea turtle. After we were done, I asked. "About the same as a chest X-ray," he replied. When I said that I was surprised that the shell wasn't more opaque to X-rays, he explained that a turtle's shell is more similar to cartilage than bone, and that this sort of radiation doesn't have much trouble penetrating it.

Without further study of the images and a comparison to photographs taken earlier, we couldn't be sure how many of the tumours on the X-ray images, if any, were internal. Before we left the clinic, Mike said in a low voice that Roxy's prognosis for a long and happy life was not promising. I hoped that Ellen hadn't heard him.

Ellen and I carried Roxy back to her enclosure, and after carefully unwrapping her, I lifted her back into her tank. She seemed to be floating a little higher than she had before, and Ellen explained that Roxy would have gulped a bit of air into her stomach and would float a bit strangely until she expelled it. I looked back at the laboratory apron that we had used to secure Roxy. It was littered with small chunks of tumour that had broken off in handling. Even though there is no way for the FPTHV to affect me, I was extra diligent in washing my hands.

MEMBERS OF SOME ABORIGINAL COMMUNITIES are entitled, by heritage, to capture and consume sea turtles. Some traditional custodians of the land have also become involved with the monitoring of sea turtle populations. Because of this constant involvement with the comings and goings of turtles, there is no doubt in anyone's mind that the sea turtle tumours we see today in Australia were not present much before 1990. Where had the virus come from and how had it arrived on Australia's far-flung shores? I would be fibbing if I said that anyone knew with absolute certainty. We are not even certain yet how the virus is communicated from one turtle to another. Perhaps the virus has always been present, but it is only now expressing itself in tumours. Given the global pattern of distribution of FPTHV, it is possible that the disease was introduced to Australia by accident by humans. Maybe it arrived along with the dreaded cane toad.

Australia has a long history of plant and animal introductions, both intentional and accidental. Dingoes didn't evolve in Australia, and they certainly didn't swim there. Mediterranean rabbits and Central American cane toads didn't come to Australia on their accumulated frequent-flier points. Early in the European history of Australia, naturalization societies were formed with the express goal of making Oz look more like home by introducing plants and animals. If the turtle virus was introduced by humans, it wouldn't be the first. Both calicivirus and myxomatosis were brought to Australia in hopes of knocking back rabbits.

But now a hatred of alien invaders by Australians has become almost cliché. Dedication to preventing the introduction of any new creatures borders on mania. I can prove it. On January 29, 2011, my local newspaper ran a story about a former Qantas flight attendant who had avoided a prison term, despite being involved in the importation of 165 kilograms of cocaine, ecstasy, and ice, worth almost $100 million. The same issue of the newspaper reported on a woman who tried to illegally import to Australia live crystal red shrimps, worth about $1,000 each. She was sentenced to fifteen months in prison.

A FEW WEEKS HAD PASSED since Roxy had been X-rayed, and her condition hadn't changed. Ellen was asked to make a presentation on sea turtles in the community of Bowen and offered to take me along. Two hours south of Townsville, Bowen is a regional centre for the fruit-growing industry and boasts magnificent beaches that are ideal for fun and sun. The Queens Beach Action Group, the organization with the third-worst acronym in Australia, was going to help with a large-scale capture of sea turtles a month later. A presentation on sea turtles was seen as a good way to help ensure local interest and support.

The group met at the Bowen Surf Life Saving Club headquarters, just off the beach. The small building was decorated with notices reminding people to swim where lifeguards could see them, and making suggestions about avoiding dangerous jellyfishes. While we waited for the appointed hour, one of QBAG's organizers took us to proudly show off some newly installed plaques, close to the beach, describing the two species of sea turtles most likely to be seen in the area. The hope was that more people would become sensitive to the needs of turtles.

Ellen began her talk by explaining that FPTHV was first described from sea turtles in the Florida Keys in 1930. The first cases in Australia were noticed in Moreton Bay in 1990. Tumours on turtles on this part of the Queensland coast had first been found in 2004. Although the disease had been seen in all sea turtle species, it was mainly a condition of green turtles, most commonly those in their middle years.

As with herpes virus in humans, the appearance of the condition seems to be stress-related. Curiously, in this area, almost all of the sick turtles had been captured in a small region known as Brisk Bay. Ellen reviewed several possible explanations. Perhaps noxious chemicals from earlier mining or military operations were leaching into the bay, causing stress. Brisk Bay might be a focus for infection, or perhaps sick, weakened turtles got washed to the spot by some trick of tide and topography. Like so many aspects of the virus-induced illness, no one knew with certainty.

Ellen elaborated on the impacts of FPTHV. She explained that sea turtles are beautifully hydrodynamic, slipping through the oceans. Large growths on the body's surface probably require more swimming effort. She showed pictures of large growths in the lungs of a turtle that had died near Townsville; it was hard for me to believe that it had been able to breathe at all. Ellen explained that individuals like Roxy had difficulty finding food when growths on eyelids hindered their vision.

Questions from the audience showed that they were paying close attention. "Do the growths have a blood supply?" Ellen was asked. "Do sick turtles ever get well again?" "Is it something that could make us sick?" The answers were "Yes," "Sometimes," and "Not as far as we know."

ROXY'S X-RAYS HAD SHOWN HER LUNGS to be clear of tumours; if they had been infiltrated, her chances of long-term survival would have been virtually nil. But in the weeks following the imaging, her weight had continued to decline, now down to 12.1 kilograms. It had become increasingly apparent that the growths around her eyes were seriously impeding her vision, making it difficult for her to find food in her tank. She could smell food but had difficulty seeing it, although this likely wasn't the only source of her weight loss. Surgery always involves risk, but in trying to balance Roxy's quality of life against the potential hazards of treatment, the time had come to attempt to remove the ocular growths. Ellen called on Dr. Vaughan Seed, a specialist in veterinary comparative anatomy.

The Internet can be a wonderful source of information. It doesn't take much searching to find instructions on How To Jump Out Of A Moving Car, How To Steal Someone's Boyfriend, How To Hunt For Magic Mushrooms, or How To Land A Boeing 747-400. However, the Internet is strangely silent when it comes to How To Surgically Remove Conjunctival Tumours From A Green Sea Turtle. Vaughan was going to have to combine what he knew about general principles of analgesia and anaesthesia with his skill as a veterinary surgeon, mix in a bit of conjecture about marine reptile physiology, and then wing it.

Joining Vaughan, Ellen, and me around the operating table were Bronwyn Orr and Krissy Bell, students of veterinary science. Bronwyn would take photographs to document the progress of the operation. Krissy was to keep track of Roxy's reflexes and general condition. I would stick my oar in when Vaughan needed me to cradle Roxy's head or hand him a surgical instrument.

As Vaughan surveyed the situation in and around Roxy's eyes, Ellen explained that some of the external tumours were regressing, blackening, and sloughing off. It seemed to me that fresh pink growths had formed in Roxy's flipperpits since I had last seen her.

Vaughan started off with an intramuscular injection of a synthetic opioid to relax Roxy. He emphasized that this was a matter of analgesia, not a general anaesthetic. Like a dental patient breathing nitrous oxide, Roxy would be aware of what was going on but wouldn't much care. He then applied an ophthalmic anaesthetic to both eyes. From there, it was a matter of carefully assessing each growth, using fine surgical silk to ligate it close to its point of origin, and then slicing it off with a scalpel. In some cases, Vaughan injected additional anaesthetic directly into the tumour before cutting it off. Most of the growths came from the conjunctiva, the delicate moist membrane that lines the interior surface of the eyelid. Others grew directly out of the corneal surface.

Assess, ligate, cut, reassess. Vaughan worked carefully and methodically for ninety minutes. In the end, Roxy still had significant tumours on the remainder of her body, but her head looked distinctly turtle-like. It would be some time before the operation's success could be gauged, but things were looking good. Vaughan applied an additional ointment to Roxy's eyes to lubricate and soothe them, then gave her an injection of a general anti-inflammatory, which would ease the pain in the following twenty-four hours.

Vaughan then performed a bit of veterinary magic. He injected into a vein an "antidote" to the opioid he had given Roxy at the start. Within ten seconds, she went from dull and lethargic to active and alert. After a general peek and poke to ensure that there was nothing more to be done, Vaughan released Roxy back into our care, promising to come by the following day to give her another injection of the anti-inflammatory. We carried Roxy back to her room to rest. Ellen was needed off-campus but left the patient in the capable care of Bronwyn. It all looked very promising.

Forty minutes later, Roxy lost consciousness. Bronwyn rushed her to the emergency veterinary clinic, and staff stabilized her.

Twenty-four hours later, I got to visit Roxy again. It was time for Vaughan and Ellen to assess her progress. She was back in her pool, which had been drained of most of its salt water to keep her from drowning if she lost consciousness again. She was out of her element and did not look happy. But as Ellen began to refill the pool, it was as though all of Roxy's switches had been flipped to the "on" position. She began to swim, cautiously and slowly, but with a sense of purpose. She extended her head further out of her shell than I had seen before, as though keen to spy on the world that had been earlier shrouded by the growths on her face. Vaughan checked Roxy's reflexes and noted that she was able to close her eyelids completely.

It was really too much to expect so soon after her surgery, but we all wanted to see if Roxy had any desire to eat. Ellen thawed a package of squid and tossed a small piece into the pool. Roxy immediately swivelled her head, grabbed the chunk of food, and swallowed it. The relief in the room was tactile. Ellen threw in a larger piece of squid, and I was overjoyed that Roxy not only saw it, but was able to track it as it moved in the current created by the tank's water pumps. She stuffed down one chunk of squid after another until the whole 600-gram package was gone.

I WAS PLEASED NOT TO BE IN CHARGE of the turtle rodeo. Ninety people were to be involved, including representatives of two aboriginal groups, researchers from James Cook University, the World Wildlife Fund, the Sea Turtle Foundation, the Queens Bay Action Group, first-aid providers, and members of the media. Boats would be plying the waters of Mount Gordon Bay the following day, all attempting to capture sea turtles. As we prepared to leave Townsville, Ellen was so consumed with myriad details that she was able to speak only in sentence fragments. At one point she wanted me to stand watch over equipment while she retrieved paperwork from her office. She put her hand out with the palm facing me, and said, "Stay here." I have used that same command on dogs.

I think it very unlikely that I will ever fully understand the subtleties of the cultures of Australian aboriginals and Torres Strait Islanders. Instead, I do my best to be sensitive to differences, pick up what I can, and try to avoid making a complete ass of myself. On this expedition, there were to be boats from the Gudjuda aboriginal group living on lands around Bowen, and others from the Girringun group living further north near Cardwell. I was told that members of the two groups would be sticking to their own boats because of issues involving authority.

I also learned that, by tradition, women were forbidden from jumping out of boats to catch turtles. On a turtle-catching expedition, women were not even permitted to pilot a boat while men jumped. Exceptions were made in the case of women on university-owned boats, but only because turtles were being captured for research, and not for consumption.

After buying provisions for Saturday and Sunday's breakfasts, we drove to the Life Saving Club for an orientation to the weekend's activities. The event was catered by the folks from QBAG. Ellen had explained to the Townsville crew that the event would be a dry one. Some young aboriginal persons in the community were experiencing significant difficulties associated with alcohol consumption, and the most sensitive thing was for us all to avoid drinking. It seemed a strange restriction given that when we arrived there was a group of young men and women drinking in the shadows.

The evening's first speaker was Gudjuda Elder "Uncle" Eddie Smallwood, who welcomed us all to the country. He said of the weekend, "It's gonna be deadly." I started to worry about sharks but was later told that "deadly" is an Australian expression, used particularly by aboriginal people, roughly equivalent to "awesome." "This is all about turtles," he said. "It's all about sharing." Eddie commented on the widespread opposition of white Australians to the consumption of sea turtles by aboriginal groups. "Yeah," he said unprompted, "we do eat them, but how many? Not many."

Gudjuda Elder Jim Gaston was then introduced as one of the traditional custodians of the land. Jim had been capturing turtles for research purposes for many years, and would be piloting one of the boats. He explained that there would be six boats in operation, each with a designated pilot and turtle jumpers. These vessels would also

transport members of the media who had come to film the proceedings. Jim spoke at length about safety, the number-one concern of the
weekend. All jumpers were required to protect themselves with wet
suits, boots, gloves, and helmets. Each boat pilot would ensure that
he had a GPS unit and reliable radios for ship-to-shore communica-
tion. He then explained that we were all to meet at the community's
boat launch at 7 a.m. It seemed to me that small countries have been
successfully invaded with less preparation.

Jim claimed that the experience of catching turtles and the
resulting surge of adrenalin was better than any drug. "You want
a good hit? Come with me; I'll give you a good hit. And it's free!"
He finished off by saying, "Have a good weekend. If you don't, it's
your fault."

Ellen spoke briefly about FPTHV and the resulting tumours, and
explained how it had first been spotted in the region by Jim and his
colleagues. In their turn, each group sent forward a representative to
address the crowd. The mob from Cardwell, QBAG, WWF, first-aid
providers . . . A lot of groups were involved with this project, each
with very different backgrounds and very different priorities.

It was then time for a brief question-and-answer session. The
single most elegant question had an unexpected answer. "Will
we be cleaning up the turtles? Will we be taking off the barnacles
attached to their shells?" Ellen responded that we would leave the
barnacles in place. First, they didn't hamper the turtles at all. Second, because these barnacles were found nowhere other than on
sea turtles, and because sea turtles are endangered, the barnacles
are also endangered.

HAVING GROWN UP in a landlocked province on the Canadian prai-
ries, I had never been called upon to wear a wetsuit. However, it was
the tail end of jellyfish season on the north Queensland coast, and
local stingers were not to be dismissed; people have been known to
die from the pain. I visited five stores in Townsville without finding a
suit that would fit without making me look like a fur seal with bloat.

On Saturday morning, I rose at five thirty and stepped outside to watch a rare alignment of planets in the rapidly brightening sky. Despite predictions to the contrary, the world didn't end. After breakfast, I walked to Bowen's boat launch with my companions. Locals using the boat ramp to launch their pleasure craft looked at us, decked out in our unlovely wetsuits, as though we were Martians. In their turn, all six boats were offloaded. *Turtle Researcher 8* was a 4.5-metre yellow polyethylene craft and looked like a giant bathtub duck. The mob from Cardwell would be sailing in *Girringun Wulgu* and *Girringun Bruce.* I assumed that the name Bruce was based on an Australian cliché. Thank goodness I asked before making a joke, as the boat was named for an elder who had died the year before.

I was fortunate enough to be assigned as a jumper on *Gudjuda Gungu,* an Ensign 4.93-metre aluminum sport-fishing boat piloted by Jim Gaston. In the local language, *gungu* meant "sea turtle." It was hard to believe that anyone knew more about capturing sea turtles than Jim, as he had personally caught 900. We were joined by Lydia Gibson, a WWF marine policy officer, and three members of a film crew working for Channel 10's *7 pm Project*—Simon Wise, a producer and director; Jac Tonks, a field producer; and Serge Negus, a reporter. Like me, Serge was to be a jumper.

Just minutes from the boat launch, Jim's outboard motor started giving him grief. Sputtering was followed by wheezing, followed shortly after by not much of anything. Thinking that the problem might be the result of water in the fuel, Jim changed tanks. Sputter, sputter, wheeze, belch, silence. All six of us stared at the outboard motor as though our glares would shame the device into more cooperative behaviour. We agreed to blame the situation on a dodgy fuel pump, which was resolved by periodic squeezing of a rubber pump in the fuel line.

We passed stingrays in their dozens. Mistaking one of those for a turtle could be a terminal experience. Flying fish roared away from our boat with only their tails touching the water. We then spied a massive dugong, which sped away at a rate that seemed impossible for such a bulky creature, leaving a big bow wave.

When we got to the correct general area, Jim handed over control of the boat to me while he got into position to make the first jump. We spied a candidate, and I manoeuvred the boat to bring our target to the starboard side. With a zig to starboard and a zag to port, I tried to match the turtle's heading and speed. Jim hurled himself from the boat and surfaced a moment later with our first turtle of the day. We recorded the time, latitude, and longitude, and applied a numbered metal tag to the trailing edge of the turtle's front left flipper.

"Would you like to catch one now?" There are probably things that I would rather do on a Saturday morning than try to catch an endangered green sea turtle, but I couldn't think of any. I had to remove my prescription sunglasses in preparation. And so, slightly blind, I positioned myself on the starboard bow while Serge and Jim used their superior vision to find me a target.

"Turtle!" cried Serge, pointing off the forward port side. Jim throttled up and steered the boat to bring the turtle starboard, where he could most easily keep an eye on me. From the turtle's furious pace and evasive manoeuvres, it was pretty clear that it didn't want to be caught. But I was having none of that, and launched myself into the ocean. I made the rookie mistake of jumping where the turtle was, and not where it would be by the time I got there. My palms slipped down its back, and I watched it disappear much faster than I, or anyone else, can swim.

"Did you have breakfast?" asked Jim. "Well, there's the problem—you're not hungry enough." I was learning to love his smile.

Surely nothing could keep me from my second prey. Fifteen minutes later, Jim got another turtle into position and I jumped, only to find that I had made my dive too shallow, and it escaped under me. When I surfaced, I spied Serge diving in, and moments later he came up with my turtle.

By my third attempt, it seemed that word of my incompetence had spread amongst the turtles of Mount Gordon Bay. A moment before I jumped, the turtle deked right and then swerved left. I missed it by about a metre. Surfacing and swearing, I again saw

Serge with my turtle in his arms. After my first two attempts, I had hauled myself over the gunnels, but trying after my third jump, I lost my grip and fell back in. I asked for the ladder to be put over the side. I must be getting old. Even before we had the chance to tag and measure that turtle, Jim spotted another. Serge hurled himself forward and surfaced, victorious.

"You're going to get one," said Jim. "You've got to believe in yourself."

Now, I am usually the poster boy for self-confidence, but I was starting to have doubts. Everything we passed looked like a turtle. Every rock, every piece of seagrass . . .

"Turtle!"

On my fourth attempt, I magically found my hands around the shoulders of the large, struggling creature. I had caught a sea turtle, and no one could ever take that victory away from me. I now found myself in a very awkward situation. My legs were trailing behind, but when I tried to right myself I found that the bulk of the turtle kept me from getting my feet under me. It was trying to pull me down. No power on Earth short of loss of consciousness was going to make me let go of that turtle. And so I craned my neck just enough to get my lips above water, took a breath, submerged, slowly pulled back on the turtle as hard as I could, and gained purchase. I surfaced to applause.

I caught my turtle at 10:45 a.m. on Saturday, May 14, at 20.04924° south and 148.23346° east. It was a beaut. Its plastron was 54.0 centimetres, and we gave it a tag numbered K52482, which contained instructions to return it to P.O. Box 15155, City East Queensland 4002, if found. Like the other four turtles we had caught, mine showed no evidence of FPTHV tumours.

"How does that feel?" Jim had been right. It felt like the rush of the greatest drug, an injection of emotion. He shook my hand and seemed amused that I couldn't stop grinning and talking.

We tried for one more capture, but this turtle had an interesting escape tactic. It turned in circles that were almost the same as the turning radius of Jim's boat. After we had completed our third circle, the turtle disappeared into the ring of silt kicked up by the propeller and refused to come out of hiding.

The falling tide had left the waterline 200 or 300 metres from the beach. This meant that we had to lug our captives across the sand to the folks who would process them. While carrying one of our captured turtles, I admired its gorgeous flecked grey eyes. After putting it in the shade, I fell into a telling conversation with an aboriginal fellow. He said that if the courts would turn young transgressors back to the community instead of incarcerating them, many could be helped to turn their lives around. It might be possible to get them involved with sea turtle work.

"But the courts aren't willing to do that yet?" I asked.

"No, it's not the courts; it's the young fellas." He didn't elaborate, and I didn't ask. I suspect that if every young fellow, and perhaps every young woman, had the opportunity to be part of a team that jumps out of a boat to catch sea turtles in order to better understand their natural history, a lot of lives would turn out differently. Unsolicited, my companion started talking about the white community's attitudes about sea turtle harvest by the aboriginal communities. I had heard disparate estimates of how many turtles were taken each year, but I didn't feel that it was right to ask for his guess. Instead, I asked what sea turtle tasted like. It wasn't a fair question. How do you describe a taste, except by comparing it to another taste? Green sea turtle, I was told, tastes a lot like green sea turtle.

I now had the opportunity to help the ground-based crew. My first job was to move, with Serge, a particularly big turtle from one station to the next. Ellen showed us how to position ourselves on either side of the turtle, on our haunches, with our knees outside of our elbows. We grabbed it with one hand over the shoulder and the other at the back of the carapace and lifted, using our legs. When it was necessary to turn the turtle upside down, it was crucial that we turn it clockwise, and then turn it right-side-up counter-clockwise. Ellen explained that it was possible, by turning a sea turtle over and over, to twist up its internal organs.

Between them, the six boats had captured thirty-nine turtles. Only three showed tumours caused by FPTHV. I spotted a couple that were missing portions of flippers, probably carried away by sharks. The turtles were brought to the beach in groups, but the folks on shore could process them only one at a time, and so each arriving boat created something of a logjam. Tents had been erected to keep the turtles and their handlers out of the sun as much as possible. The head of each turtle was cloaked in a hood with a drawstring to help keep it calm.

A blood sample was drawn from each subject. This was quite a challenge, since blood vessels aren't as obvious anywhere on a turtle as on a human arm. Then the length of the carapace was recorded. A small skin sample was taken, and swabs were made of the skin, mouth, and cloaca. A comprehensive set of photographs was taken of each subject. A drill was used to sample a small core of the carapace for studies of environmental contaminants. Each turtle was then weighed before being released. While the remaining turtles waited their turns to be bled or swabbed, children poured seawater over them to keep them damp and cool.

As operations wound down for the day, I walked back to the boat with Jim and the television crew. They needed additional video footage to round out their coverage of the turtle rodeo. We stopped a few hundred metres offshore so that Serge could interview Jim about his involvement in sea turtle research.

Jac must have forgotten about the chain of command. "I need everyone but Serge and Simon to sit in the front of the boat," she announced. Jim put her in her place by explaining, gently, that it was his boat and that he gave the orders. "Can I get everyone in the front of the boat?" Jac tried a little more modestly. Simon captured footage of Serge jumping off the boat, as though trying to catch a turtle. Simon then got into another boat to film Serge jumping from a slightly different angle. This was followed by several jumps by Serge while Simon bobbed around in the sea filming him. Television is as authentic as a Sasquatch.

On the ride back to the boat ramp, Jim told me about his first experiences catching turtles many years earlier. He explained that, when a community celebration was coming up, "Uncle" would tell him, "Go out and catch a turtle."

Jim's reply would be "But we don't have a permit."

"Go out and catch a turtle."

Jim told me that in his culture you don't say no to an elder, and so he would head out to catch a turtle. Today, he catches them for studies of their natural history. Occasionally, for a big occasion, he catches a turtle for consumption but finds that he must leave the killing to someone else.

While writing up my notes that evening, my shoulders reminded me that I had climbed back into the boat too many times and had carried too many turtles across the wet sands of Mount Gordon Bay. The aching in my shoulders would disappear in a day, but my memories of catching turtles would persist.

In the hours before dawn, I could hear my wetsuit slapping wildly against the cabin, where it hung to dry. It seemed unlikely that we would be heading out to catch turtles in a strong wind. When folks showed up for breakfast, they were wearing heavy jackets to protect them against a cool wind. "I know that I wouldn't be out fishing in this," said one of the helpers.

But the order of the day was to wait for Jim. He was in charge of operations on the water, and he would decide on the suitability of the sea. Assuming that we would be driving back to Townsville without getting back on the water, the crew from the university had scarfed down mounds of bacon, eggs, baked beans, and coffee. When the word came through that we would be heading out despite the weather, a few faces turned to the sea and seemed to regret their choice of breakfast foods.

Jim's reconnoitring had shown that Queens Bay was less choppy than other spots in the region and held some promise for the capture of turtles. When we arrived at the put-in point, Ellen asked if I wanted to go jumping again. I told her that I would be very pleased to give someone else the opportunity. After a rethink, I realized that this was the wrong response.

"Do you need me to jump?"

"Well, it looks like we are short one jumper."

I gathered up my gear, squeezed into my wetsuit in record time, and ran to Jim's boat. As we sailed away, Jim explained that he had never failed to catch at least one turtle. His perfect record was on the line. Our efforts weren't helped by the breeze that generated ripples, making it difficult to resolve detail below the water surface. We and the others sailed slow loops across the bay, concentrating on shallow spots with seagrass that turtles might feed on.

The bay might have contained one hundred turtles or none at all. The latter seemed more likely, until one animal made the mistake of sticking his head up for a breath not too far away from our boat. We raced over and soon landed it. Only two turtles were caught that day, but we were two subjects closer to a more thorough understanding of the lives of green sea turtles and the impact of the FPTHV virus. Measurements were made, blood taken, skin swabbed, weights recorded, and photographs snapped. Just after I helped to release the last individual back to the ocean, someone asked, "Did you remember to take its hood off?"

I WANTED A DOG. I got a turtle. Imagine my disappointment in receiving, not a faithful and playful childhood companion, but an introduced pest. In some ways, that red-eared slider, roughly the size and shape of a deflated, green toy balloon, was the start of my introduced-species adventures. Those adventures had come to an end with me leaping onto an endangered sea turtle off the east coast of Australia.

Whether a 25-cent pet turtle or a million-dollar racehorse, many responsibilities come with ownership of an animal. One of those responsibilities is a willingness to say that enough is enough. I suppose that some people might argue that Roxy should never have been taken into captivity, no matter how sick she was. I am

not one of those people. Like Ellen, I believe that it is necessary
to balance the possibility of Roxy making a recovery sufficient to
release her back into the wild against the quality of her current life.
As much as anyone can judge these things, she seems comfortable
in her pool. Surely there is also merit in keeping Roxy alive in terms
of what we can learn about FPTHV and its impact on sea turtles in
the wild.

Given sufficient time, it is probable that green sea turtles will
evolve a degree of resistance to FPTHV. That assumes that green
turtles will survive that long. Many, many people are working
to ensure that survival. If Roxy makes a sufficient recovery, it is
my sincere hope that one day, twenty years from now, she will be
munching away on seagrass as some guy jumps from a boat and
lands on her back. And I hope that guy is me.

Epilogue

IN THE EPILOGUE of my previous book, *The Curse of the Labrador Duck,* I posted a $10,000 reward. I offered to hand over that sum to the first person who could produce a legitimate stuffed specimen of the extinct Labrador Duck that I had not described in the book. As soon as the title hit bookstore shelves, I began receiving messages from individuals claiming my reward. A number of people explained that they had spotted a Labrador Duck in this or that museum, but the curators of each of those institutions verified that they had no such creature in their collection. Others sent messages about stuffed Labrador Ducks in their possession, without any supporting evidence. When I asked for a photograph, the correspondents went silent. I received photos of stuffed ducks in attics and on sideboards, but each of these turned out to be either an eider or a Long-tailed Duck. Two expectant individuals told me that they had Labrador Duck eggs, in the hope that they might get some portion of the $10,000. In both cases, the eggs had been laid fifty years after the species had fallen to extinction, and so there seemed little need for follow-up. One wag sent me a photograph of a Labrador retriever wearing a rubber duck bill. Worthy of a chuckle, but not worth any money. After a year, my offer expired, and I wiped that amount off my mortgage.

I had fun with the Labrador Duck offer and so would like to make another one. I was completely serious in soliciting poems about lupines in Iceland. In an attempt to get you to put pen to paper, I promise to put the best poem in pride of place on my website: www.glenchilton.com.

And what about Roxy? As I write this, she is still swimming lazy laps of her indoor swimming pool. It is my sincere hope that, as you read this, she will be swimming much larger laps of the Pacific Ocean, or laying eggs on a beach 1,000 kilometres away. Feel free to write to me at glen@glenchilton.com for an update on Roxy's condition.

It must be just about time for me to go on another quest.

Acknowledgements

I offer endless thanks to all of my travelling companions for providing me with their unique perspectives on the world. Goodness knows why they put up with me. I would have no story to tell without the generous aid of many experts in the field, including Ellen Ariel, Chris Barron, Legese Begashaw, Ken Brown, John Cortez, Norbert Dankers, Clint and Irene Davy, Lincoln De Silva, José Luis Echevarrias, José Antonio Torres Esquivias, Ed Freytag, Andy Green, Hector Garrido Guil, Carlos Gutierrez, Michelle Hookano, Gabriel Laufer, Jan Light, Mariano Paracuelos, Charlie Perez, Perry Ponseti, Brian Self, Iain Sheves, Andrew Tyler, Raphael Vega, and Carmen Yuste. My colleagues at St. Mary's University College and James Cook University provided tremendous moral support throughout my adventures. I am truly grateful for the guidance and patience of my friends at HarperCollins Canada, particularly Jim Gifford and Noelle Zitzer, and for the enthusiastic support of my agent, Rick Broadhead. My loving family, the Chiltons and the Volks, have never once asked if I was on the right track. Loving thanks for the understanding.